MIXED GAS DIVING

THE ULTIMATE CHALLENGE FOR TECHNICAL DIVING

by Tom Mount and Bret Gilliam
with Randy Bohrer, Dr. Larry "Harris" Taylor, Dr. Lee H. Somers,
John Crea, and Richard Nordstrom

Disclaimer

Mixed gas diving is a potentially hazardous practice that can expose the diver to considerable risk including death if practiced incorrectly or with incomplete planning and procedures. It requires specialized training, equipment and experience. This book is not intended as a substitute for the above or for the diver to abandon common sense in pursuit of diving activities beyond his abilities. Although the practice of mixed gas diving has become more widespread, it should be noted that the national scuba training agencies do not consider the use of mixed gas appropriate nor do they endorse its use for recreational divers. Therefore, specialized training must be acquired before pursuing mixed gas diving. This book is intended as a source of information on various aspects of mixed diving, not as a substitute for proper training and experience. The reader is advised that all the elements of hazard and risk associated with mixed diving cannot be brought out within the scope of this text. Those divers that choose to pursue mixed diving activities do so at their own risk. The authors neither condone nor advocate mixed gas diving per se, and this book is offered for informational purposes only. The authors, publisher, and manufacturers presented in this book, are not liable for damage or injury including death which may result from mixed gas diving activities, with respect to information contained herein.

Cover photo by Bret Gilliam

First Printing 1993
Watersport Publishing, Inc., P.O. Box 83727, San Diego, CA 92138

Printed in the United States

International Standard Book Number
ISBN 0-922769-41-9

Library of Congress Catalog Card Number: 92-080705
Mount, Tom, Gilliam, Bret,
with Bohrer, Randy, Taylor, Dr. Larry "Harris", Somers, Dr. Lee,
Crea, John, Nordstrom, Richard

Mixed Gas Diving
The Ultimate Challenge For Technical Divers

MIXED GAS DIVING

THE ULTIMATE CHALLENGE FOR TECHNICAL DIVERS

by Tom Mount and Bret Gilliam

with Randy Bohrer, Dr. Larry "Harris" Taylor, Dr. Lee H. Somers,
John Crea, and Richard Nordstrom

Watersport Publishing, Inc.
Post Office Box 83727 • San Diego, CA 92138

TABLE OF CONTENTS

TABLE OF CONTENTS

ABOUT THIS BOOK

Whenever a technical book is written by "committee" there will be inevitable differences in writing style, opinion and occasional overlaps in information. We made our best efforts to obtain professional contributors from different areas of expertise and these individual authors are specifically identified at the beginning of each chapter. Some chapters are quite lengthy while others are condensed to a few brief pages. In some, the impact of photography has been liberally utilized while other sections are necessarily less visual. Our intent was to structure the book in such a manner that information on a specific topic was easy to find and then was presented in a modular style. Some chapters are more technical in nature because of the subject matter while others have an opportunity to be of more general interest.

Mixed gas diving is not a light subject. It requires the diver to acquire a fair amount of diving experience to be obtained in conventional compressed air applications before taking the next step into Trimix and Heliox. A background in NITROX diving is extremely valuable since the principles of gas analysis, mixing, equipment handling and the relevant limits of oxygen exposures should already be familiar. It is certainly not our intention that the science and technology of mixed gas be regarded as another trivial stepping stone in a diver's entry level training. Within the traditional recreational certification agencies there is some confusion over diving ratings. What is an advanced diver? It is possible to obtain such a rating within some agencies with as few as 15 dives. In the case of mixed gas diving, a true requisite of advanced diving and an appreciable number of logged dives is mandatory.

A background in deep diving is also desirable since the realities of inert gas narcosis, gas supply management, dive planning, decompression technique, and contingency methodology are all similar. Deep diving for our purposes is best defined as beyond 130 fsw and in a variety of site conditions.

In the limited space of this book it is impossible for us to cover every aspect of diving, and therefore we make certain assumptions as to our readers' prior knowledge and command of subject matter. We have included in the bibliography a selection of recommended reading materials. As a building block to this book we highly recommend that readers obtain copies of *"DEEP DIVING: An Advanced Guide to Physiology,*

Procedures and Systems" by Bret Gilliam, et al (Watersport Publishing), and either the *"NITROX Manual"* by Dick Rutkowski (IAND) or *"The Application of Enriched Air Mixtures"* by Ed Betts (ANDI). These texts will provide an excellent base of information in a variety of subject matter pertinent to mixed gas diving.

The layout content of the book has been set up to provide logical groupings of chapters in sections by overall topic. Although the book has been laid out to provide a systemized sequence to development, the reader can easily jump directly to a subject of interest for quick reference without requiring the chapters to be read in order. Each chapter is extensively referenced as well to aid the reader if he needs more information on a particular topic. The glossary and bibliography also provide further detail.

One thing the reader will note is that actual tables for mixed gas diving are deliberately absent. We are reluctant to provide a specific recommendation for a generic Heliox or Trimix table for a variety of reasons. First of all, we don't want anyone charging off to attempt such dives without proper training. Secondly, there are so many variables to "poor man's mix" or even Heliox that the inclusion of only a few tables would be inadequate to safely cover the subject. We urge you to get involved through a professional mixed gas training program which will provide the proper tables for your particular diving applications. As you gain experience, you will probably want to discuss custom tables with one of our table experts listed in the Resource Guide.

One of the most important sections of this book is the Resource Guide in the back of the book. Here you will find contact information for suppliers, training, manufacturers, and specialized services that mixed gas divers will find invaluable. We hope that you will find this expanded section useful and informative. Those listed are reputable professionals and the reader can be confident of their expertise.

In conclusion, it is necessary for us to reiterate that this text is not to be considered as a substitute for proper training. It is an ideal reference manual but the need for practical in-water training supervised by a qualified professional is absolutely required for safe mixed gas diving. Additionally, we recommend that all breathing gases be obtained from professional dispensers.

It is our sincerest wish that this book will provide needed information to make this aspect of diving safer and more efficient. We appreciate your support and welcome your comments for future editions.

FOREWORD

The original idea for this book was Tom Mount's. He came to me with a suggested format as far back as 1990 and devoted a fair amount of time trying to entice a publisher into having some interest. Most simply felt that mixed gas diving was a "fringe" market that did not have enough participants to justify such a printing. The project stalled and was relegated to extreme back burner status.

But the diving public with an active interest in deeper diving and more advanced technical applications came bursting out of the closet in 1991 and *demanded* access to information that had been selectively guarded and suppressed for years. In 1991 at the DEMA show in Las Vegas, Michael Menduno's *Aquacorps Journal* celebrated its first year of publishing by producing its third journal issue entitled "Deep" and a newsletter called Technical Diver devoted completely to enriched air NITROX (EAN). The simple fact that *Aquacorps* could survive in a troubled economy while featuring editorial material that was inherently controversial was pause for thought. Ragged third or fourth hand copies were jealously hoarded and passed along like trophies or baseball trading cards. An entire underground of newly named "technical divers" now had their own magazine that spoke their own language and made no apologies for addressing subjects like decompression, NITROX, mixed gas, deep diving, specialized training, and equipment outfitting in detail. Heresy! Insurrection! Burn them, they're witches!

Meanwhile Dick Rutkowski, who had been long crying in the wilderness about the benefits of NITROX, suddenly found a renewed interest in his lectures and seminars. He published the *NITROX Manual* as the industry's first dedicated reference source and Ed Betts adapted an excellent instructor manual for ANDI from that work. Suddenly IAND and ANDI found a new legitimacy beyond passing regional interest. As Dick and Ed crisscrossed the country like some mutated versions of "Johnny Appleseed", the NITROX revolution blossomed. The numbers of instructors and entry level NITROX divers soared. Somewhere in the background Dr. Morgan Wells, the godfather of the NOAA NITROX program over two decades ago, was smiling.

Not everyone was so pleased though. The public discussions of deep diving and mixed gas use invaded forums such as NAUI's International

Conference On Underwater Education in March 1991. A one hour panel discussion on deep diving issues was the best attended session of the two day program. A standing room only crowd was polled by the session moderator and it was determined that over 90% of the attendees actively practiced deep diving to as much as 200 fsw! Such public admissions would have been unheard of before within a professional group of instructors. Wow, the next thing that will be revealed is that some people, politicians aside, actually smoked marijuana in America and *liked* it! (I guess I'm really going over the edge now, but hey, maybe Bill Clinton is an ex-deep diver. We know he had to inhale then.)

All this honesty and candor did allow issues to be opened up for scrutiny but, as usual, it also rallied the forces of darkness. By late summer the naysayers had managed to effectively stall any advancement of NITROX positions within the national training agencies. Several prominent industry "experts" had published editorial opinions and professional journal diatribes against the proliferation of NITROX training and use. Never mind that most of their arguments were not founded in fact, quantifiable data, or even common sense. No, they were the "experts" and they were bound and determined to save the diving public from the dreaded menace of NITROX and deep diving. And, of course, they were also going to deprive the public of an informed choice.

Their lobbying had its desired effect. In October 1991, the Diving Equipment Manufacturers Association (DEMA) banned all exhibitors that were involved with NITROX from their annual trade show. "Now we've solved that little problem," they said. The outcry was swift and organized. Hundreds of letters, faxes, and phone calls hit DEMA and various members. A meeting was hastily arranged between NITROX professional community members and DEMA's directors. Almost as fast as NITROX was out, it was reinstated. It's funny how when intemperate actions are taken to ban something, it stimulates a reaction to focus the spotlight on that which is banned (usually with a favorable outcome). It doesn't seem to matter whether it was banning books such as Salinger's *The Catcher in the Rye*, Twain's *Huckleberry Finn*, or even *Playboy* magazine at the local 7-Eleven. People have a tendency to resent being told what they can or cannot read or take part in. The banning of NITROX, however briefly, brought it to the attention of everyone in a manner unprecedented. The genie was definitely out of the bottle and DEMA was not going to put him back in.

In an effort to coherently address the NITROX issues, a two day pre-DEMA Enriched Air Workshop was organized by the joint efforts of The

Scuba Diving Resource Group (SDRG) and *Aquacorps*. Dr. Bill Hamilton of Hamilton Research Ltd. was asked to be chairman and coordinate the program. He invited, cajoled, threatened, and, by other nefarious means, produced the top professional experts from within the scientific, military, commercial, hyperbaric, manufacturing, and technical communities. This group specifically concentrated on the pros and cons of NITROX and the varied arguments, opinions, and position papers that had led to the past controversy. Some opinions that had been accepted without challenge were effectively rebutted. Other areas such as manufacturers' concerns of improper use of equipment were realistically evaluated. In a unique peer-reviewed summation report, the technology of NITROX was found to be a viable alternative breathing gas for use by recreational divers and that adequate safeguards, standards, and training existed within the NITROX agencies. Further action items for future implementation were identified and a full version of the workshop session was published by the SDRG. NITROX had come of age.

The DEMA show of 1992 in Houston saw *Aquacorps* survive another year to produce a special mixed gas issue, ANDI unvielded a new student NITROX book, and Watersport Publishing premiered *Deep Diving: An Advanced Guided to Physiology, Procedures and Systems* (Gilliam, et al). The latter became Watersport's fastest selling book in 1992. My office phone rings several times a day with anxious calls from England, Canada, Europe, and Australia for air-mail copies. *Aquacorps'* Mix issue sold out and became a collector's item like their previous editions. In May of 1992, every major diving magazine and professional journal had included a feature article on NITROX. NAUI's *Sources* devoted an entire issue to the subject. It seemed that the bandwagon had started to roll and nobody wanted to get left behind.

The NITROX agencies, IAND and ANDI, have almost quadrupled in size with new facilities coming on line monthly. Both have now expanded to include mixed gas training. NASDS and NAUI have formally recognized NITROX as training specialties with NAUI going the extra step to include liability insurance for enriched air mixtures at no extra charge on instructor policies.

About now, the guys who used to manufacture "buddy mirrors" in the early seventies must be desperately trying to figure how to get their product banned.

I don't know, it's almost getting too respectable. Guys who are more comfortable in wet suits are having to put on suits and ties and start wearing shoes again. I knew it was time to worry when Mike Menduno showed up in pin stripes, only two earrings, and his version of a haircut.

With NITROX coming into almost universal acceptance, the next rung of the high-tech ladder will be the many applications of mixed gas diving. NITROX paved the way. Most of the same proponents and spokesmen now lead the way for mixed gas. Somewhere behind closed doors, self-righteous opponents are whispering about this new threat to their status quo and formulating anti-mixed gas position statements. Just wait until they get wind of what's happening with rebreathers... nah, let 'em chew on this bone for a while longer.

It is to the enlightened thinker who believes that knowledge and learning are best nurtured in an open forum of intellectual exchange, that this book was written. Mixed gas diving will not be for everyone. But for everyone who can use this technology to make diving safer, more efficient, and more fun... this book may open the door for you to its benefits. I have enjoyed working and diving with the people involved in putting this text together and I hope you will enjoy reading it.

BRET GILLIAM, JULY 1992

Gilliam began diving in 1958, since logged over 12,000 dives around the world. Twenty-year veteran of the diving industry including military/ commercial projects, liveaboard dive vessels and luxury yachts, retail dive store and Caribbean resort operation and ownership. Licensed as USCG Merchant Marine Master, submersible pilot and recompression chamber supervisor. Author of scores of articles and author/contributor to seven books on diving. Recipient of NAUI's Outstanding Contribution to Diving Award. Sponsored research projects in decompression sickness, diving computers and multi-day repetitive diving. Developed one of the first certification specialty courses in dive accident management and recompression chamber operation. Through his consulting corporation, OCEAN TECH, he provides services in the design and operation of high pressure air systems, recompression chamber facilities, diving vessels and risk management systems. He is one of the U.S.'s foremost legal experts on diving specializing in defense litigation. He is a member of the Board of Directors of the National Association of Underwater Instructors (NAUI), the International Association of NITROX and Technical Diving (IANTD), and the International Underwater Foundation (IUF).

ACKNOWLEDGMENTS

Pulling a project like this together would have been impossible without the cooperation of several key individuals who gave generously of their time and expertise.

A special thanks to Dr. Bill Hamilton who consented to provide review and valuable suggestions to portions of the manuscript and whom has always been ready to assist technical diving with his bottomless insight and experience. He also makes a damn fine barbecue. And to Patti Mount for graciously putting up with a house full of divers.

Many thanks to our primary divers who served as photo subjects on several deep projects: Kim Cochrane (red hair moussed to the max), Richard Bull (whose mustache has more hair than Gilliam's head), Rob Palmer (that was a female sheep, of course; nothing queer about old Rob Palmer!), Bill Gardner ("Uphill" to his friends), and Lynn Hendrickson (ferret mother). Now if the Brits could just learn to speak proper English and develop a sense of humor...

For interviews in the historical section, thanks to Gary Gentile, Sheck Exley, Hal Watts, and Rob Palmer. Your patience with detailed quotes and retrospectives helps the past live again vividly.

Our appreciation goes to Dick Rutkowski and Ed Betts for their cooperation in preparing sections on NITROX and blending systems. Also to Glenn Butler for help with schematics.

For help with extra photography, a nod to Rock Palermo, Richard Bull, Rob Palmer, Ned DeLoach, Gary Gentile, Lynn Hendrickson, Pete Nawrocky, Jim Baden, and Joel Silverstein. Your efforts to dredge up the missing and vitally needed shots are especially appreciated.

A bent knee and a kiss to the ring of Bob Warkentin, the wizard of repair for Nikonos cameras and lenses when silly divers take them too deep and don't look after them. "I promise to clean and rinse according to your directions", only 5000 more times and I'll have the blackboard full, teacher. Thanks to Fred Dion of his timely turnarounds on cameras as well.

For their time and valuable input including support with equipment we would like to recognize Mark Leonard and Lamar Hires of Dive Rite Mfg. Inc., Dick Long and Joe Martinez of DUI, Joe Schelorke of Poseidon/Viking, and Kevin Gurr of Quatek Ltd.

A very special acknowledgment to Jim Mims of Ocean Diving in Pompano, Florida who toiled over gas mixtures, supplied extra equipment as needed, provided his dive boat to get us into the deep wreck sites in difficult conditions, tended surface supplied decompression lines, and indulged our blown operating schedules. But next time be sure to turn Bret's oxygen regulator on...

For assistance in editing, computer translations, preparing the manuscript and laying it out, hat's off to Mark Flahan, Blake Hendrickson, and Theresa Lambert. Couldn't have done it without all of you!

And a deserved salute to our publisher, Ken Loyst, who didn't always know what we were doing until he read the entire manuscript, but was always supportive and let us bring this esoteric text to the public. Thanks Ken! Take the rest of the day off...

Bret Gilliam • Tom Mount • John Crea • Randy Bohrer • Dr. Lee H. Somers • Dr. Larry "Harris" Taylor and Richard Nordstrom.
July 1992

Photo by Bret Gilliam

CHAPTER 1

THEORY

A Brief History of Mixed Gas Diving

Bret Gilliam & Larry "Harris" Taylor, Ph.D.

It's April 5th, 1988 in Tamaulipas, Mexico and even though it's a bright , hot , sunny day Sheck Exley is cold and alone in the dark. Oh yeah, he's also nearly 760 feet deep in Nacimiento del Rio Mante cave system in pursuit of the deepest dive ever accomplished by an independent, untethered, surface-to-surface diver. Right now he's got a little problem: over 100 feet deeper than a free-swimming diver has ever been and almost 450 feet deeper than his nearest alternate gas source (cylinders staged at 320 fsw), he has paused to check his pressure gauge that monitors the Trimix (He / N_2 / O_2) tanks on his back.

Even on mixed gas, there are traces of narcosis at this depth. The small percentage of nitrogen in his mixture has produced a partial pressure this deep equivalent to approximately 260 fsw on compressed air. He has been fighting an upflowing current for over 20 minutes on his descent and time has become a factor. "As I entered the unexplored cave zone, I was concerned about the slower than expected rate of descent. I forced myself not to pick up the pace. Instead of continuing its vertical drop, the crevice began to narrow and run at a 60-degree angle. Flashes of narcosis were becoming more prominent. I glanced at my pressure gauge; the reading hadn't changed since my last check. I banged the unit on the tank. The needle jumped a few hundred pounds lower. Pressure had forced the lens against the needle, but had it stuck again? I had no way of knowing. A projection to tie off on was just below. I passed it and dropped deeper. The tunnel began to flatten out, falling at a 45-degree angle. I looked at the pressure gauge; it showed a third of the gas was gone. Was the reading correct? I had been down just over 22 minutes. It was time to get out."

"My light beam fell on an excellent tie-off 20 or 30 feet down. I took a breath and moved toward the projection, when suddenly a jolting concussion nearly knocked me unconscious. I tried to look behind me for a ruptured valve or hose. There was no leak. Something had imploded from the pressure, but what? I drew another breath and kicked the last eight feet to the tie-off. Quickly I threw two half hitches around the rock, reeled in the loose line and made the cut. My down time was 24 minutes, 10 seconds."

Sheck Exley returns from his record dive in Mante cave to resume a lengthy decompression and retrieve stage decompression cylinders. Photo by Ned DeLoach

Suspended at 780 feet, Exley has shattered the old mixed gas depth record (set by Germany's Jochen Hasenmayer) by 124 feet. But the surface was still a long way up and the implosion shock was numbing.

"I wanted to move fast from the deep water, 120 feet a minute if possible. The current that I had battled during my descent helped to lift me up the incline. I drew a breath and felt a slight hesitation from the regulator. The next breath came harder. Was I out of air? Again, I hit the gauge on my tank but this time the reading didn't change. If I was forced to use the gas in my belly tank, I would miss all the decompression to 330 feet where my first stage bottle was tied off. I switched over to my back-up regulator and with relief drew a full breath."

Proceeding steadily upward in the chasm, he reaches 520 feet and retrieves his conventional depth gauges where he has tied them off. Beyond this depth he has had to calculate depth by means of a knotted line since no gauges had yet been made to handle such pressure.

"At 520 feet, it was strange to be *decompressing* at such a depth. I knew that only one person had *ever gone deeper*. I remained a minute and then began to ascend at the rate of ten feet a minute until I reached 340 feet.

When I saw my first stage bottle and knew that I had spare gas around me, I finally began to relax. My stress was gone, but the long decompression stops were only beginning."

For 22 minutes bottom time, he would pay a decompression obligation of nearly ten and a half hours followed by 30 minutes breathing pure oxygen at the surface.

"Now with the extra time, I began to search for the cause of the deafening implosion. The source was the large plexiglass battery housing for my primary light. The pressure had been so great that the three-quarter inch lid was forced into the casing crushing the battery pack. Amazingly, the light still functioned."

Sheck completed his decompression uneventfully and surfaced at 9:30 PM wrinkled and exhausted. Hours later, support diver Ned deLoach broached the inevitable question:

"Will you ever do it again?"

Exley paused and considered his answer, "I don't know."

Only days before his 40th birthday and almost exactly a year later on March 28, 1989, Sheck Exley eclipses his own world record in the same cave reaching 881 feet!

There is good reason that he is considered to be one of the finest scuba divers of all time. But what makes his accomplishments all the more compelling is that he has devoted virtually his entire career to the most challenging diving environment of all: deep caves. A veteran of over 3000 cave dives, Exley is the undisputed king of the hill. But he remains an almost reluctant hero, virtually unknown until recently outside of the cave and "high tech" communities. In addition to the mixed gas record of 881 feet, he holds the record for longest swimming penetration into a cave: a 10,444 foot push into Chip's Hole, a sinkhole in Tallahassee, Florida. He also set the record for longest scooter/DPV penetration at Cathedral Canyon at 10,939 feet, a distance of over two miles!

Sheck is also a prolific writer with over 100 articles and six books to his credit. He has been honored as a Fellow of the National Speleological Society and was a recipient of the prestigious Lew Bicking Award as America's top cave explorer. Even so, "experts" gave him only 50/50 odds at best to survive the 780 foot dive. His custom Trimix tables were totally experimental having been developed by decompression physiology pioneer R.W. "Bill" Hamilton. The computerized tables called for Exley to stage 16 bottles and then carry four tanks with him for the final drop. Eleven different blends of Trimix were used with 52 decompression stops. The following year on the 881 attempt, the skeptics were less vocal. That required 34 stage bottles and 13 and a half hours of decompression. It's strictly lim-

Sheck Exley donning thermal underwear and dry suit before record dive in Mante cave in Mexico 1988. Photo by Mary Ellen Eckhoff

ited participation at this level of diving, Sheck essentially can compete only with himself.

The cave diving community has consistently been on the cutting edge of technology. Their continual drive to go deeper and farther than anyone before has given rise to much of what is known in the recreational dive community about the use of gas mixes other than air for deeper diving. Sheck's dive was not an isolated event, but rather the pinnacle of a series of carefully planned advances in knowledge about deeper diving. The advancement of knowledge has not been without its price. Along the way, pioneers and adventurers have died while seeking to dive deeper, extend bottom time and cover more distance. We, who sport dive today, owe our "recreating" to those who have gone before.

HELIUM

In 1919, Professor Elihu Thompson, an electronics engineer and inventor, speculated that nitrogen narcosis could be avoided if the oxygen in the breathing mix were diluted with a gas other than nitrogen. Thompson had previously established a record as an innovator with 700 patents including electric welding, the centrifugal cream separator and street arc lights. His business had earlier merged with Thomas Edison's company to form General Electric. He suggested that helium would be a suitable gas for deep diving without narcosis. Since at the time, the price of helium was over $2500 per cubic foot, the suggestion was viewed as an economic impossibility. About this time C.J. Cooke applied for a patent on the use of helium as a breathing gas mix. Additionally a series of experimental dives was begun on the *U.S.S. Falcon* which included at least one dive to 150 feet on a Heliox mix. Later, the discovery of helium in four Texas natural gas wells gave the United States an exclusive monopoly on the world's supply of helium. Its abundance dropped the price of helium to a few cents per cubic foot.

Thompson convinced the Bureau of Mines, which controlled the world's supply of helium (and was desperately seeking some use for this gas), and the U.S. Navy to begin examining the potential for deep diving using helium and oxygen as a breathing gas mix. By 1925 a lab had been established in Pittsburgh and lab animals were doing simulated dives in a chamber using helium-oxygen mixes. This work established that animals breathing an 80% helium / 20% oxygen mix could be decompressed at 1/6 the decompression time of an air breathing animal. Later, human subjects breathing 80% helium / 20% oxygen were found to have no apparent problems with Heliox decompression schedules that were 1/4 the time required for air breathing dives. More importantly, however, was the ability for humans to function "clear-headed" at depths where air breathing divers were incapacitated by nitrogen narcosis. Thompson's second major contribution to deep diving followed this early effort. He suggested that since the helium was not consumed during the dive, it could be conserved by developing a recirculating system for the diluent gas. His idea would ultimately prove sound; it needed only the development of high efficiency absorbents to remove the carbon dioxide generated from human metabolism so that the exhaled gas could be recirculated.

Divers commented on the ease of breathing helium, but noticed that they always felt chilled while breathing Heliox mixes. The change in voice characteristics often made communication at depth difficult. It was apparent that the narcosis-free advantage of helium breathing would create problems as well as solutions. It was obvious that much work still needed to be done.

Funding for deep diving training was very difficult to obtain in the post World War I economy. Although the U.S. Navy Experimental Diving School in Newport, Rhode Island had successfully trained divers that had salvaged the sunken submarine F-4 in 304 feet of water off Amala Bay near Honolulu, Hawaii in 1915, Congress could not be convinced to provide the funds for continuing the U.S. Navy Experimental Diving School in Newport. This school had, before the first World War, conducted over 300 test dives on air to depths of 258 feet. This work was the foundation for the first diving manual published in 1924 by the Bureau of Construction and Repair.

On September 25, 1925, the submarine *S-51* sank after a collision with the *S.S. City of Rome* near Block Island in 132 feet of water. Since the Navy had not had the funds to maintain their deep diving training program and associated submarine rescue proficiency, the salvage of this vessel took many months. (There simply were not enough divers qualified to dive below 90 feet. Bad weather and extreme cold also hampered the salvage effort.) Despite the disaster and modest public inquiry, funding was still denied. However, the public began to slowly build interest in improving the

Navy's ability to function at deeper depths.

In 1927 another sub, the *S-4* sank in 102 feet of water with loss of all 40 men. One sad aspect of this disaster is that six men survived the sinking and their taps on the hull could be heard by divers working to raise the vessel. For a short time, two way communication via rapping on the hull existed until, eventually, the taps from inside the hull ceased. The salvage operation lasted for over three months. An indignant public began to demand an improved Navy capability. As a result, the Navy established an Experimental Diving School in Washington, D.C. The two primary missions were to develop diving techniques to limit the effects of nitrogen narcosis and to develop rapid, effective methods for the rescue of crew trapped inside sunken submarines.

One significant early achievement of this Navy research unit was the development of the McCann rescue bell. This was a diving bell or chamber that could be lowered on cable to mate with the escape hatch on a submarine. Once attached, the water in the chamber between the bell and the submarine could be blown away by the use of compressed air. This then allowed trapped submariners to open their hatch and move into the rescue bell. The bell hatch could be closed and the chamber pulled back to the surface by winch. This bell would prove itself as many trapped submariners were saved by this rescue device.

In the late 1930's, an intern at Milwaukee County General Hospital, Edgar End, investigated the use of helium and oxygen as a breathing gas mix. His friend, Max Gene Nohl, an MIT graduate student, had developed with the assistance of John Craig (later of "Danger Is My Business" television fame), a new type of diving helmet. This helmet was part of a self-contained helium-oxygen system with on-board scrubbing of carbon dioxide that had been developed with the goal of photographing the *Lusitania* in 312 feet of water. During their pre-expedition trials, they were able to work at 312 feet for up to two hours with only three brief stops on their thirty minute ascent to the surface. When the expedition to photograph the *Lusitania* was abandoned, it was decided to attempt a world depth record. On a cold December day in 1937 the self contained Heliox helmet was tested in near-by Lake Michigan. Max Nohl set the world's depth record at 420 feet. The dive was conducted using a suit that was definitely not conventional. The diver wore a fashionable rubber coverall with Eskimo-like mukluk boots and a helmet that was described as looking like a lighthouse top with windows on all sides. The diver wore two self-contained tanks of breathing gas.

About the same time, the U.S. Navy research program began gathering significant momentum under the guidance of Behnke and Yarbrough. They successfully completed a simulated chamber dive to 500 feet using Heliox. It is interesting to note that during the Navy tank dive, the diver did not know his depth. When asked about his depth, the diver replied, "It feels like a hundred feet." During his decompression, the diver was told his actual maximum depth.

This success prompted the Navy to increase investigative efforts in the use of helium in diving gas mixes. By 1939 experimental research was a reality when the submarine, *U.S.S. Squalus,* sank off the Isles of Shoals in 243 feet of cold North Atlantic water. Since the submarine had been quickly located, there was a frantic effort to rescue the men trapped on

U.S.S. Squalus *breaks the surface off the coast of Maine in 1939 following successful salvage efforts. The submarine had sunk in 243 fsw and marked the first operational use of Heliox mixtures by Navy divers. The vessel was lost during a test dive, trapping 59 men on the bottom. Although 26 sailors were drowned, the first use of the new submarine rescue bell by frantic Navy divers and surface support crews enabled them to save 33 men imprisoned in the forward section. Photo U.S. Navy.*

Sport diving pioneer and early underwater photographer Hans Hass in 1942 with oxygen rebreather. The unit allowed about an hour bottom time and required him to manually add oxygen to the breathing bag as needed.

A self-contained oxygen rebreather developed by the Japanese for use during World War II.
Photos by E.R. Cross

board. A downhaul cable (for the McCann Rescue Bell) had parted and a diver on compressed air had been unable, due to the crippling effects of nitrogen narcosis, to repair the cable. It was decided to try the new helium-oxygen mixture. A diver on Heliox was successful. The McCann rescue bell made four trips in 12 hours to the sunken submarine and 33 men were successfully rescued. The submarine was then salvaged. Over 100 dives without injury were conducted by the U.S. Navy in the rescue/ salvage effort.

The *U.S.S. Squalus*, renamed the *Sailfish*, served in World War II. The rescue of 33 men and the successful salvage of the *Squalus* demonstrated to the U.S. Navy and the American public that Heliox was a viable protocol for deep diving operations. The successful rescue of these trapped men and the subsequent salvage of the sunken vessel are considered to be two of the most significant accomplishments in the history of marine life saving and salvage operations. The completion of the *Squalus* salvage and the appearance of war clouds on the horizon, prompted Congress to increase the funding for U.S. Navy deep diving training and research. Incidentally, Congress, fearing both the ingenuity of German research under the political

The first exploration of England's underwater caves including the infamous Wookey Hole were conducted using oxygen rebreathers such as this. Photo by Rob Palmer

control of Adolph Hitler and the use of helium in lighter-than-air dirigibles, prohibited the export of helium. For the next 20 years the U.S. Navy, with the world's sole supply of helium, was the primary user/investigator of Heliox as a breathing gas mix.

Jack Browne devised a triangular light-weight mask and tested his system in 1946. Diving in a pressurized tank, with decompression guidance from End and Behnke, he did a simulated dive of 550 feet. His system came to be known after its inventor, and the "Jack Browne" enjoyed a widespread popularity in compressed air use as well. During the 1950's and early 1960's, Browne's mask was standard equipment on most commercial diving job sites and strayed into the then fledgling sport diver markets as well.

Following the second World War, the British, using helium that had been obtained with the approval of the U.S. Secretary of Interior, Secretary of Defense and the U.S. President, began experimenting with Heliox mixtures. In some of their first dives, the divers developed extreme claustrophobia during diving and in screaming fits demanded to be hauled out of the water. Although the physiologists were convinced that the oxygen con-

Commander Gil Gilliam in early "Jack Brown" mask off Key West, Florida 1960. This surface supply mask was adopted for heliox and compressed air use by Navy, commercial, scientific and recreational applications. Photo by Bret Gilliam

Ed Link's "Man in the Sea" mini-habitat being winched over the side in 1962 for the first Heliox saturation experiment. Photo by U.S. Navy

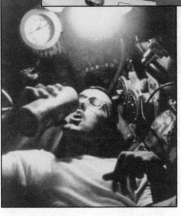

The first Heliox aquanaut, Robert Stenuit, inside "Man in the Sea" during decompression following a 24 hour dive to 200 fsw. Stenuit's original dive plan was cut short when a launch containing extra helium cylinders capsized returning to the support ship. He decompressed for 58 hours in the habitat chamber after being abruptly winched aboard ship on Link's orders following the helium loss. Photo by U.S. Navy

centrations were too high and thus the source of the problems, the divers blamed the helium. It was referred to as "Yankee gas" or "Stuka juice." (The Stuka was a German dive bomber used during WW II.)

The British diving experiments were conducted from the vessel *Reclaim*. This vessel anchored near a vertical wall in Loch Fyne that bottomed out at 540 feet. Since the Olympics were being held in London, Captain Shelford devised a "diver's depth thermometer" and sent divers on 18 dives, each deeper than the previous. The depths reached were recorded on the "thermometer." A Diver's torch was created and each new depth reached was rewarded with the diver receiving the "Olympic torch." The diver would accept the torch and run a victory lap around the vessel while wearing diving boots. Using nearly all of the remaining British supply of helium, Diver First Class Wilfred Bollard took seven and a half minutes to descend to a new world record depth of 540 feet. After five minutes on the bottom the diver took eight hours and 26 minutes to ascend (ascent time was increased because of a three hour treatment for the bends; the diver suffered elbow pain when transferring from the Davis submersible decompression chamber (which he had entered at 190 feet) to the main decompression chamber at 30 feet.) After leaving the decompression chamber he received the "torch" from the "hand" of a Neufeldt and Kuhnke armored diving suit. Since this state-of-the-art suit was rated to 500 feet, Bollard scratched "out of date" on the suit and then did his victory lap!

THE HABITAT EVOLUTIONS

1962 saw the introduction of the first significant advances in man's attempts to actually *live* in the ocean. Habitat and submersible pioneer Ed Link launched two short duration but important projects back to back in August and September of 1962. Using himself as a guinea pig in the first project nicknamed *Trial Link* , he spent a cramped eight hours at 60 fsw in a tiny 11'x3' cylinder in the Mediterranean. Robert Stenuit followed him the next month in the same cylinder now called *Man-in-the-Sea* ; this time for 24 hours at 200 fsw breathing Heliox.

On the heels of Stenuit's dive, came the first of Jacques Cousteau's *Conshelf* missions with two divers spending a week at 35 fsw off Marseilles. Much as the "space race" was heating up, so it seemed the race for advances in underwater saturation habitats moved forward. In 1963, Cousteau followed up dramatically with *Conshelf II* in which seven "aquanauts" lived at 36 fsw on the ocean floor of the Red Sea for a month! During this same mission, Raymond Kientzy and Andre Portelatine spent a week in a specially staged mini-habitat called *Deep Cabin* at 90 fsw allowing them "excursion" dives with virtually no decompression to as deep as 360 feet.

Captain George Bond directed the Navy's best known experiments with large scale saturation diving. *Sealab I* kept four men at an average depth of 193 fsw for 11 days in 1964. *Sealab II*, a year later, was more ambitious. Three teams of ten aquanauts were saturated at 205 fsw for 15 days. One hardy participant remained in *Sealab II* for a month.

The follow-on seafloor experiment, *Sealab III*, was planned for a depth of 600 fsw. This huge undertaking required not only extensive development and testing of equipment but also assessment of human tolerance to high pressure environments. Between 1965 and 1968, 28 helium-oxygen saturation dives were performed at the Navy Experimental Diving Unit to depths of 825 fsw. In 1968, a record-breaking excursion dive to 1025 fsw from a saturation depth of 825 fsw was accomplished at NEDU. The culmination of this series was a 1000 fsw, three day saturation dive conducted jointly by the Navy and Duke University in the hyperbaric chambers at Duke. This was the first time man had been saturated at 1000 fsw. The *Sealab III* preparation experiments showed that men could readily perform useful work at pressures up to 31 atmospheres and could be returned to normal pressure without harm.

"The great depth intended for the *Sealab III* habitat necessitated highly specialized support including a diving bell to transfer divers under pressure from the habitat to a pressurized deck decompression chamber. The Navy had gained valuable experience several years earlier with a small deep diving system, the *Advanced Diving System* (ADS) *IV*, deployed in the Pacific. The ADS IV, later called the SDS-450, had a depth capability of 450 fsw. For the *Sealab III* experiment, a much larger and more capable deep diving system, the MK 2 MOD 0, was constructed and installed aboard the sup-

Raymond Kientzy leaves Conshelf II *to begin a one week saturation on heliox at the* "Deep Cabin" *located at 90 fsw in 1963. Kientzy made excursion dives from the habitat to as deep as 360 fsw. Photo by Cousteau collection*

Conshelf II *aquanauts dress in early Heliox rigs before swimming to the* "Deep Cabin" *1963. Photo by Cousteau collection*

port ship *Elk River*. With this system, divers could be saturated in the deck chamber under close observation and then transported to the habitat for the stay at depth or could cycle back and forth between the deck chamber and the seafloor while work was being performed on the exterior of the habitat.

"The *Sealab III* experiment was marred by tragedy. Shortly after being compressed to 600 fsw in February 1969, aquanaut Barry Cannon convulsed and drowned. This unfortunate accident ended the Navy's involvement with sea floor habitats. Deep saturation diving was not abandoned, however. The utility of deep diving systems in conducting saturation dives had been demonstrated." (U.S. Navy Diving Manual, Vol. II, 1992 revision)

In 1964, Link sponsored his *Man-in-the-Sea II* mission off the Bahamas and the U.S. NAVY deployed *Sealab I* near Bermuda. A plethora of

Tektite II *aquanauts collect samples using MK XV NITROX rebreathers in 1971 off St. John, Virgin Islands. This program marked the first all-female saturation mission including Dr. Sylvia Earle. Photo by NOAA*

progressively deeper and longer saturation projects followed including the two month mission of *Tektite* in the Virgin Islands in the late sixties. *Tektite* was utilized for multiple missions and in 1971 marked the first all female aquanaut team led by Dr. Sylvia Earle, now chief scientist for NOAA. Link also produced the venerable *Hydrolab* habitat that began operation in 1966 and into the mid-1980's before being retired to the Smithsonian Institution in Washington D.C. During its operational life it provided an underwater home to literally hundreds of scientists and researchers at its sites in Florida, the Bahamas and finally St. Croix in the Virgin Islands. Ultimately *Hydrolab* was replaced with the massive *Aquarius* habitat now in the process of relocating to a site in the Florida Keys. The saturation habitat fascination tapered off in the mid-1970's and now only a handful of projects remain in existence. Renewed interest is surfacing, however, as the possibilities of saturation exploration of deep wrecks and cave systems are discussed by the emerging high tech community.

MIXED GAS IN EARLY TECHNICAL DIVING

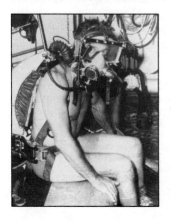

In 1970, two divers were lost while diving at nearly 400 fsw in Mystery Sink, a popular Florida cave system. Hal Watts, one of the U.S.'s top cave divers, was enlisted to organize a recovery of the bodies.

Astronaut Scott Carpenter turned aquanaut during Navy Sealab saturation training in the Mark XI rebreather, circa 1968. Photo courtesy of the U.S. Navy

Hydrolab *provided a saturation research base for literally hundreds of aquanauts during its operation in Florida, Grand Bahama, and St. Croix. It is now enshrined in the Smithsonian Institution.*
Photo by Bret Gilliam

Although Watts was one of the country's most experienced deep divers on air (he still holds the cave diving record for depth on compressed air: 415 fsw set in 1970), he felt that Heliox would give him a safety edge at these extreme depths and the added exertion of dealing with multiple body recoveries. He was successful retrieving the victims but suffered a serious case of decompression sickness during his shallow stops. The gas had eliminated his narcosis but the DCS hit so unnerved him that he never used Heliox again.

A year later during the height of the Vietnam war, Bret Gilliam was involved in a U.S. Navy project evaluating anti-submarine warfare (ASW) detection systems for tracking fast attack submarines in deep water. The project was based out of St. Croix in the Virgin Islands and was supported by two research vessels, several Navy Orion P3V patrol aircraft, various U.S. Navy submarines, and a host of electronics support technicians at a top security field headquarters located on a prominent mountain overlooking the Caribbean. Several defense contractors including General Electric and Magnavox had developed deep deployment sonar bouys with hydrophones suspended at depths approaching 500 fsw. As part of the test-

Bret Gilliam with oceanic white tip shark on Navy research ship in 1971. These aggressive sharks consistantly interfered with the divers and prompted the team to experiment with early versions of accelerated decompression schedules using oxygen to get out of the water faster following extended deep dives. Surface support crews attempted to distract the sharks by fishing for them while the divers were in the water.
Photo by Dan Farrar

Bret Gilliam operating high-volume compressor at oxygen plant in St.Croix 1971. For deep work on Navy evaluation contracts for submarine detection systems, he resorted to mixing his own heliox with the "cooperation" of a local industrial gas supplier.
Photo by Steve Arden

ing, evaluation and acceptance protocols, it was necessary to observe and film the hydrophones in active operation. Initial dives in the 250 to 300 fsw range were conducted on compressed air but as the depths were increased beyond 400 fsw, the divers in his team considered the use of Heliox to minimize narcosis and limit oxygen toxicity.

"It was kind of a strange working relationship," he remembers. "We were working for the Navy, using Navy ships, Navy planes, Navy staff, and a Navy budget... but the Navy really wanted nothing to do with us officially. Their dive teams out of Roosevelt Roads naval base in Puerto Rico had already declined to work on the projects due to the depths involved and the rather enthusiastic shark population we were forced to deal with in the open water. It was hard enough to work in such depths, but when the bottom is over 12,000 feet below you, many divers had big problems with spatial disorientation since everything is just a blue abyss. It was real easy to lose track of which way was up sometimes."

The large population of oceanic white-tip sharks were a major problem during decompression in the open ocean and unnerved several members of the dive team with their aggressive runs on the divers during long hangs. It was not uncommon to have decompression obligations of well over an hour and a half for their routine deep dives (far longer for others that required longer working bottom times), and Gilliam began experimenting with NITROX and pure oxygen as decom gases to get them out of the water faster. Sometimes the sharks were attracted to the ship by the low frequency sound impulses generated by the hydrophone test equipment. On those occasions, it was often necessary to push the sharks away from the dive cockpit with the long metal poles used to retrieve the sonobuoy floats. This amused the ship's crew and technicians, but was less than comforting to the divers.

"Just getting into the water to start one of these dives was a major exercise in stress some days. Those are the most pugnacious sharks I've ever encountered. We had a diving supervisor from the Navy who came to observe one day and was literally chased out of the water when the sharks kept bumping into him. After that we were pretty much left to ourselves. We paid a bounty to the deckhands to hook the sharks while we were in the water," Gilliam relates. Ironically, these same shark species attacked and killed a diving partner with him 18 months later on a deep dive on St. Croix's north shore. Gilliam was dragged down over 300 feet in trying to rescue his buddy, Rod Temple, from the attack.

Although he and his team were technically independent of Navy diving regulations, their liaison officer balked when they requested helium to supplement their regular compressed air dives. "We were in a ridiculous Catch-22: the Navy wanted the film on these hydrophones and other work recording wake vortexes from high speed sub runs by us in incredible depths, but they didn't want to provide us with Heliox to make the operations safer and more efficient," says Gilliam looking back after over two decades. "It was sort of a situation where nobody wanted to know what we were doing as long as we got results but they were not going to get hands-on involved with condoning even deeper work on Heliox. So we improvised."

They got a local industrial gas plant to make the raw mixtures by transfilling welding oxygen into helium tanks and then having them topped off. But they had to tumble the cylinders themselves. "The gas plant had no idea that we were using the gas to dive on. I guess they thought we were blowing up balloons or something. When asked, we'd mutter something vague about top secret testing or insulating sensitive electronics. We'd pick up the storage cylinders and drive them back to the ship where we would tumble the mixture by rolling them up and down the pier. We must have looked like some crazed hippie soccer team using 200 pound cylinders instead of balls but it worked fine. One day some admiral happened by and caught us at it and that was the end of our Heliox period. It was tough to go back to air after getting spoiled on the mix but we adapted." Gilliam would later set the world record for compressed air diving at 452 fsw in 1990.

During this same period ex-Navy diver Tom Mount took over the duties of Diving Officer for the University of Miami Rosenteil School of Marine and Atmosperic Sciences. In addition to a broad program in conventional scientific diving, Mount instituted a supervised deep diving program with various qualification levels. The initial success of the deep compressed air program led him to introduce the use of Heliox in 1970. Over 70 scientist/technician divers qualifed in the mixed gas training and several hundred dives were completed without incident through 1976. Mount and his associates also served as aquanauts for the early *Hydrolab* and *FLARE* projects in both Florida and the Bahamas.

In 1975 Heliox entered the world of cave diving again. On the first dive to 265 feet, convulsions during O_2 decompression at 40 feet cost the life of an experienced cave diver, Lewis Holtzin. His buddy, Court Smith, somehow managed to surface and survive the dive. Dale Sweet, in 1980, used Heliox to reach 360 feet in the cave Die Polder #2. Although six months later, Sheck Exley made the same dive on compressed air, the cave diving community was beginning to notice the existence of mixed gases for deep explorations. It would take three years, but in 1981, a German

Members of Rob Palmer's Bahamas Blue Hole expedition swim through the spectacular "Stargate" room.
Photo by Palmer, Deep Into Blue Holes

cave diver, Jochen Hasenmayer, descended into the French Vaucluse to reach a depth of 476 feet using Heliox. This was a new world record for a surface-to-surface scuba dive. In 1983, Jochen made another Heliox dive. This dive was to 685 feet and another world record.

One of the most well known uses of mixed gas within the cave diving community was the 1987 exploration of the Wakulla Springs Cave system. Using 12 divers, the team penetrated the cave more than 4000 feet at depths near 300 feet. The dive operation decompression profiles were controlled by a new computer analysis protocol developed by Bill Hamiliton and Dave Kenyon. Much of the success of the exploration was due to the use of mixed gas under the new decompression guidelines. Now, with reasonable decompression predictions, the depth records would move downward and more cave systems would be systematically explored. Eventually the practical operational limits of open circuit technology would be reached and serious explorers would turn to mixed gas rebreathers.

Stuart Clough, Dudley Crosson, and Neil Cave began preliminary work in 1985 with modifications to the Biomarine Mark XV rebreather in conjunction with Dr. Bill Hamilton who ran tables designed on constant oxygen partial pressures. During this same period the team experimented successfully with neon/oxygen (neox) mixtures. This set the stage for the first practical demonstration of the unit's capabilities in a 1987 expedition to the Blue Holes of Andros in the Bahamas. This team, led by noted British cave explorer Rob Palmer, marked the first use of the modified Mark

Rob Palmer with the CR155 Heliox rebreather. Photo by Rob Parker

XV's in actual cave penetrations. Joining Palmer were fellow U.K. diver Rob Parker and U.S. rebreather innovator Dr. Bill Stone.

Palmer recalls, "At that time, Bill had assorted bits and pieces of his prototype CIS-LUNAR model sort of littered about various work tables and garage benches. He was so captivated by the applications of the Mark XV's that he dashed off to home afterward and pulled everything together in less than two months for the Wakulla Project in Florida." Stone's company, CIS-LUNAR, is poised to introduce a triple redundant mixed gas rebreather to the market in 1993. See chapter 20 for more detail.

In correspondence with Gilliam (May 1992), Rob Palmer remembers the rebreather breakthrough:

"In 1987, I headed a cave diving expedition to Andros Island in the Bahamas, to continue the exploration of the many blue holes in an area we'd looked at before. On this project we had a large scientific contingent, and part of the program was to recover speleothem and wall rock samples from as deep as possible. We looked at several ways of working at depths of up to 330 feet in remote caves, often at a considerable distance from the nearest road. Surface umbilicals and one-atmosphere suits were ruled out almost immediately. Open circuit scuba was a possibility but air wasn't. To get the amount of helium and oxygen on site that we'd have needed to go open circuit was not only daunting, but excessively expensive. That left rebreathers."

"As luck would have it, we managed to negotiate use of Carmellan Research's CR155 units, modified Rexnord Mark XV's that utilized a partial pressure of 1.4 ATA's of oxygen. These gave us the potential of long bottom times with reduced decompression and no narcosis: an ideal blend! Because we had not prior experience of using them in caves, we made it a rule that each diver had to carry a bail-out cylinder of Heliox, pre-mixed to a composition suitable for breathing at the target depth. On the return, an umbilical hung down the entrance to 70 fsw allowing a back-up gas feed and the ability to decompress from 30 feet on open circuit oxygen."

"We did make some open circuit Heliox dives at more remote sites, down to about 290 feet, but these were only short exploratory penetrations and not work dives. Though our main target, Stargate, only hit 300 feet below the entrance, many safe and successful collection dives were made with the rebreathers and we all came away feeling that the future lay in this technology. Two years later we were making 330 foot dives in ocean blue holes on Grand Bahama with the units, working out of Zodiac inflatables miles from anywhere with only a two or three man support crew on the surface."

"The big problem with the CR155 rigs was that deep dives had to be pretty much pre-planned. Constant oxygen partial pressure tables aren't common and the ones we were using, developed by Carmellan in conjunction with Bill Hamilton, were still effectively being tested. We were the guinea pigs. The most recent high-profile project we used them on was an archeological recovery in Andros Blue Hole, collecting Lucayan Indian remains. Here I was testing the rig solo at a much shallower depth, between 60 and 120 feet. It allowed me a bottom time of between an hour and an hour and a half with only a few minutes of decompression. I could have spent all morning at the 60 foot level without needing to decompress at all."

Palmer's expeditions provided the basis for two fascinating books, The *Blue Holes of the Bahamas* and *Deep Into Blue Holes*. (See Bibliography page 382.)

Also in the later 1980's, the merits of mixed gas technology were recognized by the East coast wreck diving community. Bill Deans set up one of the first mixed gas filling stations on the East coast in Key West and then established a training program specifically designed to introduce NITROX and Trimix diving to recreational divers. Others have followed in his steps and now high-tech mixed gas training facilities have opened in several areas of the U.S. to meet the demand.

Deans' interest was fired initially by his desire to safely explore the deep wrecks, including the heavy cruiser *Wilkes-Barre*, located only a few miles from his dive operation. His success with Trimix and Heliox influenced other wreck diving explorers to make the switch from compressed air.

Among the first was Gary Gentile. Since 1970 Gary has devoted himself to exploring some of the United States most exciting and inaccessible shipwrecks. His first dive on the legendary *Andrea Doria* off Nantucket almost twenty years ago has fueled a passion for that one site that has seen him return almost 90 times. In 1985, he and a group of dive buddies recovered the ship's bell of the *Doria* that had somehow eluded discovery despite manic searches by artifact-crazed divers spanning four decades.

Like many explorers, Gary is a compulsive researcher into the histories of the ships he seeks. His most celebrated wreck dive came about while boning up on the circumstances of the sinking of the Civil War era ironclad, the *Monitor*. Sunk in 230 feet in a storm off the coast of North Caro-

Wreck explorer Gary Gentile prepares for 380 fsw dive on the battleship Ostfriesland in 1990. Photo by Ken Clayton

lina in 1862, the *Monitor* had never been visited by divers. NOAA had declared the wreck a protected sanctuary in 1975 and denied all access. Beginning in early 1984, Gentile and attorney Peter Hess filed suit to gain a permit to dive the historical site and photographically preserve its majesty. Thwarted at every attempt, it required almost six years of litigation before he emerged triumphant in 1989. His expedition to the wreck that next summer produced some of the best still and video images of the ship ever recorded.

One month later he would be part of the first team to dive the massive wreck of the *Ostfriesland*, a World War I battleship, sunk in 1921 off Virginia Beach. Gary recalls, "This was really a major step in deep exploration on scuba at the time since we would be using Heliox at 380 feet as free-swimming divers. I enlisted Ken Clayton and Pete Manchee as dive partners and after an exhausting search finally located the wreck. I remember thinking that this was really a unique experience because I had now dived two ships that delineated an era in U.S. naval warship history. The *Monitor* was the first of the ironclads back in the mid-1860's and the *Ostfriesland* marked the end of that tradition when Gen. Billy Mitchell demonstrated that supposedly invincible battleships could be vulnerable to attack by aircraft."

The benefits of mixed gas in sport diving and exploration applications have been apparent for decades. Now finally in the 1990's the availability of reliable professional dispensing stations and training has brought mixed gas to the forefront in deep working dives to make the sport safer. Mixed gas and NITROX have seen such explosive growth since 1990 that it is difficult to speculate on the number of divers actively involved in alternative breathing media. One thing is for sure, however, the genie is out of the bottle and no one is in a hurry to stuff him back in. Bill High, noted NOAA scientist and ex-president of NAUI, has predicted that NITROX will replace compressed air for sport divers by the end of the century. The popularity of other mixtures increases as education catches up with technology.

Rick Nicolini and Dustin Clesi of Team DiePolder '91 made the farthest and deepest penetrations in that system to pass lines laid in by Dale Sweet and Jim Lockwood almost eleven years earlier. Photo by Florida Speleological Researchers, Inc.

Almost $50,000 worth of high-tech mixed gas equipment, DPV's and surface supplied decompression gases were employed on the Team DiePolder '91 push. Here multiple sets of doubles await "staging" into the cave system. Photo by Florida Speleological Researchers, Inc.

HYDROGEN

The first recorded use of hydrogen as a breathing mix was in 1789. Lavoisier (The Father of Modern Chemistry) and Sequin exposed guinea pigs to mixtures of hydrogen and oxygen (Hydrox). They observed that the animal's oxygen consumption appeared to be similar in hydrogen/oxygen as in nitrogen/oxygen. Prior to WW II, a Russian scientist, Lazarev, subjected a single mouse to elevated pressures of hydrogen and oxygen. However, the use of hydrogen as a breathing gas for diving operations is generally associated with the Swedish engineer, Arne Zetterstrom.

Hydrogen is a desirable breathing gas component because it is the lightest element known. This means it is the least dense at depth and breathing resistance is minimal. The major problem with hydrogen-oxygen mixtures is the potential for explosion. (The destruction of the Hindenburg dirigible was due to hydrogen reacting with the oxygen in air; hydrogen-pure oxygen mix explosions are more violent!)

Paving the way for other mixed gas users today, were early experimenters such as Arne Zetterstrom and Hannes Keller who conducted some of the most daring open water dives with then theoretical gases for divers. Zetterstrom, a Swedish engineer, was fascinated with diving and sought to extend the working depths of divers by manipulating the oxygen content of a gas mixture and replacing the narcotic nitrogen with a more "workable" inert gas. Alternatives such as helium and neon were in such short supply as to be virtually unobtainable in Sweden in the early 1940's, so Zetterstrom focused on hydrogen as a replacement. It had favorable properties with respect to density, viscosity and narcotic potency but had the major disadvantage of forming being explosive if mixed with oxygen percentages in excess of 4%.

He was faced with several operational problems from the outset:
1. A 4% O_2 percentage would not support human life underwater until approaching the 100 fsw depth range.
2. Therefore a "travel" gas mix would need to be utilized to allow the diver to safely travel through the surface to 100 fsw range and back.
3. Now the curve ball... regular air as a travel mix could be used to 100 fsw and satisfy the oxygen requirements. However, if the oxygen-hydrogen mixture were to come into contact with a normoxic air mix, at least theoretically, the diver would explode. So a third mix, a transition gas mixture, would be necessary to protect the diver.

Zetterstrom decided to use one of the earliest NITROX blends as his transition mix: a 4% oxygen and 96% nitrogen mixture. This would allow a safe bridge between the O_2/H_2 "bottom mix". The diver would switch to the NITROX cylinder at 100 fsw and breathe for a period sufficient to flush out the higher O_2 percentage and then switch again to the "bottom mix". This cycle would be repeated during ascent.

It should be noted that since Zetterstrom manufactured his own hydrogen aboard ship at sea by breaking down ammonia to yield 75% H_2 and 25% N_2, his final mix was actually a Trimix of 4% O_2, 24% N_2 and 72% H_2. This was one of the earliest uses of Trimix; nitrogen in such reduced percentages was not a narcotic factor. In his experimental dives to 130 fsw he encountered no difficulties but was unpleasantly surprised to discover the highly conductive thermal properties of hydrogen and quickly became uncomfortably cold. Also, the light density of hydrogen, like helium, produced "Donald Duck" speech making voice communications with his surface tenders virtually impossible.

His second attempt would be conducted much deeper. The 300 fsw barrier was largely regarded as the limit of practical diver performance, so deliberately he would test his mixture at 360 fsw. Lowered on a wooden stage by a winch from the stern of his support ship *Belos*, he negotiated his mixture switches flawlessly and reached his planned depth where he reported "slight breathing resistance and the narcotic effect practically nil". His dive was regarded as a huge success with implications for commercial applications and for submarine rescue operations.

On August 7th, 1945, Zetterstrom planned a monumental dive to 500 fsw for the first time, far in excess of any dives successfully attained at that point by any method. Tragically, a breakdown in communications within his surface support team led to disaster.

Once again, he employed the diving stage to control his descent and ascent with prearranged signals and time allotments for his mixture switches and bottom time. All went well on the descent and he reached 500 fsw without mishap. He signaled the surface that he was well and the ascent phase was initiated in accordance with his pre-planned schedule. He was winched up to 166 fsw to begin his decompression when all hell broke loose. He had rigged the stage platform not only with a lifting cable but with two lines on either side to counteract any effects of current or tide. Somehow the tender handling the line to the bow of the ship misunderstood his instructions and winched his end of the platform all the way to within thirty feet of the surface. The stern tenders held steady with the intention of leaving Zetterstrom at 166 fsw. An impossible angle of tilt along with rapid decompression resulted in the diver's inability to negotiate gas mixture switches or to conduct normal decompression. The 4% O_2 mix was insufficient to maintain proper oxygenation and Zetterstrom died due to hypoxia and severe embolism.

Zetterstrom had dramatically demonstrated the practicality of his revolutionary gas mixes and shattered the depth record only to fall victim to the ineptitude of his surface support crew.

The death certificate stated that death was from "acute lack of oxygen and caissons disease of a violent nature." Although his death was totally unrelated to the use of hydrogen or his transition technique, (but by what was termed "an unpardonable mistake"), research on this gas was discontinued for many years.

During the mid 1960's research into the use of hydrogen in breathing gases resumed with animals breathing hydrox for up to 24 hours at 70 ATA. One interesting aspect of the animal research was the suggestion that hydrogen reduced the HPNS (high pressure nervous syndrome) often observed with helium based gas mixes on deep dives. Ultimately animals would be taken to 3500 feet on hydrox.

By 1967 there were two successful human chamber dives using hydrogen as a breathing mix to 7 ATA for 10 and then 20 minutes. More experimentation was resumed during the early 1970's to begin to develop realistic tissue saturation times for the future development of hydrox decompression tables. In 1974 the U.S. Navy initiated a series of dives termed hydrox to further evaluate problems associated with switching from hydrox to other gases.

In 1983 COMEX, the French deep diving concern (perhaps more fa- mous in the US as the company providing the submersible used in the re- covery of artifacts from the *Titanic*), began a series of dives to investigate the narcotic potential of hydrogen. Divers including H.G. DeLauze, Presi- dent of COMEX, descended in open sea to approximately 300 feet for five minutes. The divers could not perceive a difference between hydrox and Heliox at that depth. Chamber dives to 300 m (984 ft) demonstrated that hydrogen possessed a narcotic effect different from nitrogen. Hydrogen narcosis (the "hydrogen effect") had a tendency to be more psychotropic - ie. more like LSD, while nitrogen narcosis had an effect similar to alcohol. This deeper work suggested that hydrox as a binary gas mix would not be too useful at depths below about 500 feet.

MIX-MASTERING

Hannes Keller began experimental dives in 1959 that would ultimately more than double the depths of Zetterstrom but again with fatal conse- quences to dive team members. Keller, a Swiss mathematician, joined forces with noted physiologist Albert Buhlmann to explore the highly con- troversial elements of accelerated decompression in conjunction with he- lium and oxygen mixtures (Heliox). Both men could see the financial gain to be made by refining a system to place divers in working situations at incredible depths and bring them back to the surface without unreasonable delays due to decompression obligations. Much of their research was con- ducted cloaked in secrecy.

A young mathematician and Zurich engineering school instructor, Keller, saw his first aqualung while vacationing in Greece in 1958. After talking with local divers and with no previous experience in diving he was said to have proclaimed, "diving techniques were 30 years behind the times." He decided that his life's work would be to improve diving tech- nology. A voracious reader, he soon had read much of what was then avail- able on deep diving technology. He convinced Buhlmann to join in his ef- forts. Together they developed a technique for utilizing nine different gas mixes at various depths and proposed that deep diving was possible by varying the proportions of the gases at different depths.

Although no money was available for computer time, Keller convinced IBM to give him four hours of computer time to do the necessary calcula- tions for developing tables based on the hypothesis of multiple mixes for different depths. The result was 400 different tables for depths up to 1312 feet. Next, he went to Jacques Cousteau and with his assistance was able to have access to the French diving chamber which was operated by the

Atlantis *being lowered into the water off Catalina for the first 1000 fsw ocean dive in 1962. Photo courtesy of the U.S. Navy*

French Navy Group for Undersea Research and Development at Toulon. There, Cousteau and a team of Swiss scientists watched Keller attain a pressure of 630 feet and ascend without illness or apparent difficulty. When news of his success circulated within the international diving fraternity, this community assumed that Keller was some sort of physiological freak with extraordinary tolerances for breathing exotic gas mixes at depth.

Keller went to the U.S. to try to convince the U.S. Navy to finance further work. Although many in the U.S. scientific diving community were intrigued by his claims, funding was denied. (He insisted that he would retain all commercial rights and that his gas mixtures remained a secret.) Keller then returned to France.

Although the French could not fund his work, they did allow him access to the chamber in Toulon.

Working with a hyperbaric chamber capable of simulating 1500 fsw in November of 1960, Keller prepared for the first practical test of his new gas mixes and decompression schedules. This was to be a dual dive: Keller in the lower "wet" chamber and a team of French doctors in the upper "dry" chamber. Keller, equipped with a battery of diving equipment and varied cylinders for his mixes would dive alone to a simulated depth of 830 fsw! This was beyond conception even to theoreticians at this time. The French team would be exposed to a pressure equivalent to 200 fsw. Keller's rapid compression to 25 atmospheres was accomplished in only ten minutes and the consensus opinion of outside observers was that he could not survive

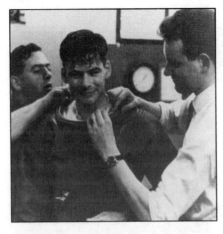

Hans Keller suiting up for the 1000 foot dive. Although Keller's tables were proven and he reached his target depth, two less experienced team members were killed in a tragic double fatality that clouded his accomplishment. Photo courtesy of the U.S. Navy

such an exposure. However, Buhlmann was in voice contact with him and reported him well at the bottom depth.

An equally rapid decompression to the 200 fsw level of the French team was conducted and Keller opened the connecting hatch to join the doctors in the "dry" chamber. Removing his gear and drying off, he then entered the access lock six minutes later. Following only 30 minutes more decompression, he emerged at the surface! By contrast, the French team exposed to only a maximum of 200 fsw would require twice as much decom time under their conventional tables. Keller had been over four times deeper.

He would not stop there. The second pivotal dive took place in actual open water conditions in Lago Maggiore and this time, incredibly, he took along a LIFE magazine reporter named Kenneth McLeish. They would reach 730 fsw while being lowered on a similar platform stage as utilized by Zetterstrom. This time the topside commands were personally supervised by Buhlmann to avoid any possible problems in operational execution. The dive required four mixes to be employed and broke the in-water record of 600 fsw held then by British Royal Navy diver George Wookey. In startling contrast to Wookey's decompression time of 12 hours, Keller and McLeish completed their decompression in less than 45 minutes. Keller had proved the validity of his decompression theory and McLeish had forever set a new standard in "on scene" reporting. It's hard to imagine one of today's blow-dried news anchors donning a dive suit to report the story from the sea floor.

The Lago Maggiore dive finally prompted the major financial support Keller and Buhlmann so desperately needed. Funding was now supplied by a group of U.S. corporations including Shell Oil, General Motors and the Navy. Keller announced his goal to reach the average limit of the continental shelf and thus open up the exploration of mining raw mineral deposits and food resources previously unreachable. This 1000 fsw dive was scheduled off Catalina Island in southern California.

A custom built diving decompression chamber named *Atlantis* was constructed capable of carrying two occupants to the sea floor over 30 atmospheres down. It was fitted with two chambers and a connecting lock to allow Keller to exit *Atlantis* and then re-enter and conduct his decompression in the upper chamber. With an evermindful eye towards the international press, Keller once again chose a journalist to accompany him. Peter Small, a British newspaperman, was only an amateur diver but had obtained a commission assignment for a substantial fee on the stipulation that he personally write the article.

Hans Hass was a personal friend of Small's and writes of his misgivings about the upcoming dive in **Men Beneath The Sea** (1973), "Peter Small had been married only shortly before this, and his wife, Mary, as attractive as she was energetic, was vital to his resolve, or so it seemed to us. From a long conversation with Peter, I got the feeling that deep down in his heart he was undertaking more than he really wanted. I don't mean by this that he was afraid, but that he lacked the freedom from doubt, the confidence of Hannes Keller. Various circumstances soon deprived him of his freedom of choice. {the newspaper commission among them, Ed.} Mary saw in him a hero, there was no escape... Somehow I felt uneasy. Peter was a true Englishman, and did not betray his feelings, but I knew him and all divers well enough to understand him."

Several practice dives were conducted working up to the 1000 fsw exposure and in the process two bends hits were sustained, one on Hermann Heberlein and one on Peter Small only two days prior to the planned primary dive. Keller and Small had taken *Atlantis* to a depth of 330 fsw and exited to spend over an hour outside on the bottom. Small had a minor hit in his elbow after surfacing and was recompressed. On Monday, December 3, 1962 all was finally ready and the support ship *Eureka* was moved into position where the sea floor was exactly 1000 feet deep. An umbilical hose linked *Atlantis* with the ship down to 330 feet to supply gases and pressurization to the chamber. Beyond this depth the divers were on their own connected only via the steel lifting hawser. Keller had installed back-up cylinders in *Atlantis* to provide extra breathing gas if needed. Each diver was equipped with a back mounted rig capable of providing 15 minutes time. It could be replenished by filling off the back-up cylinders. Unfortunately, it was discovered that the back-up units were leaking and Keller was forced into a difficult decision heavily influenced by the financial pressures of corporate endorsement and the desire to still maintain the secrecy of his mixes and decom schedules.

Keller related to Hass, "Before the attempt, this was the situation: barely enough gas in the equipment carried on the back; on the other hand, the team in top form, weather perfect. Personally, I had a strong fear that it might be all called off. Knowing that one never has perfect conditions, an attempt under perfect starting conditions never happens. Never. There are only adequate starting conditions... Well then, I decided to make the attempt."

His goal was to briefly swim out of the chamber and plant the Swiss and American flags on the bottom. He determined that his primary gas units would allow him a sufficient safety margin to exit the *Atlantis* and return. Upon reaching the planned depth, the divers opened the exit hatch and Keller dropped the short distance to the bottom. But the flags became tangled in his breathing apparatus and it took him over two minutes to free himself and drop them. After he and Small successfully closed the hatch he was exhausted. At this point he should have refilled their breathing gear from the back-up cylinders but felt himself passing out. He was just able to activate the compressed air vent to flush the knee-deep water from the tiny chamber before losing consciousness.

The remote television cameras linked the surface crew with the developments on the bottom and they immediately instructed Small to remove his mask and breathe the air atmosphere. This would probably result in his unconsciousness as well but with Keller unable to operate the inside gas selections during ascent, it was felt that Small was better handled in this manner. But Small froze in horror and continued to breathe the deep mix and collapsed shortly thereafter out of camera view.

The tenders quickly raised *Atlantis* to 330 feet where divers were sent down to reconnect the umbilical. But at the 200 fsw level, the chamber proved to be leaking and could not be raised without risking explosive decompression to the occupants. Dick Anderson, a professional California diver, and Chris Whittaker, an English friend of Small's, went down to ascertain the problem but could not locate the source of the leak. To Anderson it seemed that the chamber had solved its problems and the two returned to the surface. Whittaker was not nearly the experienced pro that Anderson was and had difficulty on the ascent with this safety vest. He arrived on the ship with a profuse amount of blood in his mask and thoroughly worn out. The surface crew informed them that the chamber was still leaking.

Since they were the only two safety divers, Anderson knew he would have to go back down but preferred to go alone. "The boy was not very strong, and rather exhausted. He undid his weight belt and took it over his arm. I nodded to him. In an emergency, he could drop the belt and would then float to the surface. We swam down again. On top of the chamber I signalled to Chris to stay there and wait. I swam down again to the hatch. I had more than enough air and had a good look around... The cover was firmly attached but when I looked very closely I discovered a small crack in it. Something small was stuck there. I tried to get at it with my knife. Then I simply propped myself on the ladder and pressed myself upwards with my back as hard as I could. I did this for quite a while. Finally the hatch appeared to be sealed. When I swam up... Chris had disappeared. I thought he must have surfaced already since I couldn't see him anywhere. When I got to the top, they asked me where Chris Whittaker was..." (excerpted from Hass' **Men In the Sea**)

Whittaker was never found. The *Atlantis* was hoisted aboard and Keller regained consciousness and hastened to cut Small from his dive suit and examine him. He reported to Buhlmann that he was alive. Later he came around and said he was thirsty. Keller got him something to drink while Small briefly spoke to Buhlmann on the phone. He then went to sleep seemingly OK. However, when Keller checked his pulse later he discovered that Small had died. He was stunned at Small's death. Keller was completely fine. The double fatality cast his remarkable achievement in shadow. Hillary Hauser, Dick Anderson's ex-wife, notes in her book **Call To Adventure**: "The Keller dive was an awful paradox. It was a success because one man made a 1000 foot dive and lived, proving that the mysterious mixture of gases had worked. It also was a disaster because of the deaths involved. No one knew whether to cheer or boo. The effect was the same as if Neil Armstrong had landed on the moon and lived, while fellow astronaut Buzz Aldrin had not made it back to Earth. In that case, would the moon landing have been considered a success or failure?"

Hass speculates that Keller's determination and confidence insured his survival while the less experienced and less motivated Small succumbed. Hass felt that had Dick Anderson been Keller's diving partner no lives would have been lost. With the benefit of hindsight, Keller would have been wise to ensure a more professional companion but Small had performed satisfactorily on the practice runs. Keller remained shaken but undaunted and continues today with consulting work in varying fields of diving and computer technologies. His vision of man's ability to work in extreme depths would provide the basis for commercial and naval systems that followed.

HPNS AND THE BIRTH OF TRIMIX

The trend has been to investigate and use multiple component mixes for extended diving. It was found in 1965 that divers breathing Heliox mixtures at depths below 500 feet developed nervous tremors known as High Pressure Nervous Sydrome (HPNS). A series of deep dives at the F.G. Hall laboratory at Duke University under the direction of Peter Bennett found that using small quantities of nitrogen in the Heliox (termed Trimix) helped eliminate this problem. In their *Atlantis* dive series, three divers reached a depth of 2132 feet breathing Trimix.

During Hasenmayer and Exley's deep cave penetrations both divers found that the "buffering effect" of nitrogen in the mix smoothed out the "shakes" they had experienced earlier on Heliox. The addition of nitrogen also made the mixture less expensive and easier to blend. Although Trimix is in widespread use now for a variety of applications in high-tech diving, the motivations have been primarily financial. Nitrogen (in atmospheric air) is free. A "poor man's mix" can be be prepared using helium as the low pressure gas going into the cylinder first, and then compressed air can be used as the "add gas" to reach final working pressure. This is economical and fairly simple operationally. None the less, as open circuit divers explore deeper depths, the original benefit in Trimix as a combatant to HPNS will once again be utilized.

It has been found that adding helium to hydrogen-oxygen mixes (termed Hydreliox) helps to eliminate the "hydrogen effect" narcosis associated with breathing only a hydrogen-oxygen mix. Theoretical limits of hydreliox are currently placed at about 1750 feet.

NITROGEN

The first use of nitrogen-oxygen mixes of other than normal air concentration was the self-contained dress of the Westfalia Machinenfabrik in Geisenkirchen, Germany. In 1912 they used their suit with a mixture of 45% O_2 and 55% O_2 for depths to a 100 feet and a 30% O_2 mix for diving to depths of 200 feet. This suit, or the NITROX blend did not receive wide distribution. Based on this work, in 1913 Draegerwerk produced a similar device which automatically mixed nitrogen and oxygen supplies to produce a 60% O_2 mix. Some time before WW I, the Fleuss-Davis Scuba unit appeared. This device consisted of two 10 cubic foot tanks; one for compressed air and one for oxygen. The gases were mixed in a manifold between the two tanks and the diver's mouthpiece. The manufacturer claimed success of this unit to depths of 66 feet.

Between the two World Wars Siebe Gorman & Co. introduced the technique of using different concentrations of oxygen mixed with nitrogen. It had been established that oxygen concentrations greater than 2 ATAs could not be tolerated by divers for extended periods of time without difficulty. The divers affected by this incapacity and convulsions associated with high O_2 concentrations invented a mythical monster, "Oxygen Pete," who was supposed to lurk on the bottom of the sea waiting to molest unwary divers. Oxygen toxicity hits during this time were referred to as "getting a Pete."

Since it was known that increased oxygen (decreased nitrogen) increased available bottom time without decompression obligation in the 60 -100 foot range, a number of mixes were utilized primarily by the commercial diving community during the period following WWII. Workman developed decompression schedules for nitrogen-oxygen and helium-oxygen diving and published these tables in 1965.

In the late seventies, the Canadian research institute DCIEM, was asked to develop a diving apparatus for the Canadian military to be used in clearing mines. The ideal system would not disturb mine sensors which would detect motion, magnetic fields, and/or sound. It was decided to utilize a semi-closed system which would use a nitrogen-oxygen mix and would vary in O_2 concentration at depth to supply a constant PO_2. The constant PO_2 is delivered via a pneumatic manifold,

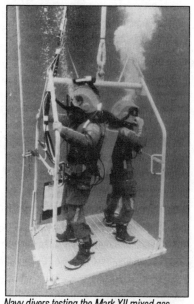

Navy divers testing the Mark XII mixed gas diving system are recovered from nearly 400 fsw on an in-water diving stage. This system replaced the far heavier and less efficient hard hat gear in earlier use. Note the closed circuit TV camera mounted on the diver at left. This enabled topside technicians to monitor the equipment's performance and the divers. Photo by Gilliam/U.S.Navy

as opposed to an electronic PO_2 sensor controlled relay system. This system was made available in the late 80's.

In 1978 NOAA formally established procedures for a standard mixture of 68% N_2 / 32% O_2. It is known as NOAA NITROX I. A second standard mix which contains 36% O_2 is known as NOAA NITROX II. Since that time, a number of users, including the U.S. Navy, commercial and academic diving operations have successfully used NITROX in operations shallower than 130 feet. NOAA has developed a reasonable compact shipboard continuous gas mixing system to supply NITROX for diving operations. Credit is generally given to Dr. Morgan Wells for developing the NOAA NITROX program. His associate Dick Rutkowski, former NOAA deputy director of diving operations, introduced NITROX to the sport diving community in 1987 as founder of the International Association for NITROX Diving (IAND).

During the last five years, approximately 32,000 logged dives using NITROX were surveyed. Although rigorous statistical analysis is not yet complete, the trend is that NITROX is a safe, easily handled mix when used by properly trained divers. Two different agencies, ANDI (American NITROX Divers, Inc.) and IAND, have been formed to introduce this technology to the sport diving communities. The sanctioning of NITROX training by recreational training agencies NAUI and NASDS indicates that NITROX mixes are becoming a permanent part of the sport diving community.

SHAKING HANDS WITH THE "KRAKEN": AN AFFORDABLE MIXED GAS REBREATHER

When sport divers talk about equipment innovations they are generally referring to modifications or refinements to existing models. Rarely is a piece of equipment introduced that fundamentally changes the way we dive. The last real breakthrough has been with diving computers to enable the diver to make practical use of in-water multi-level dive planning and decompression management. Brace yourself... a new product will be out in 1993, that has the potential to dramatically alter the way we look at equipment packages and life support systems. It will come through the miracle of mixed gas rebreathers available at an affordable price for the first time.

There is nothing new about such units. Military versions in various configurations have been around since the 1940's. What's new and exciting is that Carmellan Research's "Kraken" model has been deliberately produced to address the operational needs of the advanced sport diving and scientific markets. The "Kraken", which will be introduced in 1993, is essentially a redesigned Rexnord Mark XV. This unit was originally produced for the U.S. Navy and carried a corresponding "military/industrial complex" price tag of around $50,000. (Undoubtedly the screw driver to work on it sold for about another thousand dollars.)

But the brain trust at Carmellan (Stewart Clough in England and Dudley Crosson in the U.S.) have managed to hone the price tag on the

NITROX version of the "Kraken" down to a projected retail of $5000! That's less than most high tech wreck or cave divers are currently lugging around on their backs with open circuit equipment. And it is far safer with significant operational advantages.

First of all, it will be able to provide approximately two and a half hours of life support *regardless of depth*. It accomplishes this by what is termed closed circuit gas use. In traditional open circuit scuba, the gas we inhale is completely exhaled (exhausted) into the water with each respiratory cycle. With a closed circuit system in rebreather mode, the gas is re-cycled via a carbon dioxide scrubber to remove the waste product of our metabolic process and the "cleaned" gas is then available for reuse. There are no bubbles in such a system since all the processes are contained within the system. Two small cylinders, not much larger than a candlepin bowling ball, store the oxygen and an inert diluent gas (usually nitrogen or helium). Since the gases are rebreathed after scrubbing, far less volume of gas needs to be carried by the diver. The resulting package is smaller, lighter and presents far less drag coefficient to swim with in the water.

Fully equipped, the "Kraken" diver wears a backmounted equipment package that includes an integrated bouyancy compensator, instrumentation, decompression computer, regulator, breathing gas etc. that weighs about 60 pounds. In the NITROX version, he has a practical operational depth of approximately 165 feet and can stay submerged well over two hours. Compare that to the multiple tanks, regulators, stage cylinders, decompression tanks or surface supplied gas, redundant BC's etc. that the typical high tech diver employs for deeper diving or penetrations into cave systems. It's not uncommon for the open circuit diver to wear over 200 pounds of equipment and he will still be limited to a relatively short stay underwater.

The "Kraken" features a sophisticated computer soft-wear module that carefully monitors and adjusts the diver's oxygen partial pressure to remain constant regardless of depth. This eliminates the hazard of oxygen toxicity and maximizes decompression efficiency. Once the working portion of the dive is completed the "Kraken" can be programmed to feed a richer oxygen mixture to speed decompression stops. The entire system can be monitored by the diver and manually overridden in the event of failure of the three separate and independent O_2 sensors.

A wrist mounted display monitor provides status updates on remaining gas supply, bottom time, sensor display, depth, oxygen partial pressure, and even cumulative oxygen dose expressed in OTU's (oxygen tolerance units). The training necessary for safe operation of the NITROX "Kraken" can be accomplished in three days.

While the NITROX version will handle the needs of most divers, the second edition (available at a slightly higher cost) will be a Heliox unit capable of providing similar dive durations to around 300 feet. By replacing the inert diluent gas with helium, the problems of nitrogen narcosis are eliminated. Imagine a 300 foot wreck dive with no narcosis and a two hour bottom time. An even deeper Heliox version will be available in 1993. Rob Palmer, Carmellan's special projects director, is actively involved in the operational field testing of the units and will be lead diver in test exposures for a new Heliox model. Dives to nearly 600 feet are planned in the Bahamas this December. Palmer is one of England's premier cave diving explorers and has used the prototypes to extensively explore some of Bahamian "blue hole" systems on expeditions dating back to 1981.

The applications for the NITROX "Kraken" are varied. Underwater photographers such as reknowned film maker Howard Hall have already discovered the benefits of no bubbles and extended freedom of bottom times. He used a rebreather to swim with schooling hammerhead sharks and was accepted as just another fish. Previously the animals had fled when closely approached by bubble snorting divers. Cave divers and wreck divers can now eliminate the cumbersome burden of extra cylinders and equipment that used to be required just to provide enough breathing gas to get into the desired site for exploration. Scientists, researchers and even everyday sport divers will benefit if their diving calls for longer, deeper or multiple repetitive dives per day.

Rob Palmer reflects in conclusion, "Sport diving began with oxygen rebreathers, home made regulators, low pressure aircraft cylinders, and a lot of cautious, forward looking experimentation. That was 50 years ago, and with little material development, there have been few real changes since then. These new techniques are making diving an adventure again for all of us. There is a lot of unexplored ocean out there, and I can't help feeling that there is something missing in sport diving today when the most exciting thing at last year's trade show was a new shape of snorkle..."

LOOKING AHEAD

Undoubtedly, rebreathers will be the next technological advance for serious sport and scientific diving applications. Once reserved only for the military or those on similar budgets, recent breakthroughs in the private sector promise to bring the price of such units down to affordable levels. Dudley Crosson, President of Delta P, has speculated that a NITROX rebreather under $3000 is not far off. As the market expands and manufacturers apply themselves to the realities of a civilian based consumer economy, the pioneering research and development costs previously under-written by the military should result in a variety of mixed gas systems available to the general diving public that would have been unthinkable only a few years ago.

Several players have already entered the niche market for NITROX and mixed gas diving computers. With several major international and U.S. diving manufacturers sniffing around these fringe marketers, the prospect of larger scale production looms with its attendant price advantages. Where will we be by the turn of the century (only eight years away)? For the high tech diver, open circuit equipment is already bordering on obsolescence. Look for self-contained rebreathers capable of 12-24 hours of life support to depths approaching 1000 fsw. All this will be packaged in a system that weighs and costs less than conventional compressed air scuba. Sounds exciting...

"What improvement may hereafter be made in diving, I will not pretend to say; yet I am convinced that there can be much progress in the art." These words were written in 1859 by Johnny Green. They are still valid!

REFERENCES

Brauer, R. *Hydrogen as a Diving Gas,* Undersea and Hyperbaric Medical Society, Bethesda, MD. 1987, 336 pages.

Davis, R. *Deep Diving and Submarine Operations*, St. Catherine Press, London, England, 1962, 713 pages.

DeLatl, P. & Rivoire, J. *Man and the Underwater World,* G.P. Putnam's Sons, New York, NY. 1956, 400 pages.

Loach, N. *The Deepest Dive: A Study In Controlled Paranoia,* Ocean Realm, Summer, 1988, p.80-89.

Loyst, K. *Diving Computers: A Consumer's Guide to History, Theory, and Performance,*

Dugan, J. *Man Under the Sea*, Collier Books, New York, NY. 1965, 443 paages.

Gilliam, B. et. al. *Deep Diving*, Watersport Publishing, San Diego, CA. 1992, 254 pages.

Green, J. *Diving wtih and without Armour*, Faxon's Steam Press, Buffalo, NY, 1859, 62 pages.

Hamilton, R. *Workshop Conclusions,* Scuba Diving Resource Group, Boulder, CO, 1992, 22 pages.

Larsen, H. *A History of Self-Contained Diving and Underwater Swimming* National Academy of Sciences, Washington, D.C. 1967, 50 pages.

Marx. R. *Into the Deep*, Van Nostrand, New York, NY. 1978, 198 pages.

Miller, J. & Koblick, *Living and Working in the Sea,* Van Nostrand Reinhold, New York, NY. 1984, 433 pages.

Palmer, Rob *Deep into Blue Holes,* Unwin Hyman Ltd., London, 1989, 165 pages

Rutkowski, D. *Nitrox Manual,* Hyperbarics International, Key Largo, FL. 1989, 103 pages.

Schilling, C. *A History of Development of Decompression Chambers,* Undersea Medical Society, Bethesda, MD. 1981, 131 pages.

Smith, E. *Techniques for Diving Deeper than 1500 Feet,* Undersea Medical Society, Bethesda, MD. 1980, 159 pages.

Vallentine, R. *Divers and Diving,* Blandford Press, Poole, Dorset, England, 1981, 169 pages.

Zinkowski, N. *Commercial Oil Field Diving,* Cornell Maritime Press, Cambridge, MD. 1978, 316 pages.

CHAPTER 2

THEORY

Psychological Aspects in Diving

This chapter discusses the greatest contributor to technical diving accidents and emergencies — diver stress. It will present exercises for instructors and divers to use in developing the self-discipline required for safe technical diving. Application of the information presented here and the use of these self-discipline exercises is basic to producing competent mixed gas diver's or, for that matter, producing competent divers at any level. Adequate survival skills to use when faced with real or perceived threats to a divers safety are an absolute requirement. It is well documented that people react to stress through a survival response that employs both physiological and psychological instincts that includes the use of overlearned emergency skills and techniques.

All the classroom lectures and discussions, examples of diving emergencies and their solutions, and even non-stress related practice of diving skills will not develop the required subconscious reaction needed to handle a true life threatening situation. To control stress, divers must be exposed to specific controlled exercises during training that simulate "realistic and stressful" situations that the diver may face during his diving career. These exercises allow the mind and body to work together and develop the necessary skills which may someday allow a diver to save a life — their own. The knowledge and skills described in this chapter are designed to help the technical diver develop instinctive and effective survival reactions. These openwater exercises use various forms of stress inducing techniques such as time pressure, task loading, physical exertion, and ego threat. When overlearned these skills pay a dividend in self rescue. In actual decompression, deep, mixed gas and other technical diving environments adding stress control drills will tone up and round out our survival abilities.

We must all recognize two fundamental facts: 1) Mixed gas and technical diving are fun, especially for well trained divers, and 2) Mixed gas and technical diving are serious diving activites. It can be a health threatening or even life threatening experience. Mixed gas instructors, technical diving instructors and technical divers must be aware of both of these facts and be capable of providing training or completing training that recognizes both the pluses and minuses of the particular diving activity.

To develop adequate training programs means an evaluation of present day concepts. First, what really causes dive accidents? Or, what is the greatest danger facing divers? Many will say "air embolism" i.e., arterial gas embolism (AGE) or decompression sickness (DCS). However, these are, in fact, end results, they are not the causes of accidents. A few will say panic. This is a more correct answer than AGE or DCS. The truly enlightened will answer diver stress or a diver's perception of his stress. Teaching divers to recognize and deal with stress during diving is the area of diver training that is most crucial and yet least explored. Dealing with stress while diving is a crucial element of surviving in the water in the event that something goes wrong. Taking this concept one step further it is the overall attitude and outlook of the diver toward the stress of the moment that in fact determines the degree of safe diving performance. Therefore knowledge of the psychological aspects of stress — understanding stress, detecting stress and management of stress — must be developed by the mixed gas diver.

PSYCHOLOGICAL ASPECTS OF DIVING

As a person thinks, so the person is. It is the mind, and spirit together that dictate the reactions of the body. What we think we are capable of doing, is exactly what we are able to do. We establish our own limitations. To develop a safe diver we must produce training that allows a diver to develop a belief system of self confidence, responsibility and awareness in the water. An awareness that he can handle any emergency. To help develop this attitude the diver must be introduced to exercises in mind control.

A diver who is terrified of decompression sickness and dwells on being "hit" is the one who gets "hit". The same is true to those who feel they will get extremely narked the moment they pass 130 feet. And so, as they think, so they are. A person who believes they cannot survive a threatening situation will not survive. Conversely, divers who believe they can survive a life-threatening situation probably will survive. Divers and others have survived almost unimaginable situations simply because they believed they could survive. You could compare this to people who develop cancer and accept the fact they are going to die and within a reasonable time they do. While others who refuse to accept their prescribed fate and instead visualize good health with the belief that they can overcome the cancer get better.

Our mind controls our fate. Our mind always achieves success. If we believe we cannot succeed, our mind will program our failure. If we believe we can succeed our mind will program our success. If we believe we can overcome obstacles, our minds will guide us along the path to success. As Tom Ford stated, "Believe you can, believe you can't, either way you are right".

When considering the psychological aspects of diving, becoming attuned to your present situation and your needs along with those of your buddies is an absolute must. The world of mixed gas and technical diving is a new, exciting and challenging experience to most divers. The perceived dangers rarely become the actual dangers. Crystal clear water and enticing scenery mask potential hazards such as loss of a decompression gas, when wreck diving the danger of an instant silt out, or cut lines, interruption of air supply or disorientation when cave diving.

Attitude - our mental outlook towards a specific objective is the first topic to be discussed. To develop a safe diving attitude one must become knowledgeable about the skills needed for mixed gas and technical diving environments. Knowledge of all inherent dangers, physiological and envi-

ronmental combined with preventative steps and emergency skills is needed to develop confidence. Training exercises which allow the diver to control and overcome his/her stress in emergency situations assist in confidence building and attitude development. An "I can do it" philosophy will evolve with patience, practice of realistic training drills and mental preparation utilizing visualization techniques. However, there is a dramatic difference between controlled practice emergency drills and actual div-

Proper training in skills, theory and equipment handling are crucial. Tom Mount conducts a pool briefing. Photo by Bret Gilliam

ing emergencies. A good example is non stressed sharing of a single breathing gas supply during training and an actual openwater out-of-air emergency in deep or turbid water involving a heavy work load. Buddy breathing using an alternate air source or a single regulator for a few lengths of a pool or at rest in open water, does not prepare a person for an "emergency" out-of-air experience.

To develop an attitude of confidence in a diver's ability to cope with a real emergency, pool or open water exercises must incorporate stress management discipline. As mentioned earlier the last part of this chapter will deal with specific exercises I have used over the years. These drills are proven attitude and confidence builders. Reading, study material and formal lectures should make divers aware of mental adaptations for the technical environment. Self-reliance and not dependency on others or the equipment should be the goal of diver training.

The best approach to the "buddy concept" in diving is a non-dependency buddy approach. Buddies are two persons, sharing the fun and enjoyment of diving together. Buddies should not over-rely on each other to make the dive. One buddy should not be the crutch for the other. Each diver should be capable of completing the dive without requiring help from the other. However, each buddy should be able to assist the other, if the need should arise. The limitations of a buddy team for making any dive is always the ability of the least capable diver. When diving in a buddy team the dive plan should not exceed nor encourage pushing the ability of the buddy team. Do not assume that any diver is capable of completing the proposed dive or of providing assistance without verification. A buddy team then is two or more divers functioning as one unit for mutual enjoyment. The buddy team is not a dependency system.

Common sense, is an inherent and learned trait. The development of common sense to a point of reflex behavior that can be relied upon in new diving situations takes time and must incorporate the following: 1) theoretical aspects and practical considerations of the diving mode being used, 2) overlearning of practical diving and emergency skills, 3) an in-depth knowledge of the specific environment to be dived, 5) practical application of the knowledge, 6) visualization, and 7) skill maintenance.

With common sense an individual can make calm reasonable decisions, demonstrating as defined in Websters dictionary *"sound prudent judgment"*. Bear in mind that in order to use common sense one has to have a thorough base of knowledge and understanding about the environment, the equipment, and diving techniques utilized. Common sense is needed to have the ability to make a risk analysis and a personal evaluation.

Self-discipline and self-honesty are paramount in developing a beneficial attitude and philosophy. Self-discipline is the ability to 1) react to conditions based on common sense and logic, and 2) to maintain that decision even if tempted to do otherwise. Self-honesty is the insight to know ones own limitations, desires and needs. Visualization is a great contributor to developing these traits and in expanding our limitations. Just as the implementation of common sense used in a diving environment must be developed through training and experience, so must our feelings of self-honesty and will power to enforce our self-discipline.

Intuition, that little understood sixth sense is one of a persons most dependable decision making guides. To develop intuition, a base line of diving skills and knowledge must be ingrained through training skills and classroom knowledge. Once the mind has sufficient understanding, intuition will, if one listens, make itself known. At this point the diver who is mentally in-tune, will be able to make accurate decisions based on input from the logical mind, the emotions and intuition. With the review of these three processes taking place, correct decisions are made.

Assumption of responsibilities is essential as the diver matures. There are three major areas of responsibility for divers: 1) to yourself, 2) to your buddies, and 3) to the diving community. Self responsibility is mandatory before acceptance of other responsibilities in life. The idioms of "know thy own self" and "to thine own self be true" form the corner stone for a safe diving philosophy. The responsible self will not give into ego threat, it will manifest self awareness and awareness of its surroundings, and it will establish personal safety criteria. The self-responsible and self-aware diver thinks ahead and anticipates the events of an underwater adventure.

Buddy responsibility incorporates the self-reliant buddy system. The dive must be within the ability range of each diver. Thus a dive plan does not overextend personal abilities; secondly, the dive is limited to the men-

Buddy teams incorporate a self-reliant buddy system. Each team member can function independently of his partners. At 260 feet these divers are carrying adequate bottom mix, travel gas, and decompression gas. Photo by Bret Gilliam

tal and physical skill level of one's buddy as well as your personal capabilities. *Reactions are prompt due to anticipation and awareness. (An example is: upon checking air pressure the buddy has 700 psig compared to 1400 psig on your gauge, air sharing is started at this point so the stress of a real out of air situation is avoided. In this manner the low air buddy if uncomfortable can switch to their regulator periodically. This also allows divers to use their own air during the critical last 30 to 40 feet of an ascent. Awareness of the breathing and possible stress reactions of a buddy are also monitored by our buddy responsible diver.)*

Dive community responsibility is simply giving something back to the sport that is giving you such a great experience. It requires behaving in a manner that does not reflect negatively on the sport of diving. Use good public relations.

At this point a good attitude has emerged as the beginning of a good diving philosophy. Contributing factors to a safe philosophy include: 1) understanding stress, 2) the ability to detect stress in yourself and others, 3) controlling stress, 4) setting personal guidelines, 5) and a constant pursuit of knowledge of the environment, advances in environmental physiology, and technological and equipment updates. This philosophy accepts that regardless of expertise in a specific environment, additional training or knowledge is needed when exploring a new diving environment.

DIVER STRESS

Stress is an emotional factor that causes mental or bodily tension. Stress alters the state of equilibrium in an individual. Simply stated stress modifies performance. As mixed gas and overhead environment divers we enter an environment that is contrary to all our previous references. Breathing patterns become more exacting, movement skills change, directional control changes, our senses are fooled and especially in the early experiences we may become uncomfortable in this new situation. With proper training, the initial discomfort is replaced with a sense of ease once we have adapted to the environmental and equipment changes. But what if the unexpected happens? It is here that accidents are born and it is for this reason that stress management exercises both physical and mental should be included in a well structured mixed gas education.

Physiologically the reaction to stress is evidenced by increased heart rate, release of adrenaline and increased respiration. Of these three reactions we can control respiration through conscious effort. At the first sign of uneasiness stop all activity, exhale, and inhale slowly for a full inspiration. Repeat this slow breathing at rest for three respiratory cycles while remaining motionless. This controlled respiration will allow the diver to regain a normal respiration cycle. The stress stimuli comes under control with the establishment of controlled breathing.

Behavioral changes induced by stress may become life threatening. If left unchecked these changes may lead to panic. Panic is the greatest threat to survival. Panic is the point that control is totally lost and a diver may react contrary to safe diving practices. Websters dictionary defines panic as *a sudden unreasoning terror often accompanied by mass flight,* or *sudden overpowering fright.* Panic indicates a breaking point where the mind and body no longer work together. It is as if the mind were shut off and the body reacts independently. Panic can be life threatening. It can be the result of a reaction to a perceived danger, more so than to a real danger. Because of this perception of a situation, rather than the logical evaluation of the circumstances, it is prudent to be trained with self-confidence drills. Training skills must allow the diver to develop a database to reference when emergencies occur. Training activities that include visualization techniques, mental and physical exercises in the safety of a pool or controlled in open water can be used to develop this database from which to draw upon in an actual emergency. These enable us to achieve a conditioned mind for reacting to stress and awareness that it can be dealt with. In short, self-confidence drills develop the, "I can" attitude that is the foundation for a philosophy of survival.

Mental narrowing is a early reaction to stress. This inhibits the ability to analyze the environment and the moment. It also limits the skills and amount of knowledge brought to bear on the problem. Again the best preventive training is self confidence exercises.

Perceptional narrowing is an early symptom of stress. Our perceived reality is what we normally react to. Thus as stress increases our perception of the problem may be worse than the actual problem we are reacting to. Therefore, it is imperative that we have over-learned emergency skills under controlled stress to avoid a doomsday perception of an emergency.

Overlearned skills such as practicing isolating a malfunctioning regulator are best mastered in training so open water situations are reflexive actions.
Photo by Bret Gilliam

Analytic narrowing occurs under stress and is frequently associated with events that lead to an accident. Frequently this accompanies breathing related problems. A good example is a diver who surfaces complaining the regulator is not working yet the tank is full and the regulator breathes perfectly. Upon investigation it was discovered the diver became stressed inhaled deeply, exhaled only a fraction and inhaled again quickly, after a couple of cycles there is no room for additional air in the lungs. Upon inhalation the diver does not receive much air and thinks the regulator is malfunctioning. What is perceived as an equipment malfunction, is actually a diver stress problem. Another problem exists when a diver breathes rapidly and fails to actually breathe effectively, becoming winded. To a stressed diver experiencing analytic narrowing, the regulator has malfunctioned. To a logically thinking aware diver the problem is within the diver and solvable. The logical diver exhales fully and slowly then resumes normal breathing at rest prior to swimming. Correct breathing is restored and usually symptoms of stress disappear.

Response narrowing is another side effect of stress and its effects are enhanced by lost skills. The skills that are lost first are those poorly learned initially. Unfortunately, in the concept of diver training today many survival skills fall into this category. Emergency skills must be "over-learned" skills — your life and your buddy's may depend on them. If you want good examples of divers falling prey to response narrowing, ask a professional dive master at any diving resort to tell you a few stories. Response narrowing is one of the reasons divers die with adequate air and functioning equipment.

Other behavioral effects are produced by errors in judgment, common mistakes, carelessness, refusing to use air management rules and failure to plan dives. Proper training can help to avoid these mistakes by making divers more aware of the environment and its demands.

What produces stress in the diving environment? Basically the same points attributed to stress anywhere except they are compounded by being underwater. In the following paragraphs we will address a few of the more prominent sources of diver stress.

Time pressure is simply a race against the clock. In diving, time pressure stress can be as simple as one buddy rushing another to get ready for a dive. It is also present in a real emergency such as air sharing situations where the time as monitored by available air has a definite limit. In all its various forms, time pressure stress is the most common source of stress to divers. In training, drills to cope with time pressure stress should be incorporated.

Task loading is the next most common source of stress to underwater explorers. This is produced by compounding the number of tasks an individual must preform at one time. To a new technical diver, swim technique combined with buoyancy control, use of safety reels and lights produces a degree of task loading. Add air sharing to this, combine this with a long swim, lengthy decompression, add a flooding mask and you may have a tragedy.

Exertion and cold are stressful to all of us. Just close your eyes and I'm sure you can visualize an experience when either doing heavy exertion or being cold you felt more stressed than normal during a dive.

Directional requirements, have you ever been lost? If like most of us the answer is yes then you most definitely know this feeling.

Buoyancy control: An over-weighted diver with little instruction in manual inflation experiencing a failure of the power inflator could be in serious difficulty. Perfect buoyancy control and the ability to manually inflate a B.C. on and below the surface is a mandatory skill for all diving.

The sudden appearance of large marine life can induce stressful reactions if their behavior is perceived as threatening. Rob Palmer observes a 500 lb. loggerhead turtle at 210 feet on a wreck. Photo by Bret Gilliam

Ego threat is a subtle threat but a definite contributor to diving emergencies. This is most common when we do something we truly feel we are not ready for. Often a friend has enticed us into it. Indeed many of the body recoveries I have made stemmed from ego threat.

Physical threat is when something is perceived to about to cause you harm. It may be the 50 foot cave monster of your dreams coming to life or an out of air situation. Whatever the cause physical threat is a real threat to divers.

Compounded sources of stress are most often the culprit in diving accidents. This occurs when two or more sources of stress present themselves at the same time. Lectures, visualization and pool drills can prepare divers for these occurrences.

Controlling stress is of major importance to divers. As you have guessed by now, one of the major ways to be prepared for dealing with stress is the process of overlearning and maintenance of skills, mastery of good dive technique, environmental information and reliable equipment. It is here that specific confidence and familiarity drills are needed in diver education. Perhaps the most important tool of stress management is mind control through the visualization process.

Anticipation is a key means of avoiding a bad reaction to stress. Again, training and visualization exercises that are stress control related will enable the diver to form a basis for anticipating events that may or may not occur in a dive. When diving mixed gas or entering hazardous environments such as caves, wrecks and under the ice there is more demand emphasis on anticipation by proper training.

Physiological control via mind control is the most effective means of coping with stress. Quietly thinking through a situation is an initial step in this direction.

Visualization is one of the most effective ways to direct and control stress and human performance. Virtually every olympic class athlete is taught this process today. Meditation combined with visualization is a positive cure to most stress related problems. To achieve this, simply close your eyes, inhale and exhale slowly while concentrating on relaxation. Mentally picture the desired goal. Simple, yet visualization is the most effective exercise known to overcome stressful conditions, achieve goals, or increase performance. There are many good books on visualization and for in-depth study visit a metaphysical book store.

Visualization of a safe dive should be undertaken by each diver immediately before a dive. The following steps are needed to correctly visualize a dive or any other activity or goal. The same steps may be used to train the mind to react to stressful scenarios. In the latter case, once in a relaxed state see a possible problem and work through it with your mind. The steps are: 1) sit or lie down in a comfortable position, 2) close your eyes, 3) breathe in slowly for approximately six seconds, pause for two to three seconds and exhale for six seconds, 4) concentrate on relaxation of the body, repeating "I'm relaxed, my legs are relaxed, my body is relaxed, my arms are relaxed, my neck and head is relaxed, my breathing is slow and relaxed, my pulse is slow and relaxed", 5) draw a mental picture of the dive or visualize the dive as planned, see the dive as safe and enjoyable, 6) count to yourself backwards from five prior to opening the eyes.

This simple exercise is effective in preventing stress and in producing a more enjoyable dive. With time it also helps develop intuition. If for any reason, there is a really bad or foreboding condition during the visualization, abort the planned dive. Once the above preparations have been made enjoy a safe and rewarding dive. An in-depth visualization, especially when used as a goal setting tool may take up to 45 minutes. A quick pre-dive visualization usually lasts three to fifteen minutes.

Affirmations are another effective means to develop controlled responses and confidence facing a crisis. Affirmation can be as simple as stating to yourself a positive statement. Affirmation should be made with emotion and intent. It is important that affirmations are made in the present tense, not future. Words like a bunch, a little bit, some, when, maybe, etc., must be avoided. I made a 200 foot dive safely today. Not, I hope to make a 200 foot dive safely today. Affirmations are even more effective if also written. The most effective affirmation is made within 30 minutes of going to sleep at night. At this time our subconscious mind is open to suggestion. Affirmations made at this time are great contributors to realization of our goals.

Overlooked in western society until recently is the total effect of breathing on the mind and bodies performance, health, stress prevention, and stress release. Improper breathing practices are responsible for a large percentage of stress felt by all people. Even back aches and other general aches and pains are often reduced or eliminated by correct breathing exercise. Combine increased density of air as one descends and the importance of breathing correctly is tripled. In the diving environment it has been my experience that most feelings of uneasiness by divers has been breathing related. It is of utmost importance to teach yourself, and repeat over and over that any time you feel uneasy to stop, slowly exhale all air (without forced exhalation) then slowly inhale, repeat three times prior to resuming physical movement. This is even more important when reacting to an emergency situation. Of course while stopped, the individual can also think, observe, visualize and analyze the problem. If divers were taught these basic skills and processes it would eliminate many of today's accidents. For more in-depth knowledge, read the chapter on the science and art of breathing.

Survival training herein lies the key to safe high-tech diving. The physical drills and evaluations to be covered later in this chapter are mandatory to key the subconscious mind. However there are numerous other ways to develop and maintain survival instincts. Mentally, a guided mediation where a tape or person places one in an adverse position (non-diving related) and the mediator solves the problem is excellent for tuning the mind, thus the body to survival. Physical exercises that place mental demands are ideal as well. One of my favorite exercises that I practice several times a week is by use of a stairmaster (stepper machine). I will address this as a progressive training drill. This is an excellent exercise for developing mind/body response patterns.

Initially, spend about three workouts on the stairmaster (bike, stationary bike, rowing machine, treadmill, running, swimming, etc. All are equivalent types of exercises) . Once familiar with its operation incorporate steps 1 through 5.

1. Begin at a slightly taxing level,
2. After a few minutes increase the pace to a difficult level,
3. Maintain this level for a group of minutes divided by two, at which time return to the previous level, remain at previous level for a comfortable period of time, then return to the higher level under the same conditions.
4. When doing the upper level of exercise if you exceed the even number without dropping down, be committed to continue to the next number divisible by two.
5. Obviously as your physical conditioning level increases, the resistance is increased and the time is increased.

Many aspects of diving require hard physical work. An ethic of fitness conditioning and honing survival instincts is recommended. Here Tom Mount exits from a 4 knot current with over 150 pounds of equipment. Photo by Bret Gilliam

After three to six months make the upper level divisible by threes and remember you can only drop down to the original setting/pace at a number divisible by three. In another three to six months change the divider to five.

I find about a 30 minute workout of this nature is ideal for mental preparation. In physical training this is a form of interval training for conditioning of athletes, however, its most important benefit is survival training and mental toughness. On days you cannot maintain the goals, equate them as "on this day I would not have survived in a critical situation". Using this attitude I push to complete my objective just as you must. I use this when teaching karate as well, by making myself and my students dig down mentally when all the physical reserves are gone. I'm alive due to this type training. Perhaps from some near-miss diving activities, and most definitely from a plane crash incident. The side benefit is you will also get into good physical condition.

Mixed gas diving is a physically and mentally demanding activity. Unlike traditional recreational diving, it is not for everyone. Mental and physical fitness are mandated in this form of diving. The ideal model for a high-tech diver is 60% mental conditioning and 40% physical conditioning. A physically unfit diver (by the way, fitness has nothing to do with the amount, or lack of body fat, many thin divers are unfit, and numerous large divers seem to have excellent fitness — look at linesmen on football teams most have sizeable mid-sections) diver does not posses the physical stamina to meet the demands on high-exertion survival. A mentally unfit diver (this person may be a real tarzan physically) does not have the ability to focus nor the discipline to survive stressful occurrences. Interesting, the only two persons I have had fail my performance test were two body builders, who were excellent swimmers, but lacked the mental discipline to control themselves. On the same test that they failed, an almost blind diver and his buddy who was 80 pounds overweight passed with flying colors. The difference in the two teams was mental conditioning/discipline. Balance is the key to strive towards.

A final phase in developing a realistic philosophy is that of risk analysis and acceptance. Herein is the division point between a high-tech diver and an explorer. It is a fine line to cross but one that exists and may be totally unforgiving and demanding. This in mountain climbers, high altitude sky diving, deep diving, wreck diving, cave diving, and extremes in all sports is where the record holders and adventurers prevail. As in all activities, there is a higher price to pay as the limits are pushed more severely. The true explorer accepts the total risk, which may be their lives or permanent body injury, and values the resultant activity to be worth the price. This should not be the goal of all mixed gas divers.

For explorers and pioneers in new frontiers, Gil Milner M.D., and psychiatrist states it best, " You have the obligation to inform one honestly of risk, and as a person you are committed to educate yourself to the total risk in any activity. Once informed and totally aware of risk, every fool has the right to kill or injure themselves as they see fit". The double-edge sword to this is the person who accepts the risk to "be the first", must take precaution not to entice others to push the envelope with them. Most high-tech divers are and should be happy to use high-tech techniques to explore a hazardous environment whether it be deep, cave, wreck or whatever with relative safety. The explorer pushes deep into the danger limit and must be aware and acceptable of the what if's. The choice is ours. Hopefully, by the end of this book you will be informed adequately to make accurate risk analysis and acceptance judgments. If combining gas diving with other forms of high-tech diving then, be prudent enough to seek out training and education in these fields.

DETECTION OF STRESS

Detecting and reacting to stress in divers is an art all instructors should be familiar with. Mixed gas and overhead environmental divers should be adept in recognition and detection of stress in themselves and dive buddies. These divers must be introduced to, and demonstrate proficiency in stress management of diving companions. Specialized water skills are used to ingrain these practices into the students mind. Master divers, dive masters, and assistant instructors should be taught to recognize pre-dive stress and management plus group stress detection and management underwater.

Self Confidence and Performance Evaluation Pool/Open Water Skills

In order to prepare a person to recognize and respond to stress and stressful situations there are numerous training exercises that will condition the mind to react safely. The specific exercises presented are ones I use in various training programs.

In order to have divers perform the skills, it is necessary to explain to them why these skills are chosen. If one simply states do it, the skills are hard, but, with explanation of their importance in self rescue/survival they become confidence builders. The skills are also on a steady progression of competence. All divers are allowed to repeat skills until mastered. On the pool/open water skill performance test, the skills are graded and students may have two tries at a skill but receive a point penalty on the repeated attempt.

A short explanation of each skill in the following paragraphs will be given as the skill is presented.

Pool/Open Water Skills for Developing Self Confidence

Example One: Breath/breathing control. The importance of safe breathing patterns and breath control are introduced. Students are made aware of normal stimuli to breathing and exercise stimuli. The psychological urge to breathe approximately every 15 seconds is explained.. The importance of slow controlled movements is discussed as a means of avoiding an increased stimuli to respiration. Correct body positioning and attitude is related to its importance on breathing stimulation and buoyancy control. This entire explanation takes approximately two minutes; in addition this has already been discussed in the classroom.

Breath control exercise one: This is a breath holding exercise that is used and explained as such as a step towards being able to manage a stressful situation in the water. It is also explained that in fact it is a survival tech-

FIGURE SYMPTOMS OF STRESS

Pre Dive	Symptoms: nervous gestures, frequent clearing of the throat, or extreme withdrawal, fixation on gauges or other pieces of equipment, clumsiness in gearing up.
Reaction	Talk calmly and reassure the diver. Remain with diver until they become relaxed. Go over the dive profile with them and discuss their concerns with the dive. Remind them to be aware of efficient breathing patterns. Point out all techniques, "tricks of the trade" etc., to make this an enjoyable experience.
During Dive	Symptoms: Wild-eyed look, white knuckles, fixation on gauges or guide line, failure to respond to communications, losing physical coordination, erratic buoyancy control, failure to clear mask, steady increase or decrease of swim pace for no apparent reason, increased respiration, failure to exhale, freezing up (failure to move, usually hanging onto something).
Reaction	Make eye contact, plus firm but not tight hand contact with diver. Signal to stop, exhale, take three breaths slowly (note!! Slow, full, inhalation, not forced. Followed by slow, full, exhalation) relax, solve problem if one actually exists. Check the divers buoyancy frequently. The perception of stress is induced due to abnormal breathing patterns. (In early technical dives it is common for divers to fail to adjust the swim pace to ventilation requirements). Communicate with and reassure diver all is okay, once correct respiration is established and diver is calm begin safe ascent procedures. On the surface, debrief the event and discuss it as a learning experience.

nique base line rather than a performance required skill. This skill should be mastered prior to any candidate being permitted into a technical environment. Take five slow (approximately six seconds inhalation and six seconds exhalation), full breaths without force on the completion of inhalation or exhalation. Force the mind to concentrate on relaxing, this is followed by a limit of three moderate hyperventilations, then surface dive keeping the chin tucked and swim slowly. The goal is 100 feet horizontal without surfacing. The important point at this stage is that the diver begins to incorporate discipline with understanding the importance of controlled movements as stress is introduced.

For those not completing it, the first question we ask immediately upon surfacing is are you really in need of air? The answer is always no, as no one is really breathing hard upon surfacing. We then review why they needed to come up; for most it is the psychological need to breathe. This mental need for air is based on a lifetime of breathing every ten to fifteen seconds not on a real need for air at that point. We refer to this as the psychological breaking point and a factor that must be overcome in surviving underwater should an emergency occur. The remainder of the students who surfaced early usually did so due to swimming too fast and developing a tremendous exercise stimuli to breathing. This is a great tool as it enables us to make the point of controlled physical exertion underwater for comfort and most importantly for survival. On a second attempt, once these errors and dependencies are explained, the vast majority of the students complete the exercise. The distance is gradually increased to 120 feet.

Example Two: Place scuba at shallow end of pool with air on. Have student do proper breathing sequence (five deep slow breaths and three hyperventilation), swim 90 feet underwater and don scuba, swim 600 feet and complete skill in under ten minutes. This is a time pressure and task loading stress management exercise. Subtract one point for each ten seconds over ten minutes. A perfect score is based on a normal swimming rate of 70 feet per minute.

Example Three: Two students side by side, in full equipment for whatever course is being taught, on the count of three, surface dive without breathing from S.c.u.b.a. (Regulator is in mouth for emergency use) swim 75 feet without breathing and then commence sharing air via alternate second stage. Remain at rest for a minimum of three breaths then swim 800 feet while continuing to share air. Skill completion under ten minutes based on swim rate of 80 feet / minute. Explain to students that the out of air swim must be at a slow relaxed pace, that swim pace must be at a normal pace. Speeding up will cause respiratory distress and slowing the pace in a real situation would not allow sufficient air for surfacing safely. One point is subtracted for each ten seconds over ten minutes.

Example Four: Place divers 40 feet apart have them remove regulator from mouth on surface and take one breath surface dive and swim to each

A variety of pool training exercises under the supervision of professional instructors can build confidence and reinforce reflexive skills. Photos by Bret Gilliam

other and commence manual buddy breathing. Again explain that this is an exercise to duplicate the stress of a real out of air management occurrence. Upon beginning buddy breathing, make it mandatory for students to exchange regulator three times at rest prior to commencing to swim. This allows them to calm down as in a real situation and should always be done in practice and most certainly in actual air sharing emergencies. Repeat this skill with both students exhaling all their air prior to surface diving. Follow this with a timed swim of 600 feet in under seven minutes.

Example Five: Repeat above drill except divers have their eyes closed, so they must find each other. In this drill air sharing is via alternate air source/octopus. The time requirements are the same.

Example Six: The skill begins with buddies (both in scuba) 50 feet apart one buddy sits on the bottom and faces the pool wall, the second buddy exhales and swims a minimum of 50 feet without air, then gets the attention of the buddy, signals to share air and commences manual buddy breathing with three exchanges at rest prior to beginning an air sharing 600 foot swim. Students are once again cautioned to stop, exhale, and breathe normally for three breaths any time they become winded. Repeat with opposite buddy roles.

Example Seven: On being signaled diver in double tanks with dual valve manifold simulates failure of an air supply. The diver is to shut down one valve and switch to the other regulator. Time limit is 40 seconds.

Example Eight: Diver tows buddy for a distance of 600 feet, brings the diver to the surface and simulates mouth to mouth for a distance of 100 feet, then with assistance removes buddy from water and simulates CPR. All accident management procedures must be demonstrated during this rescue drill. Time limit ten minutes.

Example Nine: At the end of a dive, diver closes eyes and without aid of lines etc. attempts to retrace path to ascent line.

Example Ten: On a dive where a given distance has been covered on a previous dive and the time is noted for normal swim pace (use a distance of at least 300 feet), divers close eyes and share air via octopus and remain within normal time limits. If students are slowed down, explain how this could have caused them to run low on air had the air sharing occurred at a critical air source level.

Each speciality course and advanced training program should have its associated stress management/confidence building exercises incorporated into it. When using the above examples in a mix class, the times are modified and the drills are done with both doubles and two stage bottles. These skill exercises count for one third of the total course score with the written test accounting for one third and the open water evaluations the balance. Each evaluation, practical open water or written should be passed with a score of 80%. For divers who want to become high-tech or push the envelope, a stress management program is highly recommended.

REFERENCES

"The New Practical Diving", Tom Mount and Akira Ikehara, University Miami Press, Baltimore, Md.

"Safe Cave Diving", Tom Mount NACD (out of print).

"Deep Diving: An Advanced Guide to Physiology Procedures and System," Bret Gilliam and Robert von Maier, Watersport Publishing, Inc.

CHAPTER 3

The Science & Art of Breathing

Breathing is a natural means of providing life support to the living mechanism. Why do we breathe? What causes us to breathe? What affects breathing? What is the correct way to breathe? These are all questions to be answered in the science and art of breathing. Most often the process of breathing (respiration) is taken for granted and we rely on its occurrence as a reflex. Few people actually concentrate on the art of breathing or realize the effects of correct or incorrect respiration on health, performance and stress. As divers, we need to understand the importance of correct breathing techniques to compensate for density, changes in breathing gases, and mechanical resistance factors. In fact, as we explore greater depths, dive in stronger currents, perform long decompression dives and enter the world of overhead environments, it is mandatory to master good breathing habits.

Prior to an in-depth discussion on breathing, it is necessary to review some basic physiology. While there are numerous systems within the human body, we shall discuss three that specifically relate to our subject in this chapter. The nervous system can be thought of as the central computer. It is within this system that signals are generated to induce all functions of the body. The circulatory and respiratory systems enable the process of metabolism to be enacted.

THE NERVOUS SYSTEM

The nervous system controls body function by nervous impulses. These are developed by one of the following:

- The central nervous system (C.N.S.). The C.N.S. controls consciousness, mental activity, and control of skeletal muscles. The brain and spinal cord make up the C.N.S.
- The peripheral nervous system carries out the functions of the C.N.S. It is composed of the cranial and spinal nerves.
- The autonomic nervous system controls our internal environment and emotional reactions. Most of the centers of the A.N.S. are within the C.N.S. For this chapter, the main emphasis on the A.N.S. is that it regulates respiration.

It is apparent that anything which alters the behavior of the above systems will therefore affect our health, behavior, functioning and even survival. As this text unfolds, many physiological events such as decompression sickness, oxygen toxicity, inert gas narcosis etc. will be discussed. These occurances exert a great effect on the nervous system as will be demonstrated in the respective chapters. Not quite as obvious is the total effect of breathing on the health and well being of the overall nervous system.

THE CIRCULATORY SYSTEM

The circulatory system is a closed loop system consisting of the heart, arteries, veins, tissue capillaries, and lung capillaries. The heart is the pump that propels blood through the circulatory system.

The force that pushes blood is referred to as blood pressure. Blood pressure is determined by the amount of blood being pumped and the resistance of the vessels the blood travels through. Factors that affect the blood pressure include the cholesterol and other blood fat levels of the vessels, the amount of exercise being performed, and induced stimuli such as caffeine and alcohol. The carotid sinuses are pressure sensing devices that aid in regulating blood pressure by informing the brain via nervous impulses about pressures.

Oxygen is combined with hemoglobin in the blood, becoming oxyhemoglobin and transported to the cells of the body. Carbon dioxide also combines with hemoglobin as a waste product and is carried back to the lungs. As we will see in later chapters, some diving events throw the relationship of hemoglobin transport out of balance and contribute towards adverse diving physiological reactions.

Blood chemistry factors also are affected by and affect changes in the diver's physiology, most notably the behavior of platelets that are needed to induce clotting following injuries, etc. The normal behavior of platelets is to attack foreign bodies at injury sites within the system. Unfortunately, bubbles are viewed as injury sites or foreign material in the circulation and platelets attach to them increasing the size and disruptive effects of bubbles. With frequent long duration dives, it is believed that the platelet count is diminished.

Blood plasma and serum are also important in circulatory health providing for a healthy functioning body. With dehydration due to exposure to the sun, breathing compressed dry air, and with vacationing divers partying at night etc., the volume of plasma is reduced. Thus the ability to transport gas is diminished. The circulatory system overall is viewed as one system. Within this are two separate systems: the pulmonary and the systemic. The pulmonary system supports the circulation dedicated to the lungs while the systemic serves body tissue. A healthy circulatory system is mandated for efficient transport of gases. Factors that disable its efficiency greatly affect health. For divers, a reduction in the proficiency of the circulatory system subjects them to numerous diving disabilities. Correct breathing habits greatly increase circulatory performance.

THE RESPIRATORY SYSTEM

Mechanically speaking the act of respiration is simply defined as: The use of oxygen and the production of carbon dioxide and the exchange of these gases within the respiratory and circulatory systems. Viewed from this perspective we can conveniently break the respiratory process into easily understood steps:
1. Breathing, the act of inhaling and exhaling.
2. Exchange of gases across the alveoli and into the pulmonary capillaries.
3. Transport of gases via the circulatory system.
4. Exchange of gases to the tissue fluids.
5. Exchange to the cellular level and,
6. The resultant act of metabolism (combining of oxygen and glucose to produce energy, waste, carbon dioxide, and heat.

BREATHING

Simply put: breathe in and breathe out. The act of breathing is far more complex than this statement. As we explore breathing, we see a series of events that take place to insure proper inhalation and exhalation.

First, let's examine why we breathe. Many will say it is an automatic response governed by the autonomic nervous system. In a simplified approach this is basically correct, but for correct breathing and for breathing underwater we must assist this "reflex" and we must on many occasions consciously control this activity.

Why we breathe is an action that is put into motion by various stimuli. At rest, the primary stimuli is elevated partial pressure of carbon dioxide or pH. As CO_2 increases, it sends a signal to the inspiratory center of the respiratory center located in the medulla obligate, which in turn via nerve transmission, tells the respiratory muscles to contract. Once these muscle groups contract, the elastic lungs expand following the action of the muscles. Expansion continues until the stretch sensors within the lungs sense they have stretched adequately. Upon attaining the desired "stretch goal", the sensors reflect this to the expiratory center and they in turn communicate the need to discontinue inhalation. Exhalation occurs due to two facts: 1) The relaxation of the respiratory muscles, 2) The elastic recoil of the lungs.

The lung recoil is much like a balloon as it has some elastic fibers. More importantly, the elasticity is related to the millions of alveoli. Each alveoli is coated inside by a thin layer of protein containing fluid called surfactant. Surfactant possesses a property known as surface tension. Surface tension is common to all fluids. The behavior of surface tension is most easily understood by observing a soap bubble. The walls of the bubble are primarily water with some dissolved soap in it. As the bubble is blown up the trailing edges are pulled together forming a sphere, while the soapy water exerts a force drawing it concurrently to form the smallest area possible: a bubble. Surface tension continues to maintain this shape.

In the lungs, in order to inhale, the muscles must overcome this tension for the lungs to expand. Upon relaxation of the muscles, the surface tension draws the lungs to normal shape and the chest and diaphragm follow this action. These two actions, contraction of respiratory muscles and relaxation of these muscles, combined with surface tension of the alveoli produce the acts of inhalation and exhalation at rest.

Upon contraction of the diaphragm, the lungs will expand drawing air into them. When air is drawn down the trachea, it splits into the bronchi which serve the two lungs. The bronchi resemble branches of a tree becoming smaller until they terminate into the bronchioles. They in turn end in a series of tiny air sacs called alveoli. The alveoli are so tiny that they are not visible individually. To the naked eye, they appear as a single structure: the lung. In fact, billions of alveoli make up the lungs. In breathing, inspiration follows the contraction of the diaphragm, and ideally, proper diaphragmatic breathing takes place. However, in the western world, many people have developed the habit of chest breathing, thus losing the ideal means of respiration. When diaphragmatic breathing is practiced the diaphragm moves downward on inspiration, and produces the best physiological respiratory patterns. With this type ventilation, much of the gas in the lungs is distributed to the lower portions of the lung(s). At birth this is a natural means of breathing. It is only with aging that people develop improper habits. Chest breathing usually results from being told "suck that tummy in and stick the chest out". With chest breathing, air fills the middle and upper portions of the lung. Unfortunately, in an upright position most of the blood needed for ideal gas exchange is in the lower portion of the lungs. Chest breathing also requires more work and is less efficient in ventilation. Chest breathers tend to breathe more rapidly than diaphragm breathers. Chest breathers also then cause their hearts to work harder in order to circulate more blood to the lungs.

A third type of breathing comes into play under strenuous work loads. This is called clavicular breathing. Divers should strive to maintain paces and muscular effort that is below the threshold that results in clavicular breathing. Due to all the musculature in this form of breathing, significantly more oxygen is needed with more blood flow to the lungs. In addition, density increases as the diver descends with a corresponding increase in resistance for equipment exchange of gases in the lung's airways. For at rest training purposes, breathing exercise can incorporate all three patterns of respiration.

As the act of breathing takes place, let's trace the path the gas flows through the airways down to the lungs. Normally air is inhaled through the nose, however in diving this is altered and we now breathe via the mouth. As we inhale through equipment, we encounter drag forces that are design-limited in higher quality regulators. It is for this reason that divers, especially divers exploring greater depths must be prudent in using regulators with low breathing resistance and ample volume/flow characteristics.

Gas traveling through an airway will meet frictional resistance due to the walls of the airway itself. If a diver breathes shallowly and rapidly, this will result in gas literally bouncing from the airway walls and these gas molecules opposing the flow of additional gas. This occurrence is defined as turbulent gas flow. It is measured by a factor known as "Reynold's number". Breathing (gas flow) that produces high Reynold's numbers is inefficient and may lead to respiratory distress. Inadequate ventilation yields a sensation of gas starvation and if reacted to via the A.N.S. will complicate itself by increased breathing rate and "gulping" the gas. This pattern left unchecked yields improper ventilation, produces stress and most likely ends in panic with a perception of gas failure. To avoid this reaction, it is important that divers be trained to inhale slowly and to exhale slowly. The volume should be deep and even paced. In other words, the respiratory rate and respiratory minute volume should be slow with deep volume. A Respiratory per Minute Volume (RMV) of this nature avoids turbulence, maintains a low Reynold's number, and assures the diver of proper ventilation. This type of respiration produces laminar flow of gas in the airways. Correct breathing habits must be developed by conscious practice. Thus the statement of "breathe normally", so often heard in traditional dive training, is literally untrue. We should strive to learn to breathe correctly.

The deeper a diver descends, the greater the density and resistance to breathing. The ANS reflex to density is to breathe faster. What this accomplishes is turbulence and improper respiration. Again the deeper the dive, the more awareness is needed for slow, deep breathing. On working dives i.e. current, hard swimming, physical work, mental stress, there is a reflex to increase the respiratory rate. Divers must adjust their work load and respiratory rate to a level that allows slow inhalation and exhalation with adequate volume of gas to fulfill the body's needs. It is evident that correct breathing under almost any underwater activity is not reflex, but a learned skill. Once fully trained in breathing technique, the mind will store this ability and it becomes natural. Beware though that under stress, regardless of breathing technique, a conscious effort must be made to maintain slow, deep breathing habits.

There is one other series of breathing reactions that are prudent to discuss at this point. Under stress, divers will frequently inhale then exhale only a small portion of the gas. As this process is repeated the lungs become fully inflated with, for practical purposes, no exhalation. To the diver, the sensation is that the equipment has malfunctioned and often a panic reaction follows. (see psychological aspects chapter). Again, any time a diver feels unusual they should exhale slowly fully and then slowly inhale. A third common abnormal breathing pattern is rapid shallow breathing. This of course produces turbulence and a high Reynold's number. The technique of slow breathing is one of the most important tools for safe diving and a must for deep diving. For swimming dives, experiment with a swim pace that is balanced to the ability to maintain slow deep breathing. Swimming faster than this pace will be inefficient as the breathing pattern will be altered and turbulence in the airways will most likely occur with an end result of improper gas supply to the alveoli.

As stated earlier, carbon dioxide (CO_2) is the resting stimuli to respiration. With exercise, we also incur a muscular stimuli (neuro/chemical) that provides a strong desire to breathe. In addition, emotional factors, pain, anger, and psychological stimuli also are induced. The A.N.S will induce this additional stimuli in a flight or flight response. Thus the diver who experiences stress will have an urge to breathe more rapidly and to consume a larger volume of gas. This urge can be and must be consciously controlled for survival in the water. Frequently divers will speed up their pace under stress and this may lead to loss of control of breathing. Conversely, occasionally divers (such as in an air sharing situation) will drastically slow their pace, this could lead to insufficient gas to reach the surface. All in all, the aware diver's conscious reaction is to maintain a normal pace that allows balance with swim pace in harmony with safe breathing patterns. Use of conscious control requires discipline and the diver is encouraged to train on both the physical and mind control exercises explained in the chapter on psychological aspects of diving.

Normal breathing on land is performed through the nose. Thus it is proper that we discuss this important part of respiration. An interesting fact is it takes up to 150 % of the work to pull gas through the nose as compared to the mouth. With all the extra energy consumed, there must be some distinct reasons why we breath via the nose. The nose is the narrowest part of the respiratory tract and is where most respiratory resistance is encountered. The nose actually does much more than allowing gas to flow. Rhinologists (nose specialists) list 30 functions the nose performs. It filters, moisturizes, directs gas flow, warms and conditions the gas, registers the sense of smell, brings in oxygen, creates mucus, provides drainage for the sinuses, and affects the nervous system. These are a sampling of nasal functions. There are two divisions of the nose: external and internal.

The shape of the external nose plays a major role in inhalation. The structure varies with different climates and altitudes that people come from. In colder climates, long big noses evolve and are desirable as it heats and filters the air more efficiently. Long, big noses are also common to climates where the air is very dry. In tropical and moist climates, noses tend to have flared nostrils as much less filtering of air is needed. The external nose gathers and "jets" gas into the internal nose. The external nose is composed of bone and cartilage.

The first compartment of the external nose is the vestibule. These are formed by the flare of the nose and are affected by gravity. Moving up the nose, the base of the nose is discovered. Injury to the external nose will affect gas flow through it. The common deviated septum is a good example. (In this condition one nostril is partially or totally shut off). Moving internally, the nasal passage expands with the dimensions of the internal nose being larger than the vestibule. The floor of the internal nose is also the roof of the mouth. This point is like a three story building: above is the brain and eyes, and below is the mouth (an interesting location with interactions between the nose and mental activity).

The turbinates are one of the more interesting portions of the nose. Their function is to stir air as it enters the nose. They are of major importance in moisturizing and warming the inspired gas and conditioning it for the lungs. They also serve to aid in prevention of heat loss and moisture from the body. Mucus membrane lines the inside of the nose. This material secretes mucus. Mucus picks up dust, debris, bacteria, viruses, fungi and whatever other foreign elements might be found in the nasal passageways. Thus the function of mucus is to gather exterior bodies and then move it from the nasal passageways. Cilia is a hairlike substance that grows out of the mucus. The function of cilia is to remove mucus. Diet greatly effects the mucus system. A diet high in diary products causes high mucus production. Mucus membranes also line the passageways carrying gas to the lungs. Smokers tend to accumulate mucus in the airways and smoke destroys cilia. Hence we see the classic "smokers cough". From the above description, the importance of the nasal system is obvious in good breathing habits. When performing breathing patterns (exercises) one should incorporate nostril breathing both with tandem nostrils and alternate nostrils. Yoga is a system we highly recommend for learning proper breathing habits.

EXCHANGE OF GAS IN THE LUNGS

Once gas has traveled to the alveoli the process of utilization of gas may begin. These tiny air sacs are delicate, composed of only one cell thickness, and are the units that gas exchange takes place. Surrounding the alveoli is a rich network of capillaries in which oxygen exchanges into the circulatory system and carbon dioxide is exchanged outward for exhalation. To be efficient, there must be a balance in the amount of blood flowing in the capillaries and the concentration of oxygen brought to the alveoli.

The amount of blood is not evenly distributed in the lungs. This blood supply is gravity dependent and in the upright position more blood is in the lower portion of the lungs than in the middle and upper parts of the lung. Conversely the flow of gases is at its peak in the upper portions of the lung. Thus gas transfer is not as efficient as one would suppose. Divers have a slight advantage underwater in that they are released from gravitational effects. However, even then there is a slightly unbalanced transfer of gas. To make the transfer of gas more advantageous one needs to develop good breathing habits. Again, to insure good gas exchange one must breathe slowly, evenly and deeply.

If the alveoli are injured due to a physical accident they become inefficient. Smokers of tobacco or other substances will also lose pulmonary efficiency. Smoke produces a breakdown in the lining of the lungs, resulting in a "visible hole" in them. This hole reduces the surface area in which oxygen comes into contact with blood across the alveoli, thus reducing the amount of gas exchange across the alveoli. This condition is referred to as emphysema and essentially all smokers suffer from this to varying degrees. With a long term habit of smoking, noticeable symptoms of emphysema are likely to occur. Of course, this type of lung damage, in addition to producing inefficient respiration, also predisposes one to lung overpressure accidents such as arterial gas embolism (AGE). Other areas of interference with gas exchange include exposure to elevated partial pressures of oxygen for prolonged periods of time. At partial pressures higher than 0.5 ATA on extended duration, the lungs will become irritated with swelling of the alveolar wall, reduced vital capacity, and eventually edema/hemorrhage of lung tissue will occur. Of course, the above is an extreme example and the concept will be explored more in the chapter on oxygen toxicity.

Diffusion of gases across the alveoli are due to different hydrostatic pressures. On inspiration the gas has a high oxygen level and once at the alveoli the oxygen will tend to diffuse across it to the pulmonary capillaries which at this point have low oxygen pressure. On the exhalation cycle the blood in the capillaries contains a reduced volume of oxygen. The carbon dioxide in solution is also high and thus carbon dioxide tends to diffuse from the blood across the alveoli and is exhaled.

TRANSPORT OF GAS VIA CIRCULATORY SYSTEM

Once oxygen has diffused into the pulmonary circulation it is transported by two mechanisms: some will remain in simple solution in the blood, but most of it will be bound by the hemoglobin molecule within the red blood cells. Hemoglobin is composed of four protein chains attached to one atom of iron. It is the iron in hemoglobin that attracts oxygen. This facilitates transport throughout the circulatory system. Also, oxygen enriched hemoglobin becomes a bright red. People who have low hemoglobin have reduced ability to transport and utilize oxygen and are considered to suffer from anemia. People with severe anemia should be cautious about diving activities especially deep dives where increased partial pressures of oxygen and carbon dioxide may complicate the anemic condition. Hemoglobin also transports carbon dioxide from the cells. This CO_2 enriched hemoglobin has a bluish color to it. Frequently hemoglobin saturated with CO_2 is called reduced hemoglobin. Of course, inert gases (nitrogen-helium-etc.) are carried in the circulation in solution.

With proper gas supplies, the only gases that combine with hemoglobin is O_2 and CO_2. However, if the gas supply contains carbon monoxide (CO), it will combine with hemoglobin 240 times more readily than oxygen. Carbon monoxide will not support life and renders one anemic quite rapidly. If unchecked, high levels of CO may lead to unconsciousness and possible death. How does CO get into the gas supply? The most common means divers are exposed to CO are through smoking. Thus a smoker can quite easily have five to fifteen percent of their hemoglobin combined with CO. As depth increases, so do the partial pressures of all gases in the breathing medium thus the effects of carbon monoxide are compounded. Exhaust fumes from combustible engines, cars, compressors etc., also produce CO. From this it is apparent that diving gases must be free of gas contaminates, and life support systems for diving should be free of carbon monoxide and hydrocarbons.

As gas diffuses across the alveoli it travels from the capillaries of the pulmonary circulation where it enters the arteries. It is pumped through the heart and transported to where oxygen becomes available to the tissues. Of course, the opposite is true with the elimination of CO_2. CO_2 is transported back to the lungs, diffuses across the alveoli, and is exhaled.

EXCHANGE OF GASES TO THE TISSUE FLUIDS AND CELLS, AND USE OF GASES IN METABOLISM

Once gas has been transported via blood it is available to the tissues. Initially gas diffuses from the arteries to the capillaries supplying the cells. This diffusion is referred to as exchange to tissue fluids.

Cells receive gas from the tissue fluids (via capillaries). The gas diffuses into the cells due to higher gas pressures within the capillaries. Osmosis also accounts for some of the gas exchange. Oxygen is used by the cells to combine with glucose to provide life functions of the cell (cellular metabolism). Looking at an overview of the process to this point reveals a path of gas flow from the lungs to use in the tissues. Once hemoglobin is oxygenated it must travel throughout the body to provide individual cells with oxygen. The heart is the muscular pump that drives the gas by creating blood pressure.

If we start at the right side of the heart and track the path of blood it will be rich in reduced hemoglobin (high CO_2). The blood enters the right atrium and is pumped by systolic pressure through the tricuspid valve to the right ventricle. It then enters the pulmonary circulation. The next stop is the lungs where carbon dioxide is removed from the hemoglobin by diffusion. At this point the blood is newly oxygenated from across the capillaries producing oxyhemoglobin and it transfers to the larger blood vessels for transportation. It then enters the heart via the left atrium, passes through the biscupid (mitral) valve and is pumped by the left ventricle through the aortic valve into the systemic circulation. The propelling action into the arterial circulation is the diastolic pressure. Blood with oxygen rich hemoglobin now travels a network of smaller vessels until it is at the tissue via capillaries. At the capillary — cell interface oxyhemoglobin diffuses into the cells and inert gas (nitrogen, helium etc.) is stored in them to equilibrium with the ambient pressure.

Cells receive oxyhemoglobin and react like a slow burning furnace. Cells produce energy by combining a flow of fuel with oxygen. The oxygen "burns" the fuel and energy is released. In the human body, fuel comes from carbohydrates, and fats consumed by a person. The reaction takes place in small subunits within the cell known as mitochondria. Mitochondria contain specialized protein molecules or enzymes referred to as the cytochrome oxidase system. This system takes energy released from the oxidation of food (fuel) and transfers it to an energy storage molecule adenosine triphosphate (ATP). ATP, then, is the unit for energy storage within cells.

As energy is produced, waste is also produced. As a result of the use of oxygen, a by-product is produced from its "burning" called carbon dioxide. Unlike oxygen, CO_2 does not support life. The cell pressure of CO_2 is higher than the CO_2 pressure within the circulation, thus CO_2 diffuses into the venous circulation and is transported through larger and larger veins until it is returned to the heart and the cycle repeats itself. If the body retains CO_2, or has a reduced capacity to eliminate it, then it has an adverse physiological effect on the cellular energy mechanism. As we explore the effects of increased partial pressures of gases, we will discover several instances whereby CO_2 transport is altered, or a behavior that can lead to CO_2 retention. It is easily seen that any action which interferes with this process will ultimately effect the health of the cells and our well being. Environments with elevated CO alter the function of tissues and blood. Smokers with their increased CO content may suffer from hardening of the arteries which reduces transport efficiency of blood, increases blood pressure and subjects the diver to numerous problems including carbon monoxide poisoning.

In a diving environment there are both self induced and physiological reactions that do alter the processes of circulation and respiration as well as producing changes in neurological performance. In addition, the inert gas becomes a problem. As the pressure is increased, inert gas maintains its normal transportation route to the tissues. However the gas(es) will tend to reach a new equilibrium at the depth of the dive. Discussed in detail in later chapters dealing with decompression sickness and decompression models, inert gas will eventually saturate the system. Upon ascent, the inert gases must be allowed to leave the tissues and blood at a rate that does not produce symptoms of DCS. Ideally, the gas will stay in solution without bubble formation due to exceeding supersaturation parameters.

In addition to discussing techniques and habits of breathing, I would like to present another view of the act of breathing. It is not intended that In addition to discussing techniques and habits of breathing, It is not intended that the reader accept or reject this different view but rather that he/she understands the principle that breathing control is based upon. The best way to approach

This completes *The Science of Breathing*. The reader is referred to Appendix A on page 369 for the continuation on, *The Art of Breathing*. The Appendix gives a detailed outline of breathing philosophy and exercises to develop healthy breathing tecniques.

REFERENCES

The New Practical Diving, Tom Mount and Akira Ikehara, University Miami Press, Baltimore, MD.

The Lung, Comroe, Dubois, Briscoe, Carlsen Yearbook Medical Publishers.

The Science of Breathe, Swami Rama, Rudolph Ballentine, and Alan Hymes, Himalayan Institute.

CHAPTER 4

Some Physical Principles

We are land dwelling, air breathing creatures. As such, we have developed perceptions and behaviors for operating in a breathable atmosphere. Since we have chosen to play in an underwater world and since we cannot breathe water, it is necessary to understand some aspects of that underwater realm. Understanding the environment in which we play will minimize our risk and increase our enjoyment of the underwater world we call "Planet Ocean." This chapter will define concepts to help you better understand the principles that govern many of your actions in the underwater world.

BASIC DEFINITIONS

The study of the physical world has traditionally been divided into a number of inter-related disciplines. Physics is the broad name given to the study of our physical world. Chemistry is the investigation of chemical substances that make up that world. These disciplines share a common vocabulary, philosophy and methodology. In order to utilize physical principles to enhance our enjoyment of the underwater world, we must first understand the vocabulary of these disciplines.

We define matter as anything that occupies space (possesses a measurable volume) and has mass. (More on mass later.) Matter can exist in one of four forms or physical states. These states are solid, liquid, gas and plasma. Plasma is an extremely high energy form of matter that exists only under extreme conditions (like the inside of a star). Since most divers do not frequent stellar regions, we are concerned only with the three ordinary states of matter:

Solids are characterized by rigidity and a definite form; liquids flow; Gases diffuse and will uniformly fill any container in which they are placed. Using water as an example: ice is a solid, running water is a liquid, and steam is a gas. The physical state (solid, liquid or gas) of a substance depends on the surrounding pressure and temperature. Conversion from one form of matter to another, like the melting of ice, is termed a change of state.

According to accepted scientific theology, matter is composed of atoms. Atoms are the smallest possible entity a material can be divided into and still retain its identity. For example, if we take a piece of pure iron and cut it into smaller and smaller pieces, eventually we will get to something that can no longer be cut apart and still be iron. This "something" is an atom. Materials that are composed of only one kind of atom are termed elements. There are more than one hundred such elements, each with different characteristics. Each element has a unique symbol, assigned number and atomic weight. Chemists have arranged the elements in chart format termed the periodic table. This table allows chemists to understand certain aspects of the way elements react with each other.

Atoms interact or combine with other atoms to form molecules. If the molecules are made up of more than one type of atom (or element), the resultant is called a compound. Since each element has a unique symbol, combinations of atoms, or molecules, are then represented using these symbols. The relative proportions of the combining elements are indicated by numbers after the symbol to provide a chemical formula. The individual weights of the elements (derived from the periodic table) can then be summed to give a molecular weight.

EXAMPLES:

H Hydrogen, an element; the molecule (H_2) contains two atoms;
    The element has an atomic weight of 1; the molecule has a molecular weight of two.

He Helium, an element; Note: this element does not combine with other elements under ordinary conditions; it is said to be chemically inert. This element has an atomic weight of four. Since it does not combine with other molecules, the molecular weight is also four.

N Nitrogen, an element; the molecule (N_2) contains two atoms.
    The element has an atomic weight of 14, the molecule has a molecular weight of 28.

O Oxygen, an element; the molecule (O_2) contains two atoms.
    The element has an atomic weight of 16, the molecular weight is 32.

CO_2 Carbon dioxide, a compound; the molecule contains two atoms of oxygen and one of carbon. The molecular weight is 44.

H_2O Water, a compound; the molecule contains two atoms of hydrogen and one atom of oxygen. The molecular weight is 18.

TIME

Time in both the English and metric systems is based on the second. A second, as determined by astronomical measurements, is the duration of 1/86400 of a mean solar day. For divers, who require less precise standards, a second is 1/60 of a minute or 1/3600 of an hour.

MASS & WEIGHT

The concept of mass and weight is often confusing to nonscientists. A scientist makes a rigorous distinction between mass, an intrinsic property of matter, and weight, the result of force (a push or pull) operating on that mass. Mass refers to the property of matter that resists change in movement. For example, a moving boat continues to move in the water after the power has been turned off... the boat continues to move toward the dock, even though a foolish dockhand puts out a hand to stop the boat. This tendency of the boat to resist change in movement is termed inertia. The property of matter that provides this resistance to change is termed mass. In the metric system, the unit of mass is the kilogram. The corresponding English unit of mass is the slug.

Weight is the result of some force (like gravity) acting on mass. The unit of weight in the Metric system is the Newton; the unit of weight in the English system is the pound. For example, you will weigh less on the moon than on the earth because the gravitational force on the moon is less than that of the earth's. Your mass (number of kilograms or slugs) will not change, however, you will weigh (number of Newtons or pounds) less. In practice, divers do not make the scientifically rigorous distinction between mass and weight and they will refer to kilograms and pounds as units of weight. (If unsure whether the scientific use requires "mass" or "weight," consider the following: Weight is a force; it has a magnitude (mass) and a direction. If direction is an important consideration in understanding the nature of the problem, then the appropriate term is weight. If direction is not a factor, then mass is the proper term.)

DENSITY

Density is a measurement of the "molecular packing" of a particular substance. The heavier the molecule and the more molecules per unit volume, the heavier a substance will be. Density is defined as the mass per unit volume. Density can be used to calculate the mass of an object.

MASS OF OBJECT = VOLUME X DENSITY

Pure water theoretically contains only water molecules. Since salt water also contains a variety of dissolved materials, an equal volume of salt water has more mass than a corresponding volume of fresh water.

Substances may expand or contract (ie. change volume) as temperature changes. This means that density, particularly of liquids and gases, will change with temperature. (Divers may be familiar with a thermocline, the sharp interface between colder, more dense water and warm water. Here the cold more dense water sinks relative to the warm water.) Since density changes with temperature, it is necessary to have a standard value for comparison of different materials. This standard is the specific gravity which relates the mass of material to an equal volume of water. Water has a density of 1.000 at 4^0 C. (The density is slightly less than 1.000 at all other temperatures.)

$$\text{Specific gravity} = \frac{\text{mass of material}}{\text{mass of equal volume of water at } 4^0 \text{ C.}}$$

Since divers do not operate at temperatures where there is a significant difference between density and specific gravity, for most applications, these terms may be interchanged. The specific gravity of pure fresh water may be assumed to be 1.00. (Note that density has units of mass/volume while specific gravity is a ratio and has no units.)

BUOYANCY

While playing (allegedly alone) in the public baths of ancient Greece, Archimedes, a renowned natural philosopher, noted that the level of water rose in the tub when he entered the bath. He then stated what has become known as Archimedes' principle: An object partially or wholly immersed in a fluid, is buoyed up by a force equal to the weight of the fluid displaced by the object. Translation: objects more dense than water (like lead) will sink; objects less dense than water (like cork) will float; objects of the same density will remain at the same level and neither sink nor float. Objects that sink are termed negative. Objects that float are termed positive or buoyant. Objects that stay stationary at depth are said to be neutral. Buoyancy is best understood by the application of "force arrow" principles or vectors. Vectors are mathematical constructs that have magnitude (like mass) and direction (towards or away from the surface).

TRIM

As a diver moves in the water column, the diver is subject to a number of forces. Gravity (negative buoyancy) tends to make the diver descend. Positive buoyancy (too little weight or too much air in the B.C..) makes the diver ascend. The diver moves forward propelled by the force of the kick. (Note that regardless of advertising claims, the forward thrust comes from power in the leg muscles, not the fin.) The thrust, or forward motion, must overcome drag (or friction) that the diver and equipment present to the water. A good diver tries to adjust the diving style to balance the forces involved.

Part of the unique "wonderfulness' of diving is the ability to glide, weightless, through the underwater realm. This allows the diver to truly become one with the environment. It is the most efficient and enjoyable way to experience Planet Ocean. If the diver is overweighted (a too common occurrence), then the diver must continually expend energy to overcome gravity and remain at constant depth. If the diver is underweighted, the diver must also continually expend energy in an attempt to overcome being positive with leg power. (In battles with improper buoyancy, buoyancy always overcomes leg power and fatigue is a certainty.) Please note that the way to maximize efficiency (decrease work load and thus increase enjoyment) in the water is to be neutral so that the thrust energy from the fins can be directed towards forward movement, not towards overcoming buoyancy trim errors. The drag resistance to movement can be lessened by assuming a horizontal position in the water. This presents a smaller area to the path of movement and lessens resistance. This also assists in directing the power derived from fin kick to move the diver forward, instead of wasting the power in attempts to overcome buoyancy errors.

ENERGY

Energy is the ability to do work. Energy due to a change in position is termed potential energy; energy that is due to movement is called kinetic energy. For example, a child on swing at the top of the swing, at the momentary pause before moving downward, possesses potential energy (the energy used to lift the child's mass to the height of the swing). As the child reaches the bottom of the swing, at the moment before starting to climb, the child possesses only kinetic energy (the energy of movement). Note that during the entire movement through the pendulum motion of the swing, the child will possess different portions of potential/kinetic energy, but that the sum of these two forces will remain constant. There are several types of energy:

Mechanical:	The sum of potential and kinetic energies derived from the movement of a body.
Heat:	Energy derived from molecular motion.
Radiant:	Energy in the form of electromagnetic waves such as light, X-rays, or radio waves.
Chemical:	Energy released from the chemical reactions.
Electrical:	Energy derived from moving electrons
Nuclear:	Energy derived from inter-atomic forces.

Under ordinary conditions, energy can neither be created nor destroyed. It can, however, be changed in form. For example, the potential energy of water at a high level, falls through a tube in a hydroelectric dam (kinetic energy). The water turns a turbine (mechanical energy) that drives a generator producing electricity (electric energy). The electricity lights a light bulb (radiant energy) and heats a small spaceheater (heat energy). During this entire process, energy was not created; it was transformed from one form to another.

Work is the movement of mass over a distance. Work requires energy to perform. Note that if no movement occurs, no work is accomplished.

HEAT

Heat is thermal energy. It is thought of as the sum total of the kinetic energy of all the molecules contained within a substance. It is the energy associated with the random movement of molecules. (See discussion on kinetic theory of gases.) It is convenient to measure the amount of heat as if heat were independent of the particular substance whose molecular motion determines the magnitude of heat energy present. The amount of heat necessary to raise 1 gram of pure water from 14.5 to 15.5° C is defined as one calorie. One thousand calories is a kilocalorie (Kcal). The corresponding English measurement is the amount of heat necessary to raise a pound of pure water from 63.° to 64.° F. This unit is called the British Thermal Unit (BTU). One BTU is equivalent to 252 calories.

Matter may be thought of as a heat reservoir. Different substances, due to their molecular make-up, will be capable of holding different amounts of heat. The amount of heat a particular material can hold is termed its specific heat. It is determined by measuring the amount of heat necessary to raise 1 gram of the substance 1° C. (Remember that this corresponds to our definition of calorie and thus water has a specific heat of 1.0). Substances like water or Helium have high specific heats, compared to air, and thus divers in contact with water or Helium will lose significant amounts of heat. Heat capacities of gases are listed at a specific temperature (usually 25° C at 1 ATM pressure) and are measured either at constant pressure (Cp) or constant volume (Cv). The values listed below for heat capacities of gases have the units of cal/g °C.

Examples of Specific Heat Substance

Substance	Cp	Cv
Air	0.3439	0.2943
Argon	0.1252	0.0750
Helium	4.9680	3.0470
Nitrogen	0.2477	0.1765
Oxygen	0.2200	0.1554

Heat capacity is the amount of heat required to raise the temperature of that particular body by one degree.

Heat Capacity = Mass of body x specific heat of body

The amount of heat necessary to change the temperature of a body is:

Heat Required = Mass x specific heat x change in temperature.

Example:

While holding pressure constant, how much heat is necessary to raise the temperature of 100 grams of air 10° C ? of 100 g of Helium 10° C?

a. For air: Heat needed = $\dfrac{100 \text{ g x } 0.3439 \text{ cal x } 10° \text{ C}}{\text{g}° \text{ C}}$ = 343.9 cal

b. For He: Heat needed = $\dfrac{100 \text{ g x } 4.9680 \text{ cal x } 10 \text{ C}}{\text{g}° \text{ C}}$ = 4968.0 cal

Comment: Divers in a Helium environment (breathing Heliox) will lose large amounts of heat from their bodies in an attempt to warm the gas they are breathing. This increased heat loss (compared to air) due to the high specific heat of Helium is responsible for hypothermia problems associated with breathing Heliox. This heat loss is not trivial; it can be life threatening.

Note that a large mass (physically large diver) will possess more heat capacity (more heat stored in body reservoir) than a physically smaller diver. Thus, the larger person will be more able to tolerate appreciable heat loss associated with immersion in cold water.

Temperature is a measurement of the intensity of heat energy. When two materials possessing different heat energies (different temperatures) come together, heat will always move from the warmest body to the cooler one. Heat will continue to be transferred until the two bodies possess the same energy (have same temperature.) This means that anytime a diver is immersed in water cooler than body temperature, heat will be lost from the diver. For example, if a diver enters Lake Superior at 34° F, heat will be lost from the diver in an attempt to warm the entire mass of Lake

HEAT TRANSFER

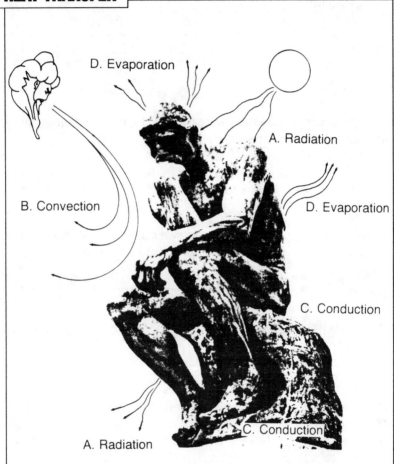

"MECHANISMS OF HEAT TRANSFER WITH THE ENVIRONMENT

The mechanism of heat transfer between man and the environment include: A. Radiation - heat transferred by electromagnetic waves from warm to cooler objects: B. Conduction - heat transfer by molecules of air or fluid moving between areas of unequal temperature: C. Conduction - heat exchange between objects in contact: D. Evaporation - heat loss by water molecules diffusing from the body surface by sweating, and by environmental wetting when this water changes from a liquid to a vapor state. The above methods are further explained in the text.

Superior to the temperature of the diver. Since the mass of Lake Superior is enormous (ie. incredible heat capacity) compared to the mass of the diver, the diver will lose much body heat. The temperature decrease to the diver will be significant, but the temperature increase to Lake Superior will be infinitesimal.

The diver loses heat by several mechanisms. They are:

Radiation; is the direct emission of infrared (heat) energy from the body. (A person may be thought of as a "living lightbulb" emitting "light" (infrared radiation) not visible to the human eye. This mechanism of heat loss is extremely important in the vacuum of space, but radiation heat loss is minimal to the diver.

Conduction: the primary heat loss mechanism in diving. This is the direct loss of thermal energy by direct contact between substances; a molecular transfer of energy. Heat moves from the warm diver to the cooler water. Note that water is more dense than air (has more molecules per unit volume); thus more molecular collisions and more heat transfer. Water will remove heat from a diver 25 times faster than dry still air of the same temperature. Note also that the diver is breathing gas at a temperature below body temperature; thus much heat will be lost from the diver in an attempt to warm the breathing gas to body temperature.

Convection; is associated with conduction. As a volume of cooler fluid in contact with a warm body is warmed, it moves away from the contact point. The area vacated by the warmer fluid is filled with cooler fluid and more transfer of heat occurs. Convection increases the conductive heat loss.

Evaporation; is the loss of heat associated with a change in state of liquid water to water vapor. It requires significant amounts of energy to change liquid water to water vapor. A diver generally breathes very dry air. The lungs need humidified air. As the diver breathes, water is evaporated along the respiratory tract to humidify the breathing mix. This can result in significant heat loss to the diver.

The loss of heat from a diver immersed in cold water CANNOT BE PREVENTED. It can, however, be slowed. The purpose of insulation, generally gas trapped in some physical matrix (like bubbles in a wet suit or dry suit underwear), is to slow the loss of heat from the diver to the water by imposing a physical barrier. Thus, heat must move through the insulation on its way from the diver to the water. The better the insulation, the longer it will take the body heat of the diver to move into the water.

TEMPERATURE

Temperature is measured by a variety of scales. Historically, the first reliable calibration of temperature was introduced by Daniel Fahrenheit in 1724. He picked the lowest temperature he could obtain (a mixture of ice, salt and water) and called that his zero point. He next picked the body temperature of a healthy man and arbitrarily gave it a value of 96. Using mercury as the expanding fluid that would mark his temperature sensing gauge called a thermometer, he found that water would freeze at a temperature of 32 and boil at a temperature of 212 on his scale. His system, the Fahrenheit temperature scale, is still used in the United States. Twelve years later, Anders Celsius, proposed a scale that would be based on 100 units between the freezing point and boiling point of water. Originally, he called the boiling point 0 and the freezing point 100, but that has been inverted to give a scale of 0 for the freezing point of water and 100 for the boiling point of water.

The two systems of measurement can be converted using the following expressions:

$$F = (1.8 \times C) + 32 \quad or \quad F = 9/5\,C + 32$$
$$C = (F - 32) / 1.8 \quad or \quad C = 5/9\,(F - 32)$$

There are two other temperature scales of importance to divers. They are the Rankine (absolute Fahrenheit) and the Kelvin (absolute Celsius) scales. The significance of these absolute temperature scales is discussed in the section on Charles' Law.

$$R\ (Rankine) = F + 460$$
$$K\ (Kelvin) = C + 273$$

LIGHT

Light is a form of energy. It provides the illumination that we use to visually perceive and characterize our surroundings. Its propagation is influenced by a number of factors. These include:

Absorption: White light is composed of a number of different colors. The splitting of white light into its component colors (Red, Orange, Yellow, Green, Blue, Indigo, Violet) is observed naturally when we see a rainbow in the sky. Each of these colors possesses a different energy. Red is the least energetic color, while blue is the most energetic form of visible light. As light moves through the water, the components of light are absorbed by the water. Since red is the least energetic, it is absorbed (lost) first. Each of the colors, in turn, is absorbed as light passes through any appreciable distance in water. The diver observes that colors "disappear."

In shallow water, only the reds may disappear, but as depth increases (light reaching a diver has had to pass through more water) the underwater realm takes on more of a bluish cast. Application of artificial white light (all the colors present) allows the diver to observe nature in its true color.

Diffusion: As light moves through water, it interacts at the molecular level with all substances present in the water. The result is that light is scattered and moves in random directions. This process of light scattering is referred to as diffusion. Divers see less light at depth because the total amount of light available at the surface has been scattered by diffusion.

Turbidity; refers to the amount of particulate material in the water. If turbidity is high, then the abundance of suspended material will increase the amount of both diffusion and absorption that occurs. The diver sees less light in turbid water.

Refraction: Light travels at different speeds in different substances. Light slows about 25% when it enters water from air. This change in velocity results in a bending of the light path as it changes from air to water. This bending has the same effect on light as if light had moved through an optical lens. This bending of light is termed refraction. The diver's mask is an air/water interface, thus the mask will act as a lens. Divers will perceive that objects are larger (by 4/3) and closer (by 25%) than they really are.

SOUND

Sound is a longitudinal wave (a series of vibrations: compressions and tensions) that moves through a fluid. In other words, sound energy is produced by mechanical vibrations. Our ears, through a vibrating membrane (the ear drum), detect sound energy and convert the vibrations to electrical pulses that the brain interprets as sound.

On the surface, we can perceive the direction of a sound source. Our brain does this determination by measuring the time delay between the sound energy striking one ear and then the other. Underwater, the velocity of sound is four times faster than in air. (Longitudinal waves, a series of vibrations, propagate more readily in dense media; the more dense the fluid, the faster the velocity.) This means that the time delay between sound energy striking the different ears is too short for the brain to interpret as a direction. Thus, divers are unable to use sound as a directional cue underwater.

PRESSURE

Pressure is defined as a force (push) acting across a unit area. The force most often encountered by divers is weight. Thus pressure is measured in terms of a weight (not mass) per unit area. The pressure that divers must cope with is a result of the weight of the water and atmosphere above the diver.

The belief that air had weight was first expressed by the Greek philosopher Empedocles in the 5th century B.C. Even Aristotle said that "nature abhors a vacuum." However, the first scientific demonstration/explanation of the weight of air was by the Italian mathematician Evangesta Torricelli. His experiment was the basis of the modern barometer. Torricelli filled a tube with mercury and, after inverting the tube, placed the tube in a dish of mercury. He noted that the mercury did not drain from the tube into the dish. Instead, it remained within the tube. His explanation was that air had weight. The weight of the air pushing down on the mercury in the dish was equal to the weight of the mercury in the tube. The height of the mercury (760 mm) in the tube was then defined as "atmospheric pressure." This is why pressure is often expressed in mm Hg. (Hg is the chemical symbol for mercury; a pressure reading given in mm Hg means that observed pressure is equal to the weight that will hold a column of mercury at the height given in the measurement. Note that the diameter of the tube is immaterial, the mercury in tube is held up by the weight of the entire atmosphere.) Equivalent measurements of pressure can be made with different fluids; mercury was originally chosen because of its high density.

DEFINITION

One Atmosphere pressure: 760 mm Hg
                           33 feet sea water (fsw)
                           34 feet fresh water (ffw)
                           14.7 pounds per square inch (psi)

Problem:

What is the pressure (in psi) exerted by 4 feet of seawater?

$$\frac{14.7\ psi}{atm} \quad x \quad \frac{atm}{33\ ft} \quad x \quad 4\ ft = 1.78\ psi$$

Note that the alveoli in the lungs can rupture if the pressure gradient across the alveolar membrane is greater than about 1.5 psi. This is why (if you hold your breath) it is possible to suffer an air embolism in less than four feet of water.

When you descend in the water column, there is water above you. Thus, your body will be subjected to a pressure from the weight of the water above you. This pressure, due to the water surroundings, is termed hydrostatic pressure. This is equal to 1 atm of pressure for every 33 feet of descent in sea water (34 ft in fresh water). However, the water in which divers play is underneath the entire weight of the atmosphere. So the total (ambient or absolute) pressure is the sum of the hydrostatic and atmospheric pressures.

Example:
Determine hydrostatic and absolute (ambient) pressure at a depth of 78 fsw:

$$Hydrostatic\ pressure\ =\ \frac{depth\ of\ sea\ water}{33\ ft\ fsw/atm}$$

$$Hydrostatic\ pressure\ =\ \frac{78\ fsw}{33\ fsw/atm}$$

$$Hydrostatic\ pressure\ =\ 2.36\ atm$$

$$=\ 2.36\ atm \times \frac{14.7\ psi}{atm}\ =\ 34.75\ psi$$

$$Absolute\ pressure\quad =\ hydrostatic + atmospheric$$
$$=\ 2.36\ atm + 1\ atm$$
$$=\ 3.36\ ATA\ \ (ATA = atmospheres\ absolute)$$

Gases in cylinders are measured in gauge pressure. However, gauge pressure reads zero at a pressure of one atmosphere. To get the absolute pressure, one atmosphere must be added to the gauge pressure.

Example: An 80 cubic foot cylinder contains gas at a pressure reading of 3000 psig (pounds per square inch gauge.)

This corresponds to an absolute pressure of: 3000 psig + 14.7 psi = 3014.7 psia (lbs per sq inch absolute)

KINETIC THEORY OF GASES

All gases, irrespective of chemical composition, demonstrate similar behavior in response to physical changes of composition, temperature and pressure. This uniformity of physical behavior was of great interest to early scientists. It is one of the dogmas of science that the behavior of a material is a reflection of the particles that make-up the substance. The differences between a solid, liquid and gas reflect the movement of the small particles (atoms) that compose all matter. This assumption is part of the **Kinetic Theory Of Gases** (Kinetic from the Greek for Motion).

This theory is based on six fundamental assumptions:
1. Gases are composed of molecules.
2. These molecules are in constant motion. This is why gases mix to uniformity and fill all portions of the containment vessel.
3. Molecules of a gas collide frequently with each other and with the walls of the containment vessel.
4. Under ordinary circumstances, the distance between gas molecules is far greater than the size of the individual molecules. This is why gases can be compressed.

5. The molecules of a gas move in all directions with an average velocity at a given temperature. At a given temperature, the average energy of molecules in the gaseous state is the same for all substances. This can mathematically be described as:

$K.E.$ $= 1/2\ m\,v^2$ *where:*
$K.E.$ *= the kinetic energy (in ergs)*
m *= mass of the substance (in grams)*
v *= velocity (in cm/sec)*

6. Molecules are perfectly elastic; thus they lose no energy when they collide with another molecule. (If they lost energy on collision, the temperature of a gas mix would always decrease with time.)

These assumptions are the basis for understanding gas behavior. For example, the gases constantly collide with the walls of the vessel. A measurement of the "intensity" (force per unit area) of the collisions is termed pressure. As we increase the kinetic energy (by raising temperature) the molecules will have more velocity and they will collide with more force on the vessel walls. This is why pressure increases in a closed container as temperature is raised.

GAS LAW FUNDAMENTALS:

CHARLES'S LAW

The relationship between temperature, pressure and volume has been extensively studied. The French scientist, Jacques Charles, in 1801, studied the relationship between temperature and volume at constant pressure. He noted that in the vicinity of zero degrees Celsius, the volume of a gas decreased by a factor of 1/273 for each Celsius degree decrease. If one theoretically continued this decrease in temperature, then a gas would have zero volume at -273 degrees C. This value is termed **absolute zero**. [Note: If a gas has zero volume, then there will be no molecular motion (velocity = zero in kinetic energy equation) and thus no kinetic energy.] Measurements of temperature based on this absolute zero point as temperature zero are termed **absolute temperature**. (Note that since gases will liquefy before absolute zero is reached, the "zero volume" state is not obtainable.) Since this 1/273 change in volume corresponds to one degree change on the absolute temperature scale, absolute temperatures are used when using "the gas laws" described below to predict variations in pressure, temperature and volume. Charles' observations have been formalized into Charles' Law: The volume of a gas at constant pressure is directly proportional to the absolute temperature. Expressed mathematically:

$$\frac{V(1)}{V(1)} = \frac{V(2)}{T(2)}$$

$V(1)$ = *the volume at first condition*

$V(2)$ = *the volume at second condition*

$T(1)$ = *the absolute temperature corresponding to measurement of $V(1)$*

$T(2)$ = *the absolute temperature corresponding to measurement of $V(2)$*

BOYLE'S LAW

Earlier, in 1662, Sir Robert Boyle measured the relationship between pressure and volume at constant temperature. He measured the volume of air trapped at the small end of a J-shaped tube. The tube was filled with mercury and the volume of the air space was measured. Adding mercury, (increasing the height of mercury in the J-tube) deceased the volume of air trapped at the end of the tube. He noted that the product of the pressure (as determined by the height of the mercury column) and the volume was always constant. Expressed mathematically:

$PV = k$ *where:*

P = *the pressure (height of mercury in tube)*

V = *volume (of air space in tube)*

k = *a constant*

This relationship, PV = k, held for a variety of P, V combinations. In mathematics, products equal to the same value can be set equal to each other.

This gives us Boyle's Law:

$P(1)\ V(1) = P(2)\ V(2)$ *where:*

P = *pressure*

V = *volume*

measured at set of conditions 1 and 2.

Boyle's Law states that at constant temperature, the volume varies inversely with the pressure. A corollary to this law states that density (mass/volume) increases directly with the pressure.

It is important to remember as pressure increases, volume decreases. Likewise, as pressure decreases (as on ascent on scuba), the volume of gas in the lungs and other air spaces increases. The greatest volume change per unit of ascent is in the vicinity of the surface.

GAS CONSUMPTION

Note that the actual volume of gas within a scuba cylinder does not decrease (all of the gas molecules have not been shoved to the bottom of the tank) upon descent. The tank physically does not shrink under pressure. However, air being delivered to the diver is at ambient pressure. The increased pressure means more gas molecules per unit volume (gas is more dense). Since the diver consumes more molecules per constant volume breathing, the gas in the scuba cylinder will last a shorter amount of time. Although gas consumption can be affected by numerous factors (such as physical size, work load, water temperature, anxiety from seeing

HOW BOYLE'S LAW WORKS

		AIR-FILLED (OPEN)
SEA LEVEL	14.7 PSI (1 ATM) VOL=100% (1)	
33 FT	29.4 PSI (2 ATM) VOL=50% (1/2)	
66 FT	44.1 PSI (3 ATM) VOL=33 1/3% (1/3)	
99 FT	58.8 PSI (4 ATM) VOL=25% (1/4)	
132 FT	73.5 PSI (5 ATM) VOL=20% (1/5)	

that 14 ft hammerhead, general physical and emotional condition), it can be approximated. The best approximation comes from personal experience. (Personal knowledge of individual gas consumption rates.) It has been stated that the "average" diver (I personally have never met or known this guy!) consumes air at a surface consumption rate of one cubic foot per minute. Individual surface consumption rates vary and must be determined from personal observation.

Estimating air consumption rate is a two step process:

a. estimate the surface duration time:

$$\frac{Surface\ duration}{Breathing\ rate} = Volume\ of\ cylinder$$

For our "average diver" using an 80 cubic foot cylinder:

$$Surface\ duration\ at\ one\ ATA = \frac{80\ ft^3}{1\ ft^3\ /\ min}$$

Surface duration = 80 minutes at one ATA

b. convert surface duration to ESTIMATE at depth:
For our "average diver" at 99 fsw:
Hydrostatic pressure at depth: $99\ fsw = 3\ atm$
     $33\ fsw/atm$
Absolute pressure at depth: $3\ atm + 1\ atm = 4\ ATA$

$$Depth\ duration = \frac{Surface\ duration}{pressure\ (ATA)\ at\ depth}$$

$$Depth\ duration = \frac{80\ minutes\ at\ one\ ATA}{4\ ATA}$$

Depth duration = 20 minutes at 4 ATA

GUY-LUSSAC'S LAW

Near the turn of the nineteenth century, a third scientist, Joseph Guy-Lussac, investigated the relationship between pressure and temperature while the volume was held constant. His observation (known as Guy-Lussac's Law) states that the pressure of a gas at constant volume is directly proportional to the absolute temperature. Stated mathematically:

$$\frac{P\,(1)}{T\,(1)} = \frac{P\,(2)}{T\,(2)} \qquad where\ P\ and\ V\ are\ as\ previously\ defined$$

Example: *A cylinder at 298 degrees K contains gas at a pressure of 3014.7 psia (pounds per square inch absolute) Predict the pressure at 334 K.*

Guy-Lussac's Law:

$$\frac{P(1)}{T(1)} = \frac{P(2)}{T(2)}$$

Substituting:

$$\frac{3014.7psia}{298\ K} \qquad \frac{P(2)}{334\ K}$$

Solving:
$$P(2) = 3378.9\ psia$$
Converting to gauge pressure:
$$P(2) = 3378.9\ psia - 14.7\ psi$$
$$= 3364.2\ psig$$

Thus, a 3000 psig scuba cylinder at 298 K heated to 334 K will show a gauge pressure of 3364 psi. Note that Guy-Lussac's, not Charles' law, is the explanation for the increase in pressure observed when a scuba cylinder is heated. (ie. a scuba cylinder is, hopefully, a constant volume device. As kinetic energy increases with temperature, the molecules travel faster, thus they hit the vessel walls harder and pressure increases.)

The above three laws have been combined into what is termed the:

General or Combined Gas Law:

$$\frac{P(1)\,V(1)}{T(1)} = \frac{P(2)\,V(2)}{T(2)} \qquad \textit{Where P, V, \& T are as previously defined.}$$

This relationship can be used to predict pressure, volume, and temperature relationships where any five of the six variables are known. Remember that when working gas law problems, both pressure and temperature must be absolute measurements.

Expanding on Boyle:

Remember that Boyle measured the product of pressure and volume and always got the same number:

$$PV = k$$

Scientists wanted a single equation that would, without having to measure multiple volumes, temperatures and pressures give reliable pressure, temperature, volume, AND quantity measurements on gases. This lead to an investigation of this constant k. It turns out that temperature and quantity of a gas can be added to this equation. This new generalized gas equation takes the form:

$PV = nRT$ where:
P = absolute pressure
V = volume
T = absolute temperature
n = number of "moles"
R = Universal Gas Constant

A MOLE is a chemical measurement of quantity. It is used to relate compounds of different molecular weights. One mole (a mass equal to M grams, where M is the molecular weight of a substance) contains Avagadros' Number (6.02×10^{23}) of molecules. For example: one mole of O_2 (molecular weight of 32) is 32 grams; this mole of oxygen contains the same number of atoms as 28 grams, one mole, of N_2 (molecular weight of 28). Chemists use MOLES because physical/chemical properties are determined by the numbers of molecules present. Using moles allows chemists to compare substances that have different molecular weights. The MOLE is also important because it turns out that one MOLE (the molecular weight (MW) of a gas expressed in grams) at so-called Standard Temperature and Pressure (STP; $O°$ C, 1 atm absolute) always has the same volume, 22.414 liters. Thus, using this equation, it is possible to derive not only pressure, temperature, and volume relationships, but quantities of a substance as well.

R is the "universal gas constant" - ie. it's a number that has been placed into the equation so that the numbers calculated are similar to the numbers observed. (A common trick in science is to add "constants", ie. fudge factors, to make equations reflect observed reality.) R has been determined from numerous physical measurements. It is equal to the value of PV/nT.

Example: *How many liters would 5 moles of any gas occupy at 25 degrees C (298 K) and 2 atm absolute pressure.*

$PV = nRT$

Substituting:

$$\frac{(2\,ATA)\,V}{deg\text{-}mole} = (5\,moles)\,(0.820 \quad L\text{-}ATA\,)\,(298\,deg.)$$

Solving:

$V = 61.1\,L$

This 5 moles of gas would correspond to:

5 moles x 32 g / mole = 160 g O_2 (Oxygen, MW = 32)
5 moles x 28 g / mole = 140 g N_2 (Nitrogen, MW = 28)
5 moles x   4 g / mole = 20 g He   (Helium, MW = 4)

Note that 20 g of He occupies the same volume as 160 g of O_2. This is because 20 g of Helium (5 moles) contains the same number of molecules as 160 g (5 moles) of Oxygen. This is why moles, not grams, are used in gas law equations.

Example: Predict the volume of one mole ideal gas at 5.1 ata and 276 K.
$PV = nRT$
Rearranging:
$V = nRT/P$
Substituting:
$V = (1\ mole)\ (0.820\ L\ ATA)\ 276\ K$
$deg\ K\ mole$
$5.1\ ATA$
$V = 44.4\ L$

REAL & IDEAL

The equation: $PV = nRT$ is called the IDEAL (or PERFECT) gas law. It is used to predict the behavior of so-called IDEAL GASES. An ideal (or perfect) gas is a gas that exactly behaves according to the laws of Charles and Boyle. In reality, NO GAS IS IDEAL! It turns out that most gases, at conditions near STP ($0°$ C, 1 ATA) behave according to Boyle's and

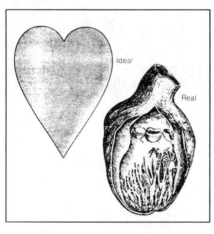

Charles' Law. As temperature and pressure move away from STP, values calculated by the ideal gas laws, including Boyle's and Charles', are different from the values measured experimentally. This deviation from ideal behavior has been explained by the fact that molecules do occupy space. Since moving molecules cannot freely move unhindered in all directions, the volume appears larger than predicted by Ideal behavior. Also, slight forces of attraction (Van der Waal's forces) exist between molecules so that individual molecules truly do not act totally independent of each other. This makes the volume appear smaller than predicted for Ideal behavior.

The proximity of molecules to each other will depend on both temperature and pressure. Low pressures and high temperatures keep molecules apart and allow gas behavior to be close to that predicted by the Ideal equations. However, low temperatures and high pressures (like that found in a scuba cylinder) tend to decrease molecular distance and significant difference from Ideal behavior is observed. Such behavior is termed REAL behavior and equations that predict gas behavior in regions where the simple IDEAL laws are inadequate are termed REAL equations.

VAN DER WAAL'S EQUATION

Since measurement of the pressure and volume of a number of gases at different conditions clearly demonstrated that the simple Ideal gas law was inadequate to predict observed behavior, it became necessary to "modify" the Ideal gas equation. Near the end of the nineteenth century, a Dutch chemist, Johanns Van Der Waals, examined the Ideal gas equation and made the following assumptions:

1. At low pressures, the intermolecular attractive forces act to cause a decrease in pressure. This causes the product PV in the Ideal gas equation to be lower than expected.

2. At high pressures, the volume occupied by individual molecules is significant with respect to the total volume occupied by the gas. Since the V term in the Ideal gas equation should represent only free space available for gas movement, a correction would be needed to account for the volume of space occupied by gas molecules. Since this correction factor is not present in the Ideal gas law, values calculated for PV at high pressures are larger than measured.

In order to make the Ideal gas law more closely conform to observed parameters, Van Der Waal introduced the following modifications:

1. The Ideal pressure could be represented as:

$P\ (IDEAL)\ =\ P + a\ /\ V^2\ where$
$P\ =\ pressure\ measured$
$V\ =\ the\ volume$
$a\ =\ a\ constant$

The constant a represents the attraction between molecules; it is different for each gas and has been determined from empirical observations.

2. The Ideal volume could be represented as:

$V\ (IDEAL)\ =\ V - b\ \ \ where:$
$V\ =\ volume\ measured$
$b\ =\ a\ constant$

The constant b represents the excluded volume of the molecules that make up the gas; it is different for each gas and it has been determined from numerous measurements. Tables of a and b values for various gases are available. One of the most common such collections in the *CRC Handbook of Chemistry and Physics*. Also note that a and b values are for pure compounds only and values for mixtures are commonly not found.

Adding these new P & V terms to the Ideal gas law gives rise to the Van Der Waals Equation for Real gases. This equation has also been called the REAL Gas Law:

$$(P + a/V^2)(V - b) = nRT$$

This equation can be used to derive pressure, temperature, volume and composition predictions for conditions away from STP.

COMPRESSIBILITY

Another approach to resolving the dilemma between ideal and real behavior is the concept of compressibility. In this scheme, the formula for predicting gas behavior is:

$$PV = znRT \qquad where \; z = compressibility \; factor$$

Note how, once again, science introduces a constant (an empirically derived measurement) to make an equation fit reality. The value z is different for each gas. Tables and graphs to find the appropriate "z-factor" at needed conditions are available. Note that for an ideal gas, $z = 1$ and the Real "compressibility" equation reduces to the Ideal gas law.

BEYOND REAL:

The Ideal gas equations adequately predict gas behavior at conditions near STP. As conditions move away from STP, more terms have to be added to the equations so that the predictions are close to observed values of pressure, temperature, volume and composition. These new terms gave rise to the Real Gas Laws. The REAL gas equations provide enough correlation with observed values to be used at scuba cylinder pressures. However, as the pressure continues to increase, the REAL gas laws begin to deviate from observed values and additional terms must be added to the REAL equations. The equations which add even more terms to the REAL equation are the expressions of Berthelot and the so-called virial equation of Kammerlingh-Onnes. These equations are well beyond the scope of sport diving.

DALTON'S LAW

A common method of estimating gas mix concentrations is the utilization of partial pressures. According to Dalton's Law of partial pressures the final pressure of a gas mix is the sum of the partial pressures of the components of the gas mix.

$$P\ (total) = P\ (1) + P\ (2) + P\ (3) + ... P\ (n)$$
where n = maximum number of components in the mix.

This law assumes that each individual gas molecule in the mix acts independently. (The pressure exerted by a gas in the mix is the same as it would exert if it were the only component present.) Thus, the final pressure of a mix can be obtained by simply adding the partial pressures of each component in the mix to derive the final pressure.

Another way of viewing Dalton's Law is:

$$P(n) = P\ (total)\ \ x\ \ \frac{\%\ of\ gas\ by\ volume}{100}$$

Example: Determine the partial pressure of oxygen in an air mix at a depth of 100 fsw using above formula:

$Air = 21\ \%\ O_2$

$P\ (Hydrostatic)\qquad = 100\,fsw\ x\qquad\quad = 3.03\ atm\quad \dfrac{atm}{33\,fsw}$

$P\ (absolute)\qquad\quad = 3.03\ atm + 1\ atm\quad = 4.03\ ATA$

$\qquad Substituting:$

$\qquad\qquad P\ (O_2) = 4.03\ ATA\ x\ 21/100$

$\qquad\qquad P\ (O_2) = 0.85\ ATA$

DALTON'S LAW & MIXING

Let's assume, for the purposes of speculation, a deep scuba diving adventurer wishes to dive on the Edmund Fitzgerald. This wreck lies at 530 feet of cold fresh water in Lake Superior. This corresponds to a pressure of:

$$\frac{530\,ft}{34\,ft/atm}\ =\ 15.6\ atm\ \ ambient$$

which is 15.6 atm + 1 atm = 16.6 atm absolute (16.6 ATA)

The diver wishes to keep the oxygen partial pressure below 1.8 ATA since PO_2 levels higher than 1.8 have been involved in oxygen toxicity hits. So, to simplify the math, the diver decides to prepare a diving mix of 10% (1.66 ATA) oxygen for diving at this depth. (Note that ideally, the concentration of oxygen in the gas mix should be varied at depth to keep the partial pressure of oxygen high enough to maintain consciousness, yet not enough to cause a toxicity (overdose!) problem. The ability to vary oxygen concentration with depth is currently not an available option in sport diving equipment.)

Estimating PO₂ for 10% mix:

Change in O_2 partial pressure: (P2 - P1) (a)
Where: P2 = absolute pressure desired at end of mixing
*   P1 = absolute pressure at start of operation*
*   a = fraction O_2 desired*
Substituting:(3014.7 psia - 14.7 psi) (0.10) = 300.0 psia
Absolute final O_2 pressure = P1 + 300.0 psia
*   = 14.7 psia + 300.0 psia = 314.7 psia*
Converting to gauge pressure: 314.7 psia - 14.7 psi = 300.0 psig

The diver slowly fills the "empty" scuba cylinder with pure O_2 to 300.0 psig. (Since this is a physics discussion, we will ignore the practical problems with "plumbing" to measure gas to that tolerance. We will also ignore, for the sake of this discussion, the hazards associated with handling pure O_2.) Our diver even remembers that calculations are only valid at constant temperature. Thus, when the cylinder cools to room temperature, the diver slowly adds He to the scuba cylinder until pressure reaches 3000 psig.

Although often ignored by sport divers, an analysis of diving gas mix is the accepted practice. The mix perfectly prepared to the above calculations would analyze about 11-12% oxygen. In other words, the mix contains too much O_2 and increases the divers risk of oxygen toxicity. (A 12% O_2 mix at 16.6 ATA corresponds to a PO₂ of 1.99 ATA). The diver, confident that the calculations provided a margin of safety, would be diving with a mix that is most likely too oxygen rich for the depth.

Note that there is a distinct difference between the composition of the mix calculated by the simple Dalton's Law equation and the actual percentages of gas present. Mixing of gases to typical scuba cylinder pressures requires application of "real" gas law equations to arrive at a calculated value that more closely resembles reality. In the field, this can be done by using computer programs or consulting tables and extrapolating. Some physical measurement, like mass (based on "mole fraction") or density, is used to arrive at the proper pressure for mixing.

When the cylinder is first filled, there may be some layering since He is much less dense than O_2. Tanks should be rolled or allowed to set for several hours before analysis or use. Once the gas has been mixed to uniformity, it will remain mixed and will not settle into layers.

Note that the "real" method that used tables derived from empirical observations gave a PO₂ that was significantly different from the value obtained from "ideal" simple proportions. (300 psi vs. 283 psi) It turns out that Heliox mixes at scuba cylinder pressures calculated from simple Dalton's Law percentages will always contain more O_2 than calculated.

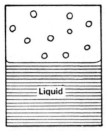

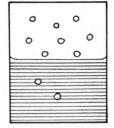

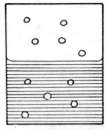

Gas molecules introduced above a liquid.

After a period of time molecules will dissolve into liquid.

Eventually the gas pressure above and in the liquid equalize.

If the partial pressure of the gas over a liquid is increased then the amount of gas going into solution will exceed that coming out and after a period of time a new equilibrium will be established.

HENRY'S LAW

1 A.T.A.

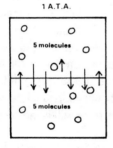

2 A.T.A.

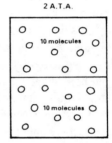

Conversely, when the partial pressure of a gas over a liquid drops, the amount of molecules coming out of solution will exceed the number going in. Therefore, a new equlibrium will be achieved after a period of time.

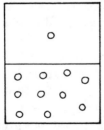

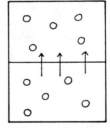

Pressure above the liquid drops.

Molecules come out of solution until equilibrium is reached.

However, if the pressure drop is too rapid, molecules will come out of solution forming a bubble within the solution.

Thus, diving at mixtures derived from simple relationships will increase diver susceptibility to oxygen toxicity since the diver will be diving with a much higher PO_2 than anticipated.

MIXING: BOTTOM LINE

No matter what method is used to calculate the gas mix concentrations, the only way to know what the cylinder contains is by obtaining a detailed chemical analysis. In diving physics, as in life, it is that which is not known that poses the greatest risk.

HENRY'S LAW

Whenever a gas is in contact with a liquid, gas will dissolve in the liquid. There is a continual movement of gas molecules; individual molecules of the gas are simultaneously moving out of solution into the gas phase and moving from the gas phase into solution within the liquid phase. Although it is impossible to predict the behavior of an individual gas molecule, the net movement of gas will be into solution until the partial pressure of the gas going into solution is the same as the partial pressure of the gas coming out of solution. When the gas reaches the state where the amount of gas molecules going into solution is the same as the amount of gas molecules coming out of solution, the solution is said to be saturated with gas. This state is termed equilibrium. At this point, although individual gas molecules will move at random into and out of solution, there will be no net change in gas concentration within the solution.

Henry's Law states that the amount of gas that will dissolve into a solution is directly proportional to the partial pressure of that gas and inversely proportional to the absolute temperature. The greater the partial pressure of the gas, the greater the driving force for solution and the more gas that will dissolve into solution. As temperature decreases, more gas will dissolve into solution.

The dissolution of nitrogen within body tissues is approximated by Henry's Law. The deeper one dives, the greater the partial pressure of nitrogen (and any gas in the gas mix) and the greater the gas load each tissue must bear. Upon ascent, the partial pressure in the gas phase decreases. The gas in solution will then escape from solution in an attempt to obtain equilibrium. If this escape from tissue is too rapid for the body to handle, decompression sickness is the result.

CONCLUSION

This chapter has provided a brief overview of some physical principles. Divers understanding these principles can utilize their awareness to make their diving safer and more efficient. It is the belief of the author that "knowledgeable, physically fit divers ALWAYS have more fun!"

REFERENCES

Adamson, A. *Understanding Physical Chemistry,* W.A. Benjamin, New York, NY. 1964, 253 pages.

Battelle Memorial Institute, *U.S. Navy Diving Manual,* Battelle MemorialInstitute, Columbus, OH. 1969, 189 pages.

Bennett, C. *Physics,* Barnes & Noble College Outline Series, Barnes & Noble, New York, NY. 1952, 208 pages.

Butler, *Getting Your Fill,* Technical Diver, Summer, 1991, p. 5-8.

Carlucci, P. Pletzke, T. & Pengler, R. *Gas Mixtures, Facts and Fables,* Matheson Gas Products, Secaucus, NJ. 1991, 24 pages.

Calhoun, F. *Physics For Divers,* NAUI, Colton, CA. 1978, 94 pages.

Dickens, R. *The Physics of Diving,* D.L.S. Enterprises, Jacksonville, FL.1981, 192 pages.

Kittsley, S. *Physical Chemistry,* Barnes & Noble, New York, NY. 1963, 217 pages.

Metz, C. *Physical Chemistry,* Schuam's Outline Series, New York, NY. 1970, 424 pages.

Moore, W. *Physical Chemistry,* Prentice-Hall, Englewood Cliffs, NJ. 1963, 844 pages.

Schaum, D. *Theory and Problems of College Chemistry,* Schaum's Outline Series, McGraw Hill, New York, NY. 1966, 257 pages.

Schaum, D. *Theory and Problems of College Physics,* Schaum's Outline Series, McGraw Hill, New York, NY. 1961, 270 pages.

Snider. E. (Ed.) *Ideal Gas Law, Enthalpy, Heat Capacity, Heats of Solution and Mixing,* American Institute of Chemical Engineers, New York, NY. 1984, 74 pages.

Tucker, W. *Diver's Handbook of Underwater Calculations,* Cornell Maritime Press, 1982, 182 pages.

CHAPTER 5

Inert Gas Narcosis

Inert gas narcosis has been the plague of deep divers using compressed air since the invention of scuba. Narcosis can lead to life threatening conditions by impairing the diver's judgment. It is a problem that affects diver behavior at increased partial pressures of nitrogen in the gas the diver breaths at depth. Usually the depths that induce the degree of narcosis and behavior changes seriously detrimental to the diver is beyond the alleged 130 fsw scuba safe diving limit promoted by the sport diver training agencies. On the other hand, studies have been made demonstrating narcosis effects shallower than 100 fsw. Different divers have differing responses to nitrogen under pressure. This is comparable to the individual differences associated with alcohol consumption. As in drinking any alcoholic beverage, some individuals are more susceptible to its effects than others. Thus the degree of individual impairment per drink varies.

Junod, in 1835, described a lively imagination, with a peculiar charm in thoughts along with an activation of brain functions and symptoms of intoxication among those exposed to increased partial pressures of nitrogen. 190 years later, Domant noted that at 10 ATA (300 fsw) divers became mentally abnormal and suffered from memory loss. Behnke, Thompson, and Motley concluded in 1935 that at pressures higher than three ATA narcosis is apparent. It is characterized by euphoria, retarding of the higher mental processes, and impaired neuromuscular coordination. By 1937, Shilling and Willgrube demonstrated the effects of narcosis on divers in chambers from 90 fsw to 300 fsw. The test used included addition, subtraction, multiplication, and division. These tests gave quantitive measurements of narcosis and indicated that experienced divers and people of higher intelligence are more resistant to narcosis.

Kessling and Magg (1962) used choice reaction time with the Purdue pegboard test and a conceptual reasoning test to study narcosis. At a chamber depth of 100 fsw they measured a 20.85% decrease in reaction time, a 33.46% drop in conceptual reasoning ability and a 7.9 % decrease in mechanical dexterity.

Miles and McKay noted that experienced and strong willed divers were able to tolerate or build tolerances to narcosis. In addition, they discovered that the onset of noticeable symptoms and measurable performance decrements did not occur as shallow in water as in chambers. In fact, at 100 fsw there was little change in diver performance in the open sea. They did, however, quantify that narcosis is a risk and that as depth increases the narcotic effects of compressed air are magnified. From their studies it was concluded that, with respect to narcosis, there is a human risk factor (to diver safety) between 180 fsw and 240 fsw. On depths exceeding 240 fsw, a serious danger zone exists for diving on compressed air. In the real world of diving, if one reviews the data, these conclusions have proven to be practical.

In 1965, psychiatrist Gilbert Milner M.D. and I, tested three groups of divers. The purpose of the test was to one, verify the results of Miles and McKay in establishing delayed symptoms of narcosis in water vs. chamber studies and two, to understand the effects of psychological modeling during diver training on the behavior of divers at depth.

Each of the three groups consisted of two male and two female divers. Group one was trained that divers do become symptomatic of narcosis at and below 100 fsw, and that the symptoms are severe as one approaches 150 fsw. The narcosis lecture was laced with all the potential problems of narcosis to be anticipated by divers. Group two was taught that narcosis is a reality of diving. It effects different persons to varying degrees. The symptoms were noted and it was explained that many divers do have high tolerance to the narcotic effects of nitrogen. Group three was trained to believe that through concentration and mental preparation divers are resistant to narcosis.

As expected, those divers in group one did became symptomatic shallower than the other groups. Group one divers had the most severe symptoms with one actually losing motor function at 150 fsw having to be assisted to 100 fsw before becoming functional again. Group two adapted to narcosis better. Our "brain washed divers" in group three were highly resistant to the severe effects of narcosis. One female diver in group three, who demonstrated noticeable symptoms on a dive to 200 fsw, actually had improved overall performance at 240 fsw on the following day. These tests indicated that diver training and mental conditioning have a great effect on a diver's susceptibility to narcosis. The group three divers also showed an adaptation to narcosis. These tests also agreed with the conclusions of Miles and McKay in that the risk and danger zones they described are true considerations of compressed air diving.

Dr. Dick Williams and I were subjects on another test dealing with the effectiveness of narcosis tolerances. These tests were performed in 300 fsw. The tests ran for six consecutive days to allow for any increased tolerance to narcosis as the tests continued. Prior to the tests, the two made five 300 fsw dives in six days to establish a baseline performance or tolerance for nitrogen before beginning the experiment. On the first five days, the divers did one test per dive. The test included two different math tests, ball bearing test, a flip card reasoning test, and the Purdue Pegboard Test. I actually scored higher on the math test at depth than on the surface. During the first five days of testing, no performance decrement was noted or measured in either diver. This led to a conclusion by the two divers that "we have proven the validity of tolerance development and adaptation". On the sixth day, the testing procedure was explained as usual and the divers were allowed to select three of the previous days' tests for experimental testing, each chose his personal best of course. The tests were then divided into three sections — sections a, b and c. Both divers breezed through part a then during the second test in part b, Dick and I both lost it. Neither diver was able to continue beyond this point during the ten minutes allowed for the test. To each, this presented a side of narcosis that had not been observed before — multi task loading and the inability to focus attention on more than one area at a time because of narcosis stress.

In 1976, I applied this same multi-task test procedure in an unsupervised situation. The difference, though, is that I utilized pre-dive visualization and at the moment the test began I spent 30 seconds in heavy focus control. The result was completion of the test within the allotted ten minutes. The actual time was seven minutes and 33 seconds. In 30 fsw, I did the same test in five minutes and three seconds. So visualization and concentration aided me in problem solving on deep air dives. However, even with this degree of mind control there is still delayed time in completion of multi-task problems. On a single task with use of these techniques my response time was as fast and accurate as on a 30 fsw control comparison. This delay in the multi-task response time could be critical in a survival situation.

During a cave dive in the Bahamas, Dick Williams and I were ascending from 300+ fsw when I observed that during his kick cycle he no longer pointed his fins and he was slowly sinking to the floor of the cave. At this time I assisted him up to approximately 250 fsw, at which time his swimming ability was again normal. After the dive he had no memory of any performance decrement or of being assisted. This type of occurrence has been cited by numerous deep divers. Again, it points towards the subtle but true dangers of narcosis.

Over the years numerous researchers such as Bennett, Hamilton, Wells, Lamphier, Lambertson, Zumrick, Hulet et al have documented the effects of narcosis. It is apparent that the degree of narcosis is variable. A tolerance of sorts may be developed, but there is still decreased performance as depth is increased. Air dives below 200 fsw are a calculated risk and those below 220 fsw are compounded by the possibility of oxygen toxicity.

Jim Lockwood has related hallucinations of a flour sack pouring over the edge of a wall and headless divers on excursions below 400 fsw. These occurred after more than ten minutes of bottom time. He has also reported amnesia during a dive from some unknown point to arriving at the 10 fsw decompression stop. It is interesting to note that on these dives he did make all of his stops, frequently beginning near 100 fsw. Thus, while the amnesia set in, the mind set or subconscious controlled the dive. This is due to extreme concentration and mental rehearsal of the dive before actual diving. Today, to avoid narcosis, Jim uses mixed gases when exploring deep frontiers.

NARCOSIS SYMPTOMS

Light-headedness
Euphoria
Drunkenness
Impaired neuromuscular coordination
Hearing Sensitivity or Hallucination
Slowed Mental Activity
Decreased Problem Solving Capacity
Overconfidence
Short Term Memory Loss or Distortions
Improper Time Perceptions
Fine work Deterioration
Exaggerated Movements
Numbness and tingling in Lips, Face and Feet
Stupor
Sense of Impending Blackout

Levity of Tendency to Laughter
Depressive State
Visual Hallucination or Disturbances
Perceptual Narrowing
Less Tolerance to Stress
Exaggerated (overrated) Handwriting
Amnesia
Loss of Consciousness
Retardation of Higher Metal Processes
Retardation of Task Performances
Slurred Speech
Poor Judgement
Slowed Reaction Time and Reflex Ability
Loss of Mechanical Dexterity

CAUSES OF NARCOSIS

Inert gas narcosis is caused by physiological changes in the human nervous system. It is also effected by the mind set of the person. In recreational diving a simplistic view of it is presented in Martini's law. Basically it states that for each 50 fsw of descent, the effects are similar to drinking a martini on an empty stomach. If this was an actual law it would probably restrict me to 50 fsw. On deep dives I do okay, but real martinis catch up to me very fast.

To relate narcosis to diving, it is best to relate alcohol to driving. With full concentration a driver under the influence may be able drive a car quite straight enough when followed by a police car. But the same driver, may not be able to put the brakes in time to stop the car should a child suddenly run in front of it. This is basically how narcosis behaves. As alcohol, the dose or amount consumed determines the exact behavior change. The Meyer-Overton hypothesis is the easiest way to relate to narcosis.

Meyer-Overton hypothesis: any inert gas will exert a depressant action on the C.N.S. When a sufficient quantity (dose) becomes dissolved in its lipid phase.

A. The solubility of a gas and the ratio by which it is distributed in solution between lipid and water are important in determining the effects of a particular gas.

B. Effects are largely dependent upon the concentration of the substance in the lipid factor of the responsible nervous tissue.

RELATIVE NARCOTIC POTENCIES

Helium (He)	4.26	(Least narcotric)
Neon (Ne)	3.8	
Hydrogen (H2)	1.83	
Nitrogen (N2)	1.00	
Argon (A)	0.43	
Krypton (Kr)	0.14	
Xenon (Xe)	0.039	(Most narcotic)

THE ICEBERG THEORY

Gas dissolved in water (liquid) causes a greater order of the liquid's molecules. This is referred to as the iceberg effect. The size of an iceberg is proportional to the anesthetic properties of the gas. Icebergs are found in bulk water (fluids) and in water in the protein and lipoprotein portion of nerves. These icebergs act as blocks to nerve conduction thus decreasing nerve transmission.

COMPARATIVE PROPERTIES OF SUGGESTED GASES FOR USE IN DIVING

PROPERTIES	ARGON	NITROGEN	NEON	HELIUM	HYDROGEN
Decompression	Not good, can only be used under special circumstances	Good in short dive; slow return from long dives	Fairly easy to eliminate in long dives. Builds up slowly in short dives.	Easily eliminated from body in long dives; builds up fast in short dives	About the same as Helium
Narcosis	Very narcotic in nominal diving range	Narcotic beyond about 200 fsw	No narcosis	No narcosis at any depth	Slight narcosis at great depth
Voice Distortion	Makes voice deep	Normal	Nearly normal	Large distortion	Large distortion
Thermal Conductivity	Good insulation	Fair to good insulation	Fair insulation	Poor insulation	Very poor insulation
Breathe-Ability	Hard to breathe	Hard to breathe at depth	Relatively easy to breathe	Can be breathed to 5000 fsw	Same as Helium
Cost and Worldwide Availability	Low cost, readily available	Lowest cost, available anywhere	High cost, depending on purity. Available many places	Moderate cost, available only in certain places	Low cost, readily available

Dose application of narcosis is explained by the physical properties of partial molar, free energy effect. Molecules have a tendency to enter a phase and remain there as long as a steady state condition exist. Thus the longer duration of exposure the greater the effect of narcosis.

Other effects of narcosis include the following: 1) an inhibition of enzymes which in turn reduces carbohydrate metabolism and 2) a histotoxic hypoxia produces a synaptic block by depolarization of the nerve axon. This may effect the consciousness of a diver, by depressing the reticular formation of the brain and apical dendrites of the cortex.

The reader can see that the causes of inert gas narcosis are varied and complex. Due to its complexity and variability it deserves respect.

Prevention and Control of Inert Gas Narcosis
- Experience
- Frequent deep dives
- Strong will
- Anti-depressant drugs (few that are not contradictory to diving)
  Acceptable: asprin, carbohol, frenquil, deriden, phenacetin
- Use of less narcotic inert gases (this is the most practical approach)

Additive Factors to Inert Gas Narcosis
- Anxiety
- Fatigue

Diving under ice requires careful selection of thermal suits. Narcosis may be dramatically elevated in a cold environment. Photo by Peter Nawrocky/ Viking

- Exercise
- Alcohol
- Cold
- Drugs
- Rapid descent (produces an increased CO_2 level and a temporary severe narcosis also usually associated with ascents faster than 120 feet-per-minute).

First Aid/Treatment/Prevention
- Avoid diving when fatigued
- Do not use drugs or alcohol while diving
- Control amount of exercise
- Control descent rates
- Ascend
- Avoid additive factors
- Limit air dive depths
- Mix gas for desired maximum narcosis level

NITROX OR ENRICHED AIR NITROX (EAN)

Although most applications of NITROX are in waters shallower than 130 fsw it does provide for a slight reduction in narcosis. An example would be a dive to 130 fsw using NOAA NITROX I. The equivalent narcosis depth (END) is:

END (same as the EAD formula) = (FN$_2$) x (depth +33)/.79)) -33
Thus END = ((.68) (130 + 33) /.79) -33) or equals 107 fsw

For NITROX technical diving applications, custom blends are used thus a dive can be planned to 140 fsw on EAN. In such a dive, the dive duration will determine the PO_2 to be used. For example, let's plan a dive with a 20 minute bottom time to 150 fsw. The desired PO_2 is 1.6 ATA.

$FO_2 = PO_2/P$ or $[(1.6/ (140/33 +1)] = .305$ or 30.5%
The END $= (.695) (140 + 33)/.79) -33)$ or equals 120.2 fsw.

Thus, this mix is less narcotic than air. The equivalent decompression schedule would be on a 120 fsw table and the higher O_2 concentration would provide a safer ascent (decompression) gas.

HELIOX

Inert gas narcosis is avoided by substituting the nitrogen in a gas mixture with helium. By referring to figure 11 it is apparent from a narcosis standpoint that helium is the ideal substitute gas. However, even this gas has limiting factors. High pressure nervous syndrome (HPNS) is the major

RELATIVE NARCOTIC POTENCIES

Helium (He)	4.26	(Least narcotric)
Neon (Ne)	3.8	
Hydrogen (H_2)	1.83	
Nitrogen (N_2)	1.00	
Argon (A)	0.43	
Krypton (Kr)	0.14	
Xenon (Xe)	0.039	(Most narcotic)

drawback to Heliox diving. This can occur as shallow as 450 to 600 fsw. With HPNS, brain wave changes occur that are different from those in nitrogen narcosis.

These changes are believed by many researchers to be due to a lack of nutrition to the brain. Helium produces a rise (constriction) in surface tension in membranes. This is felt to be the producer of the HPNS. In the commercial diving field the need for increased working depths resulted in the development of a "buffered" Heliox. It is known that nitrogen causes a fall in surface tension. This fall in surface tension produces narcosis. By adding a small amount of nitrogen in a mix, the effects of HPNS are reduced, without a significant increase in narcosis. Thus, as depths approach the 450 fsw and deeper range, a small amount of nitrogen is added to a mix. This is called Trimix.

On dives above 100 fsw, not only is Heliox non narcotic, but it also provides extended bottom times over air. However, as depth increases, the decompression requirements for Heliox diving become great. After approximately two hours of bottom time, helium once again becomes a friendlier decompression gas. In recreational diving, two hour bottom times to

Narcosis can be controlled to comfortable levels by proper selection of Heliox or Trimix blends. Here a Trimix diver explores a Florida wreck. Note his NITROX cylinder mounted between his doubles.
Photo by Bob Cunningham

great depths are rare. This is due to long in-water decompressions producing hypothermia and the inability to carry an adequate gas supply.

Symptoms of HPNS
- Tremors of hands
- Whole body tremors
- Personality change
- Convulsions

Advantages of Heliox
- No narcosis
- Fast off gassing
- Extended bottom time shallower than 100 fsw
- Less decompression on dives in excess of two hours at depth

Disadvantages of Heliox
- Longer decompression duration on dives below 100 fsw with less than two hours
- Expensive
- Critical ascent rate
- HPNS

Cave diving pioneer Sheck Exley was one of the first to use Heliox in recreational diving. Sheck used the mix to safely explore deeper depths.

Eventually he switched to the use of Trimix for shorter decompression profiles, less cost and the ability to control the extent of narcosis. Sheck is the current open circuit Trimix depth record holder. At this writing, the record depth is 880 fsw.

TRIMIX

Trimix is the state of the art for technical diving. This gas capitalizes on the non-narcotic use of helium, a less restrictive decompression duration provided by nitrogen, the absence of HPNS and a more affordable mix than Heliox. With the use of Trimix, a diver blends a mix that becomes more cost effective and limits the degree of narcosis experienced on a dive. A few divers refer to Trimix as the "dial a high" mix. In other words, a diver may balance the duration of decompression, the degree of impairment from narcosis and the cost of the mix in preparing for a dive. As in Heliox, decompression usually takes advantage of intermediate stops on EANx, with the 20 and 10 fsw stops on O_2.

Advantages of Trimix
- Less expensive than Heliox
- Controlled narcosis
- More friendly decompression than Heliox
- Increased safety on deep dives as compared to air
- Less breathing resistance than air

Disadvantages of Trimix
- More expensive than air
- More narcosis than Heliox
- More critical ascent rate than air
- Must use custom tables
- Increased equipment dependency
- Additional equipment needs

Trimix is the most "user friendly" of dive gases available to the deep diver. As has been shown in this text, deep divers need to avoid oxygen toxicity and to reduce inert gas narcosis to a predetermined safe limit. With Trimix, these objectives are realized. Decompression is not overly burdensome especially when two or more gas switches are used during ascent. As explained when discussing Heliox, Trimix was born in an effort to avoid HPNS. It soon became apparent that it offered many operational advantages, especially in regard to cost. The deep recreational diver is willing to tolerate some narcosis thus the mix is ideal. Although originally used exclusively by divers plunging to depths in excess of 220 fsw, Trimix is also becoming popular for photographers and workers who need precision abilities in the intermediate depths. Depths between 140 fsw down to 200 fsw are ideal moderateTrimix depths. Photographers discover a clearer head when on Trimix. Work is performed both more accurately and faster on Trimix in these depths. In preparing a Trimix the user has several decisions to make.

DECISIONS FOR BLENDING TRIMIX

1. Degree of narcosis to be tolerated (this will, by and large, determine the amount of helium to be added to the mix. Most divers plan for a 132 fsw narcosis depth, While some limit it to 85 fsw and others extend to 180 fsw).
2. Duration of decompression (the number of gas switches and gas mixture(s) will determine this).
3. Acceptable PO_2's for dive duration.
4. Degree of equipment dependency and support personnel
5. Redundancy considerations

At this point, it is prudent to give a few examples of planning a specific Trimix.

• A dive is planned to allow a maximum narcotic effect of 132 fsw. (this produces the accepted narcosis comparable to acceptable recreational diving programs)
$PN_2 = FN_2 \ x \ depth/(33 +1) \ or \ .79 \ x \ (132/33 +1) = 3.95 \ ATA$
From this we can plan a mix, that regardless of depth, will not allow a PN_2 over 3.95 ATA.

• The maximum depth of a dive is to be to 170 fsw. What will be the FN_2 in the final mix?
$FN_2 = PN_2/(depth/33 +1) \ or \ 3.95/(170/33 +1) = .64 \ or \ 64\%$
We now know that the amount of oxygen plus the helium added must leave a balance of no greater value than 64% nitrogen.

• The desired working PO_2 on this dive is to be 1.5 ATA.
$FO_2 = PO_2/(depth/33 +1) \ or \ 1.5/(170/33 +1) = .24 \ or \ 24\%$

• Determine the helium to add.
The total of O_2 and N_2 is 64 + 24=88%, therefore... (100-88) = 12% helium.

The above mix has just enough helium to reduce the narcosis to 132 fsw equivalent. It is also a friendly decompression mix and the PO_2 is below toxic levels for dives through two hours duration (refer to NOAA oxygen exposure chart in the oxygen chapter). This is a mix that would be efficient for decompressing on the bottom mix. However, the increased safety of oxygen at 20 fsw is recommended.

Mix a 64% N₂, 12% He, 24% O₂ blend in a 3,000 psig tank

1. Begin with an empty tank.
2. Fill the tank with 12% He (.12 x 3,000) = 360 psig He allow tank to sit for a couple of hours verify psig.
3. Determine total O_2 required in tank for 24% (.24 x 3,000) = 720 psig O_2
4. Find balance of gas to add on top of He (3,000 - 360) = 2,640 psig
5. Solve for adjusted FO_2 720 psig O_2 / 2,640 balance gas =.272 or 27%
6. Ascertain the amount of O_2 to add to mix *(FO_2 - .21) / .79 x psig or ((.27 - .21) / .79 x 2,640) = 200.5 psig* Add O_2 to He, let set for two hours verify psig
7. Top tank off with air
   A. Bring air psig to 90% of target pressure (2,700 psig)
   B. Let set for half an hour
   C. Tumble or move tanks up and down and from side to side to provide better blending
   D. Verify pressure and analyze gas.
   E. Complete topping off tank verify analysis and psig
8. Allow tank to sit for at least four hours verify psig and analyse mix prior to diving.

Maintaining the same limits, lets design another Trimix.
Working depth: 300 fsw
$FN_2 = 3.95/(300/33 + 1) = .395$ or 39.5% round off towards conservative side to 39%
$PO_2 = 1.5/(300/33 + 1) = .15$ or 15%
The total gas including oxygen and nitrogen is 54%
Helium to be added is solved: (100-54) = 46%

As the FO_2 (fraction of oxygen) is a low fraction and the amount of helium in the Trimix is significant, efficient decompression will require two or more gas switches. In planning for decompression stop gas switches it is desirable to get off the bottom mix as soon as possible. Generally speaking the diver would be prudent to make two gas switches on ascent with bottom times up to 30 minutes. For dives in excess of 30 minutes, three or more (depending on conditions) gas switches would be made. A single gas switch could be made with a resultant longer decompression duration. If a single gas switch was to be made, the two most desirable choices would be either On a work project a diver has a Trimix 18% O_2, 32% He, 50% N_2. What is the equivalent narcosis depth (END) with a planned depth of 260 fsw.

$$END = [(FN_2) (d + 33)/.79)-33] \text{ or } [(.5) (293)/.79)-33] = 152.4 \text{ fsw}$$

CONCLUSION

Inert gas narcosis is and will continue to be a limiting factor of compressed air diving. However with the state of the art in mixed gas applications, the present day diver may safely explore new depths. In addition dives in the 140 to 200 fsw range can be made more enjoyable and safer by applying mix technology.

REFERENCES

The New Practical Diving, Tom Mount and Akira Ikehara, University Miami Press.

The Physiology and Medicine of Diving, Bennet and Elliot Best Publishing.

Deep Diving: An Advanced Guide to Physiological Procedures and Systems, Bret Gilliam and Robert von Maier, Watersport Publishing, Inc.

CHAPTER 6

THEORY

Understanding Oxygen
The Good, the Bad, and the Ugly

Oxygen in our breathing gas, be it air or a mix, is the supporter of life. Keller described oxygen as the "princess of gases" — providing a beautiful marriage with our physiology. When the oxygen level in the breathing is normal we function as usual but when the amount of oxygen in breathing gas is altered from the normal we function differently — because our basic physiology is affected.

In the pursuit of diving longer and safer, we modify the fraction percentage of oxygen in the breathing gas. In order to dive longer at moderate to shallow depths (less than 130 fsw) EAN (NITROX), which uses an increased percentage of oxygen is utilized. In order to explore deeper Heliox or Trimix using a reduced fraction of oxygen is utilized . Thus in our quest to safely stay longer or go deeper, we alter the amount of oxygen in the breathing gas. For this reason we must be well educated on the behavior of oxygen and its limitations.

Oxygen is not always a friendly gas, in fact the term the good, the bad and the ugly can apply equally to oxygen and Clint Eastwood movies. The effects of oxygen are determined by its partial pressure (PO_2). Partial pressure is the product of the percentage of the gas in the breathing mixture times the total pressure of all the gases in the breathing mixture. To better understand the term partial pressures, one must review Dalton's Law. *This law states that in a mixture of gases each gas exerts a pressure proportional to the percentage of that gas that it alone occupies.*

This May Be Expressed As:

P (total pressure) = (P_2 (partial pressure of gas a) + (P of gas b) + (P of gas c) + P + = P_1 + P_2 + P_3

Thus in a mix of air at one atmosphere,

P (1 ATA) = (0.2095 ATA oxygen) + (0.7805 ATA nitrogen) + (0.01 ATA trace gases).

If we examine a container of air containing 14.7 psi or 1 ATA, the partial pressure oxygen PO_2 would be (0.2095 x 1 ATA) = 0.2095 ATA. If the pressure of the gas in the container of air were increased to 10 ATA the PO_2 would be (0.2095 x 10) = 2.095 ATA. On the other hand, if the pressure was reduced to 0.5 ATA, the PO_2 would be (0.2095 x 0.5) = 0.10 ATA. Note the fraction (percentage) of the oxygen in the mixture of gases (FO_2) has remained constant (as it would in air or a premixed breathing gas). However, the partial pressure of the oxygen (PO_2) changed significantly with the changes in the total pressure of all the gases.

It is the partial pressure of the gas that determine its effect on the body. In the case of oxygen, decreased partial pressures result in hypoxia, increased partial pressures produces oxygen toxicity. The mathematical formula we will be using to predict the effects of a particular breathing gas mix and to plan a mix is:

$$\frac{Pg}{Fg | P}$$

Where: Pg is the partial pressure of a gas

Fg is the fractional percent (%) of the gas in a mix

P is the total pressure of all the gases. It can be expressed in ATA (atmospheric pressure absolute), fsw (feet of salt water) or msw (meters of salt water).

To convert fsw to ATA's the formula is P (ATA) = (fsw/33 +1).
To convert msw to ATA's the formula is P (ATA) = (msw/10 +1).
To convert ATA to fsw the formula is P (fsw) = (ATA-1) x 33

Let's Solve The Following:

The world depth record on air held by Bret Gilliam is 452 fsw.

What is the PO_2 at 452 fsw ?

PO_2 = (FO_2 x P) or (0.2095 x (452/33 +1)) = 3.08 ATA PO_2 at 452 fsw.

If a safety diver were to accompany Bret Gilliam on this dive using a Trimix and wished to keep his PO_2 at 1.5 ATA what is the fraction of oxygen or (FO_2) in the mix ?

FO_2 = (PO_2/P (in ATA)) or (1.5/ (452/33 +1)) = 0.10 or 10% FO_2

The balance of this mix would be helium (He) and nitrogen (N_2). The bottom mix is ideal, but the oxygen content is not adequate at the surface or in shallow water. The safety diver would need a different mix for the descent and ascent to have a sufficient PO_2 for life support in shallow water. At a preplanned depth a switch to or from the bottom mix is made. During ascent the diver may switch to one or more EAN mixes and eventually will switch to pure oxygen to insure more efficient decompression.

If the gas mixture was analyzed and contained 0.09% O_2 the safety diver could have descend to a deeper depth without exceeding a PO_2 of 1.5 ATA. To illustrate this point let's determine the maximum depth for a 0.09% oxygen mixture.

$$P (MOD) = \frac{(PO_2 - 1) + 33}{(FO_2)}$$ *where mod is the maximum safe operating depth, as set by the PO_2 limits.*

Therefore,

$P = (PO_2/FO_2)$ *or* $(1.5/0.09) = 16.67\,ATA - 1\,ATA\ (surface) = 15.67\,ATA.$ *Converting ATA to fsw; fsw = (15.67ATA x 33ft/ ATA) = 517.11fsw.*

At this point it is necessary to define the limits of oxygen both in respect to its toxic effects and its inability to sustain life. As PO_2 drops below 0.2095 ATA or 20.95% it becomes less able to support life's functions. At 0.16 ATA or 16% surface Fg (fractional percent) the user will begin to dem-

OXYGEN LIMIT FOR LIFE SUPPORT SYSTEMS

ATA O_2

3.0	50/50 NITROX Therapy Gas @ ATA (165 fsw)
2.8	100% O_2 @ 2.8 ATA (60 fsw)
2.5	Decompression for Operation Diving (maximum)
2.4	60/40 NITROX Therapy Gas @ ATA (165 fsw)
2.0	U.S. Navy Exceptional Exposure to Working Diver
1.6	U.S. Navy Maximum Normal Exposure to Working Diver
.5	Maximum Saturation Exposure
.35	Normal Saturation Exposure
.21	Normal Environment O_2 (normoxic)
.16	Begin Signs of Hypoxia
.12	Serious Signs of Hypoxia
.10	Unconsciousness
<.10	Coma/Death

onstrate symptoms of hypoxia (low oxygen). As the PO_2 drops further, at 0.12 ATA or 12% serious symptoms will develop and at 0.10 or 10% surface equivalent a diver may become unconscious.

When the PO_2 increases beyond 0.5 ATA or 50% surface equivalent, the diver may begin to exhibit symptoms of whole body or pulmonary oxygen toxicity. As the PO_2 exceeds 1.6 ATA or 160% surface equivalent especially with prolonged exposures, CNS (central nervous system) oxygen toxicity symptoms may develop. CNS toxicity can be life threatening in the water.

HYPOXIA

Hypoxia is the result of reduced PO_2 to a point where it is no longer capable of supporting normal life functions. If the PO_2 is reduced to zero then a diver is said to experience anoxia - there is total absence of life sustaining oxygen. In diving, anoxia and hypoxia can develop through a variety of circumstances. Theoretically, one could skip-breathe to such an extreme as to produce hypoxia. In this instance, the hypoxia would be further complicated by carbon dioxide (CO_2) excess.

Another instance of potential hypoxia can result from the long term storage of breathing gas in a cylinder that has moisture in it. In this case the O_2 may be used up in oxidation of the metal. A check of the gas pressure will indicate a full tank except now the tank has a reduced percentage of oxygen.

The possibility of hypoxia also exists when using mixed gases. Although in NITROX diving situations this is almost impossible providing the blending has been done correctly. By analyzing the gas just prior to diving it is impossible to have a mixture low in oxygen. For the deep diver employing mixed gas this is more of potential problem. The best way to illustrate this is to look at the PO_2 for a given deep dive.

On a dive to 350 fsw the desired PO_2 for a long duration dive is 1.4 ATA. What is the required fg of oxygen in the mix?

$Fg = PO_2/p$ or $1.4/(350/33+1) = 0.12$ ATA or 12%

From this example it is apparent that if the diver breathes this gas on the surface with only 12% oxygen hypoxia is probable. With diving mixes of this low FO_2, the diver uses a starter or travel gas during descent to prevent hypoxia. On ascent the diver will again switch gases to prevent hypoxia. The diver will also utilize a higher PO_2 to wash out or eliminate the accumulated inert gas from the tissues.

Oxygen exposure tolerances vary widely in individuals. Rob Parker and Rob Palmer in chamber tests supervised by Neil Cave of Carmellan Research. Photo by Wild Track

Divers with rebreathers must verify the function of both the O_2 sensors and the CO_2 absorbent prior to every dive. Failure to do so could result in an inadequate oxygen fraction in the supply to the diver. Rebreathers can also contribute to carbon dioxide excess if the scrubbers malfunction. Hypoxia can also develop when preparing to dive at altitude as a result of surface work prior to the dive.

With reduced PO_2, the brain and bodily functions become abnormal and symptoms of low oxygen are manifested. Symptoms observed with hypoxia usually reflect changes in neurological function as the brain (nervous tissue) is most sensitive to oxygen and carbon dioxide changes.

Hypoxia Symptoms

- Sense of well being
- Light tingling sensations
- Slight numbness
- Visual disturbances
- Loss of coordination
- Unconsciousness
- Blueness (cyanosis)

First aid must be prompt because of the danger of blacking-out in the water and drowning. The first step is to have the diver breathe pure oxygen if available or breathe from a gas mixture that can supply adequate oxygen. If in the water, switch the diver to the highest oxygen mixture available that does not exceed a PO_2 of 1.6 ATA.

127

First Aid For Hypoxia
- Switch to adequate breathing mixture
- On surface breathe pure O_2
- Avoid exertion
- Avoid rapid breathing
- Administer fluids after oxygen breathing
- Discontinue diving activities for 24 hours

Prevention Of Hypoxia
- Always analyze gas
- Breathe correctly
- Use starter gas when using low fg mixes
- Get off bottom mix during ascent ASAP
- Avoid use of gas that has been stored for prolonged periods of time
- With rebreathers always verify system function

CENTRAL NERVOUS SYSTEM OXYGEN TOXICITY (CNS)

Central nervous system (CNS) oxygen toxicity is life threatening to both deep air divers and mixed gas divers. Oxygen toxicity behaves in a dose: response system just like any other drug. In other words, the greater the dose and the longer the exposure the higher the probability of a reaction. The two factors that decide the dose level are the PO_2 and the exposure time at that PO_2. There has been much research into CNS toxicity and over the years the limits have been modified several times. The reduction in PO_2 limits and exposure time have been due to practical in-water experiences. In the 1959 edition of the U.S. Navy manual the PO_2 limit was set at 2.0 ATA. In field conditions with divers swimming or working this limit proved to be too high. In the 1970's the maximum allowed PO_2 was reduced to 1.8 ATA . With additional experience, this limit was dropped to 1.6 ATA — the current oxygen operational exposure limit. In addition dose response times are now available and must be referenced when planning technical dives.

As reflected in the NOAA PO_2 and exposure time limits table. A diver can determine the CNS "clock values". The oxygen clock is the safe or maximum allowable time limit for a given PO_2 to avoid CNS oxygen toxicity. The NOAA exposure chart allows divers to chose PO_2 limits with low CNS toxicity risk. Note the 1.6 ATA limit of 45 minutes. In recreational no-stop diving this would be difficult to exceed using either a NOAA NITROX I or NOAA NITROX II, NITROX mix. The problem only exists when divers pursue longer bottom times than allowed in no-stop diving.

NOAA PO₂ AND EXPOSURE TIME LIMITS FOR WORKING DIVERS

Normal Exposure Limits

Oxygen Partial Pressure (PO₂) in ATA	Maximum Duration for Single Exposure (Min)	(Hr)	Maximum Total Duration, 24 Hr Day (Min)	(Hr)
1.6	45	0.75	150	2.0
1.5	120	2.0	180	3.0
1.4	150	2.5	180	3.0
1.3	180	3.0	210	3.5
1.2	210	3.5	240	4.0
1.1	240	4.0	270	4.5
1.0	300	5.0	300	5.0
.9	360	6.0	360	6.0
.8	450	7.5	450	7.5
.7	570	9.5	570	9.5
.6	720	12.0	720	12.0

If a diver plans a dive for 60 minutes of bottom time, by referring to the NOAA exposure chart, the maximum PO₂ must be less than 1.6 ATA. The chart recommendation is a PO₂ of 1.5 ATA. A second consideration for extended dives is that the PO₂ requirements for decompression stops must also remain within the CNS clock times. With the use of oxygen for decompression at 20 fsw O₂ toxicity is reduced by taking a five minute air or lowered NITROX (EAN) mixture break every 25 minutes. This technique greatly extends the single dive exposure limit.

A diver who ignores the dose: response curve for oxygen and uses "hot" mixes is walking a thin line. It is like playing Russian Roulette. The gun may or may not fire but there is always a possibility it will. If you continue to pull the trigger the probability goes up each time the trigger is pulled. The same is true of one who pushes oxygen limits. There is a possibility of a problem when dose limits are exceeded. The more extreme the limits are exceeded the higher the probability. The more times violations are repeated the higher the probability.

As a diver who has been involved in extended dives to 300 fsw and deeper on air for many years, I have experienced oxygen toxicity problems on two occasions. The first was a rescue effort in the 400 fsw range. All was well until I made a power kick which was immediately followed by collapsed vision consisting of a red field with black dots that was all I could see. Normal vision did not return until I ascended to 250 fsw. The second occasion was on a 37 minute exposure in a cave while I was swimming at a normal pace on a dive at 290 fsw. This time I experienced muscle spasms. These spasms were like small waves running the length of my left forearm.

Jim Lockwood, with 147 dives below 400 fsw on air, has had similar experiences. The most severe occurrence he reports was on a record attempt to 480 fsw (an attempt when co-record attempt divers Archie Forfar and Ann Gunderson both died). Jim blacked out and floated upwards until he was saved by Sheck Exley and Randy Hilton at around 300 to 350 fsw. The trio had made numerous dives below 400 fsw to 440 fsw (well below the then recognized record) building tolerances for this deep shot. It is believed they learned to deal with or tolerate nitrogen narcosis but were unable to adapt to the increased partial pressure of oxygen. The next experience that Jim recalls was in the same cave where I had experienced oxygen toxicity symptoms. The depth was in excess of 290 fsw with a bottom time in the 40 minute range. Jim reported eye twitches and spasms in the forearm and a general uncomfortable feeling. The third bad experience Jim has related to me was on a 360 fsw cave dive. On this occasion he stated, "I just felt really bad, like I was losing it". It was a dive with a moderate exposure time .

Do I still dive deep on air? Yes. Why? Cost and the availability of the breathing gas. Do I kid myself to think it is safe? No. If diving below 250 fsw I use Trimix if possible. In overhead environments and on dives below 220 fsw I use mixed gas.

My Recommendations Are:
* On dives to 100 fsw use NOAA NITROX II unless dose exposure time is extended, then NOAA NITROX I.
* From 100 fsw to 130 fsw sue NOAA NITROX I, if extended dives then the PO_2 must be reduced and the EAD depth used.
* From 130 fsw to 190 fsw use a NITROX mix with a FO_2 that provides a PO_2 of 1.4 to 1.5 ATA, depending on exposure duration. A Trimix with 20% to 24% oxygen and 12% to 20% He is also ideal at these depths.
* For dive below 190 fsw use a Trimix especially when in overhead environments.

The whole purpose of mixed gas, be it NITROX, Heliox or Trimix is to allow a PO_2 that is not threatening to the safety of the diver. An additional benefit of Trimix is the reduction in inert gas narcosis. A third reason for mix is that with the use of custom tables decompression is safer. Benefits of gas in the case of NITROX is that longer dives are made possible with increased physiological safety. With Heliox or Trimix, deeper dives are made safer. Increased safety during decompression with Trimix is due

to use of high PO_2's during decompression stops. The increased PO_2 in decompression mixes speeds the elimination of inert gas.

Many new technical divers think gas diving requires less decompression. When applied to Heliox or Trimix, this is untrue. These gases actually require longer stops. The shortened decompression duration is due to the use of gas switches which maintain a high PO_2 during stops.

What are the physiological reactions during CNS oxygen toxicity? This problem is a complex one with many events taking place.

1. The hemoglobin is already saturated with oxygen. The higher oxygen pressure forces some oxygen to diffuse directly into the blood. This results in the tissues being able to receive oxygen by diffusion directly from the blood. This process also prevents disassociation of the oxygen attached to the hemoglobin thereby limits the ability of the blood to transport CO_2 from the tissues back to the lungs. CO_2 is eliminated at a reduced rate. The buildup in CO_2 may cause an increase production of carbonic acid shifting the ph of the blood to acid. Increased CO_2 also causes vasodilation. Increased PO_2 produces vasoconstriction and reduced blood flow to the central nervous system.

2. There is a block of electrical conduction between muscles and nerve fibers. This is accompanied by the inhibition of enzymes vital to cellular metabolism. Some researchers believe that with prolonged exposure there may be an irreversible oxidation of the sulfhydryl enzymes.

3. A histotoxic anoxia occurs due to inhibition of intracellular metabolism.

4. The effects of increased PO_2 on blood flow are dramatic. Most research indicates a decrease in blood pressure (bp) and pulse rate. There is a significant decrease of blood flow to the coronary sinus, coronary artery, and myocardium. At PO_2's of one to four ATA, there is reduction of blood flow to the brain. Kety and Schmidt reported a 13% reduction in cerebral blood

flow at a PO_2 of 1 ATA. Lambertson reported a 13% reduction in cerebral blood flow at a PO_2 of one ATA and a 25% reduction of cerebral blood flow at a PO_2 of 3.5 ATA.

5.   A decrease of 46% in the size of the retinal blood vessels after a five minute exposure to a PO_2 of three ATA was documented by Saltzman. This effect is believed to be largely due to the carbon dioxide effects accompanying the oxygen toxicity.

6.   Cell membrane damage is also produced by increased PO_2's. The lipids experience oxidation of the unsaturated fatty acids. Proteins are affected by oxidation of the sulfhydryl groups. These damages alter the overall cell integrity and inhibit numerous enzyme reactions. The brain tissue undergoes lipid peroxide formation which may cause permanent damage. The inhibition of enzymes and coenzymes by lipid peroxide may be a contributor to the outward symptoms of oxygen toxicity.

7.   It has been demonstrated by Balentine that non-convulsive exposure to increased PO_2 in rats affects neural dendrites. The mitochondria are enlarged along with an increase in the density of dendritic process. This may be due to a condensation of cytoplasmic constituents or to mitochondrial degeneration. This interferes with cellular metabolism and disturbs the overall health of the cell.

8.   Changes in electron transfer pathways are well documented. The reverse pathway being the most sensitive to increased PO_2. These changes are believed to be due to reduced ATP. It has also been demonstrated that glycine, l- alanine, vitamin E and D-alanine are effective in preventing seizures. The anti-convulsant action of these substances seems to relate to their inhibitory action on neurons.

9.   Enzymes responsible for the synthesis of neurotransmitters are quite sensitive to PO_2 induced inhibition more than the enzymes that degrade compounds. Perhaps the most sensitive is glutamic acid and decarboxylase, the enzyme involved in the synthesis of GABA (gamma-aminobutyric acid). GABA is active in oxidative metabolism of the brain. The role of gaba is one of "modulating" brain activity by inhibiting transmitters in the CNS. A reduction in GABA levels is believed by many researchers to play a major role in the production of convulsions in oxygen toxicity. High levels of GABA prevent convulsions. Experimental injections of GABA have stopped the onset of seizures. Numerous researchers have demonstrated a correlation between low GABA levels and the onset of convulsions.

10.   Other areas of research suggest toxic effects of oxygen are related to free radicals and their damaging effect on enzymes and cell function. Additional research is studying the reaction of the endocrine system during

the development of oxygen toxicity. In this aspect it has been shown that the usual defense system against stress, the hormone defense system (hypophysis, adrenal cortex, cortical hormones) and the nervous defense system (sympathetic nervous system, adrenal medulla, adrenaline) no longer function in a normal manner.

CONCLUSIONS BY WOOD 1969 REGARDING GABA (GAMMA-AMINOBUTYRIC ACID)

1. Increased PO_2 decreases GABA concentration in the brain.
2. Decreased GABA occurs prior to convulsions, thus appears as a cause/effect relationship.
3. Decreased GABA is reversible as is oxygen toxicity
4. The decrease in concentration of GABA is specific among brain amino acids.
5. The critical level of reduced GABA levels is the same in animals and mice at the point of seizures.
6. Administration of GABA prior to exposure protects against convulsions.
7. Susceptibility relates with the rate of decreased GABA.

Symptoms of oxygen toxicity occur randomly and suddenly. A diver may experience convulsions suddenly and without warning. Susceptibility to oxygen toxicity differs from diver to diver and within a given diver on a daily basis.

In-water experiences shows an increased response to oxygen toxicity as compared to dry chamber work. Hard work decreases the time to onset of symptoms. One diver described by Miles convulsed within seven minutes on one day while on a repeated effort to the same pressure the diver tolerated two hours before developing only minor symptoms.

Captain John Zumrick M.D., U.S.N. has related numerous experiences to me where Navy divers, who had completed oxygen tolerance tests, convulsed on exposures that would have been within the limits of the tolerance test. A 16 year veteran of diving oxygen rebreathers related an incident to me where he had recently completed an O_2 tolerance test. On an early morning training drill, during one leg of an exercise after only a 20 minute exposure at 15 fsw, he began to feel abnormal and headed towards the surface. Enroute he convulsed. Upon examination by the diving medical officer, he returned to the exercises later that afternoon and completed a one hour drill on an O_2 rebreather at 20 fsw. As demonstrated by this example, the variability of tolerance is great, not only from diver to diver, but by an individual diver from moment to moment.

The central nervous system is primarily affected in the acute phase and the following Table will illustrate typical manifestations.

SIGNS AND SYMPTOMS OF CNS O$_2$ TOXICITY IN NORMAL MEN *

Facial pallor	Tinnitus and auditory hallucinations
Sweating	Vertigo
Bradycardia	Respiratory changes
Palpitations	Nausea
Depression	Spasmodic vomiting
Apprehension	Fibrillation of lips
Visual symptoms:	Twitching of lips, cheeks, nose, eyelids
Dazzle	Syncope
Constriction of visual field	Convulsions

*Table excerpted from *DIVING MEDICINE* (Bove and Davis, 1990)

In the Table below, the authors have provided a simplified, abridged version to the above Table. The reader is directed to note that the first letter of each of the symptoms listed in the Table above spells out the acronym **VENTID**.

CNS O$_2$ TOXICITY SYMPTOMS (VENTID)

V ision: any disturbance including "tunnel vision," etc.
E ars: any changes in normal hearing function
N ausea: severity may vary and be intermittent
T witching: classically manifest in facial muscles
I rritability: personality shifts, anxiety, confusion etc.
D izziness: vertigo, disorientation

PULMONARY/WHOLE BODY OXYGEN TOXICITY

Whole body or pulmonary oxygen toxicity is due to prolonged exposures to breathing oxygen at pressures above 0.5 ATA. This is a major problem when treating persons in hyperbaric facilities. Within the ranges of normal recreational diving, it is unlikely that a diver is subjected to this application of oxygen toxicity. However, professional divers, saturation divers and the expanded technology used by technical recreational divers does project them into regions where they may be subject to whole body oxygen toxicity. Physiological problems that are of concern with whole body toxicity must be understood by the technical diver. Again an exception to this rule would be the diver using standard NOAA I and NOAA

NITROX II mixtures as advocated and remaining within no stop limits. Advanced utilization of NITROX and Trimixes does require observance of dive plans that track the exposure to whole body oxygen toxicity.

Whole body, just as CNS oxygen toxicity, is dose: response related. Thus, the longer an exposure to a PO_2 in excess of 0.5 ATA, the greater likelihood of symptoms of toxicity. When exposures are extended a variety of reactions in the human physiology take place. Most noteworthy are those that decrease respiratory health.

1. With pulmonary oxygen toxicity there are degenerative lung changes. Inflammation, congestion, edema, bronchitis, all represent common reactions to toxicity.
2. Extended exposures such as in laboratory research produces hemorrhage.
3. There is swelling of the alveolar walls, and thickening of the walls of the pulmonary artery.
4. Fragmentation of the basement membrane between alveolar and endothelial cells along with accumulation of exudate between the basement membrane and alveolar or endothelial cell has been observed.
5. Increased PO_2 alters the lung surfactant thus changing the surface tension and interrupting the stability of the alveoli.

Whole Body PO_2 Toxicity Symptoms
*   Dry cough
*   Increased breathing resistance
*   Shortness of breath
*   Discomfort in chest

One of the ways of determining the degree of toxic exposure is to measure the vital capacity. Indeed, the units for determining whole body exposure are based on measurements pertaining to degree of vital capacity reduction. Two methods are addressed, both based on the percent reduction of vital capacity per time unit of exposure. The UPTD (unit pulmonary toxicity dose) was developed in 1972 by Wright. This is used to predict toxicity at PO_2's in excess of 0.5 ATA. It is believed that damage below this level is limited. In this concept, exposure on a dive or treatment is kept to 615 UPTD's per day or less. For extended treatments, the maximum allowable UPTD per day is 1440.

To Determine The UPTD's Follow These Procedures:
1. Find PO_2 at each depth in ATA. $PO_2 = FO_2 \times P$
2. Select the Kp value from Kp Factors for Calculating UPTD's chart
3. Multiply time of exposure by Kp value to get UPTD per depth.
4. Total UPTD's at each depth for total UPTD exposure.

KP FACTORS FOR CALCULATING UPTD'S

PO_2	Kp	PO_2	Kp	PO_2	Kp	PO_2	Kp
0.50	0.00	1.70	2.07	2.90	3.70	4.10	5.18
0.60	0.26	1.80	2.22	3.00	3.82	4.20	5.30
0.70	0.47	1.90	2.36	3.10	3.95	4.30	5.42
0.80	0.65	2.00	2.50	3.20	4.08	4.40	5.54
0.90	0.83	2.10	2.64	3.30	4.20	4.50	5.66
1.00	1.00	2.20	2.77	3.40	4.33	4.60	5.77
1.10	1.16	2.30	2.91	3.50	4.45	4.70	5.89
1.20	1.32	2.40	3.04	3.60	4.57	4.80	6.01
1..30	1.48	2.50	3.17	3.70	4.70	4.90	6.12
1.40	1.63	2.60	3.31	3.80	4.82	5.00	6.24
1.50	1.78	2.70	3.44	3.90	4.94		
1.60	1.93	2.80	3.57	4.00	5.06		

As stated earlier, UPTD's reflect degree of reduction in vital capacity. This is shown in the Vital Capacity Decrements table below.

VITAL CAPACITY DECREMENTS

	# of UPTD's	% Vc Decrements	Restart Time In Hours
	615	2	2
	825	4	4
	1035	6	6
	1230	8	8
	1425	10	10-12
	1815	15	13
	2190	20	20
NOTE:	**UPTD Kp factors have been calculated for you. For this manual we will use the arithmetic method (table top of page)**		
EXAMPLE:	One UPTD is equivalent to breathing 100% oxygen at one ATA for one minute.		
	There are 24 hours in a day or 1440 minutes (60x24). A patient breathing 100% (alveolar oxygen tension) for 24 hours will accumulate 1440 UPTD's. These can be converted to percent of Vital Capacity Decrement (%VC) from the table in this box.		
	1425 UPTD = 10% Vital Capacity Decrement		
NOTE:	**UPTD concept is a very conservative method to predict % Vc Decrement.**		

While the UPTD method of tracking pulmonary toxicity is widely used and practical for treatment purposes, it is not practical for multiday diving in the field (There really is no good set of limits for this prediction, which is why Hamilton developed the Repex method, Gilliam 1992).

For in-field use, Hamilton's Repex method is far more advantageous on continuous diving days. Hamilton (1989) notes in his REPEX paper, "The Pennsylvania unit (UPTD) has served well and is based on empirical data; it is the basic unit used in the Repex method. For two reasons however, we prefer to use an alternative term: OTU or Oxygen Tolerance Dose. first, since we are dealing with operational physiology in managing exposure to oxygen in diving we prefer to refer to these as techniques for 'tolerance' of O_2 exposure rather than for avoiding O_2 'toxicity'. They are the same thing, but we feel it offers a more positive approach." This method starts with a maximum single day exposure and then tracks with daily average toxicity units for the duration of an operation.

REPEX OXYGEN EXPOSURE LIMITS	Exposure (mission duration) (in days)	Average Daily Dose	TotalThis Mission
	1	850	850
	2	700	1400
	3	620	1860
	4	525	2100
	5	460	2300
	6	420	2520
	7	380	2660
	8	350	2800
	9	330	2970
	10	310	3100
	11	300	3300
	12	300	3600
	13	300	3900
	14	300	4200
	15-30	300	as req.

To predict the degree of OTU's, one must know the PO_2 at each depth just as in the UPTD application. All the "stages" of OTU's are added and then the diver insures the dives are within the OTU window. Note the daily average drops with multi-day exposures. It is important to emphasize that with each added day of diving, exposures for the entire mission must fall into the daily dose referenced. From this it becomes evident that while it would take a severe dive to exceed the single dosage, one could easily acquire significant exposure on multi-day dive profiles.

Mathematically, these values are computed by:

$OTU = t (PO_2 - 0.5) / 0.5)^{.83}$

The 0.5 is the threshold at which symptoms do not develop. All exposures above this can produce symptoms based on the time duration of exposure. The exponent .83 is the exponent factor best suited to fit the data on vital capacity reduction. To determine values, one can use the math involved or more practically refer to the Maximum Operating Depths for Given FO_2's and Limiting PO_2's table on the following page.

Maximum Operating Depths for Given FO₂'s and Limiting PO₂'s

FO₂	1.2 ATA	1.3 ATA	1.4 ATA	1.5 ATA	1.6 ATA	1.7 ATA
0.05	759.00	825.00	891.00	957.00	1023.00	1089.00
0.06	627.00	682.00	737.00	792.00	847.00	902.00
0.07	532.71	579.86	627.00	674.14	721.29	768.43
0.08	462.00	503.25	544.50	585.75	627.00	668.25
0.09	407.00	443.67	480.33	517.00	553.67	590.33
0.10	363.00	396.00	429.00	462.00	495.00	528.00
0.11	327.00	357.00	387.00	417.00	447.00	477.00
0.12	297.00	324.50	352.00	379.50	407.00	434.50
0.13	271.62	297.00	322.38	347.77	373.15	398.54
0.14	249.86	273.43	297.00	320.57	344.14	367.71
0.15	231.00	253.00	275.00	297.00	319.00	341.00
0.16	214.50	235.13	255.75	276.38	297.00	317.63
0.17	199.94	219.35	238.76	258.18	277.59	297.00
0.18	187.00	205.33	223.67	242.00	260.33	278.67
0.19	175.42	192.79	210.16	227.53	244.89	262.26
0.20	165.00	181.50	198.00	214.50	231.00	247.50
0.21	155.57	171.29	187.00	202.71	218.43	234.14
0.22	147.00	162.00	177.00	192.00	207.00	222.00
0.23	139.17	153.52	167.87	182.22	196.57	210.91
0.24	132.00	145.75	159.50	173.25	187.00	200.75
0.25	125.40	138.60	151.80	165.00	178.20	191.40
0.26	119.31	132.00	144.69	157.38	170.08	182.77
0.27	113.67	125.89	138.11	150.33	162.56	174.78
0.28	108.43	120.21	132.00	143.79	155.57	167.36
0.29	103.55	114.93	126.31	137.69	149.07	160.45
0.30	99.00	110.00	121.00	132.00	143.00	154.00
0.31	94.74	105.39	116.03	126.68	137.32	147.97
0.32	90.75	101.06	111.37	121.69	132.00	142.31
0.33	87.00	97.00	107.00	117.00	127.00	137.00
0.34	83.47	93.18	102.88	112.59	122.29	132.00
0.35	80.14	89.57	99.00	108.43	117.86	127.29
0.36	77.00	86.17	95.33	104.50	113.67	122.83
0.37	74.03	82.95	91.86	100.78	109.70	118.62
0.38	71.21	79.89	88.58	97.26	105.95	114.63
0.39	68.54	77.00	85.46	93.92	102.38	110.85
0.40	66.00	74.25	82.50	90.75	99.00	107.25
0.41	63.59	71.63	79.68	87.73	95.78	103.83
0.42	61.29	69.14	77.00	84.86	92.71	100.57
0.43	59.09	66.77	74.44	82.12	89.79	97.47
0.44	57.00	64.50	72.00	79.50	87.00	94.50
0.45	55.00	62.33	69.67	77.00	84.33	91.67
0.46	53.09	60.26	67.43	74.61	81.78	88.96
0.47	51.26	58.28	65.30	72.32	79.34	86.36
0.48	49.50	56.38	63.25	70.13	77.00	83.88
0.49	47.82	54.55	61.29	68.02	74.76	81.49
0.50	46.20	52.80	59.40	66.00	72.60	79.20
0.51	44.65	51.12	57.59	64.06	70.53	77.00
0.52	43.15	49.50	55.85	62.19	68.54	74.88
0.53	41.72	47.94	54.17	60.40	66.62	72.85
0.54	40.33	46.44	52.56	58.67	64.78	70.89
0.55	39.00	45.00	51.00	57.00	63.00	69.00
0.56	37.71	43.61	49.50	55.39	61.29	67.18
0.57	36.47	42.26	48.05	53.84	59.63	65.42

From this table the need to plan dives allowing for both the OTU and the NOAA CNS clock is apparent. The dive supervisor must insure dives are within both limits. To illustrate this point, let's produce a model of a dive mission. Let's assume the mission is one that requires work at a depth of 350 fsw. Because of multi-day and moderately long exposures it is decided to use a limiting PO_2 of 1.4 ATA for the bottom mix. Our dive profile will be a 40 minute bottom time once every 20 hours. By creating a theoretical table, let's assume the decompression mix changes are:

1. To air at 220 fsw
2. A mixture of 30% O_2 at 150 fsw
3. Switch to 50% O_2 at 70 fsw,
4. O_2 at 20 fsw. The 10 & 20 fsw stops are both done at 20 fsw.

In our theory table (which is not valid as we will assume all stops are at the maximum level instead of in ten foot increments just for an example purpose),

A. at 180 fsw three minute on air,
B. at 150 fsw 29 minutes on 30% O_2,
C. at 70 fsw 88 minutes on 50% O_2,
D. at 20 fsw 126 minutes on O_2.

For the O_2 clock, we will assume the diver does take a five minute break on mix instead of oxygen every 25 minutes on O_2.

1. Referring to Maximum Operating Depths for Given FO_2's and Limiting PO_2's table on the opposite page, we discover that the bottom mix is 1.4 for 40 minutes yielding 1.63 OTU/minute = 65.2 OTU
2. At 180 fsw the PO_2 = .21 x P (180/33+1)= 1.35 ATA for 1.55 OTU/min x three minutes = 4.65 OTU
3. at 150 fsw PO_2= 1.67 ATA or 2.07 OTU/min x 29= 60.03 OTU
4. at 70 fsw PO_2=1.56 ATA or 1.92 OTU/min x 88 = 168.96
5. at 20 fsw PO_2=1.61 ATA (rd to 1.6) 1.92 OTU/min x 126= 241.92
   Total OTU's 540.76 OTU's

The NOAA CNS clock is exceeded but due to the breaks from oxygen to EAN every five minutes it is a safe deco and dive. Without the off breaks, there could be a high probability of O_2 symptoms in some individuals. After referring to the mission/day OTU chart, we find this dive could only be made for three consecutive days without taking a 24 hour break in diving. From the above it is apparent that for operational missions it is essential that divers plan for the oxygen reactions on their physiology.

There are many positive applications of increased PO_2. One is that with increased FO_2, less inert gas is absorbed into the tissues and safer dives are performed. Increased FO_2 can also be used to extend bottom times. During decompression, more efficient outgassing is brought about through the use of elevated PO_2 and even pure oxygen. Of course, the use and results of oxygen in first aid in conjunction with DCS or AGE is beyond measure. Oxygen use in hyperbaric facilities treating diving and other illness is of exceptional benefit.

Oxygen is used with complete safety provided the diver remains in the established CNS/OTU limits as defined by NOAA and the Repex table. The whole concept of NITROX, Heliox and Trimix diving evolve around correct application of FO_2 and PO_2 on a given dive mission. In fact, the use of NITROX is most likely the safest advance in recreational diving in the past 40 years. Heliox has also provided increased safety for deep diving requirements. Trimix is the mix of choice for most divers who explore greater depths. The use of these mixed gases within planned exposures opens a vast frontier of exploration and increased safety.

DIVE EXAMPLES

A diver wishes to use NOAA NITROX I on a dive to 130 fsw with a bottom time of 30 minutes. The diver plans the dive on the NOAA I tables and has a decompression stop time of seven minutes at 10 fsw. The diver plans to do the decompression stop on oxygen. Can this dive be completed safely within the oxygen C.N.S. Clock? By referring to the NOAA partial pressure and exposure time charts the answer is yes. At 130 fsw, the diver has a PO_2 of $PO_2 = .32 \times (130/33 + 1)$ or $4.94 = 1.58$. Rounding this off to 1.6 the chart tells us we have a safe exposure of up to 45 minutes. The dive will have 30 minutes at a PO_2 of 1.58 and seven minutes at a PO_2 of $PO_2 = 1 \times (10/33 + 1)$ or $1.30 = 1.3$ ATA.

The same diver returns the next day and dives to 130 fsw but needs a 45 minute bottom time with a decompression on oxygen. As the sea state is rough, the diver plans to use oxygen and remain at 20 fsw throughout the decompression ATA. How will the dive be planned? We already know the PO_2 at depth is 1.58 from the previous day of diving. The decompression on pure oxygen would be a PO_2 of $PO_2 = 1 \times (20/33 + 1)$ or $1.61 = 1.61$ ATA the stop time is 23 minutes. Thus this dive would exceed the limits of exposure for a NOAA NITROX I dive. The diver has two choices: remain on NITROX during decompression and the dive can be completed on NOAA NITROX I. The second choice is to reduce the Fg so a PO_2 would allow the completion of the dive using oxygen for decompression.

Looking at the NOAA chart we see that a PO_2 of 1.5 ATA allows time for completion of the dive. In this case, the diver will not be able to use NOAA NITROX I as it contains 32% oxygen. A new FO_2 must be planned.

$FO_2 = 1.5/(130/33)\ 4.94 = .30\ or\ 30\%$.

The diver may now plan an equivalent Nitrogen depth (END) schedule, or plan the dive based on standard air tables benefiting from the increased safety. To plan an EAD the following equation is used.

$EAD = \{ (FN_2)\ x\ (depth + 33)\ /.79\} - 33$

On an END table the 130 foot dive with 30% O_2 would be:

$\{(0.70)\ x\ (130 + 33\ )\ /\ .79\} - 33 = 112\ fsw$

The 120 fsw air table is used. The decompression is 46 minutes at 20 fsw on O_2 due to combining the 10 and 20 foot stops at 20 foot. On this dive a five minute break off O_2 is taken at 25 minutes into the stop time.

Total exposure is 40 bottom at 1.5 ATA and 46 minutes at 1.6 ATA during decompression. To provide additional safety the diver should ascend to 15 fsw after the five minute break off oxygen. It is generally regarded as safe to breathe oxygen at 20 fsw during decompression when the diver is at rest, Hamilton 1992.)

In no stop diving the NOAA NITROX I and NOAA NITROX II mixes and tables are ideal and can safely be followed. The only concern is to remain within the normal depth and time specifications in the NOAA O_2 limits. It is highly recommend that divers incorporating longer and harder dives, whether they be actual work dives, cave dives, heavy current dives or wreck dives, incorporate a general rule of using between 1.4 and 1.5 PO_2 bottom mixes and decompression gases in the .8 to 1.6 PO_2 ranges to insure efficient inert gas elimination.

An example of this type dive planning is a dive is planned for a two hour bottom time at a depth of 100 fsw. It is a hard exertion dive, what gas should be used?

To allow for exertion, for a two hour bottom time and to plan on use of oxygen at the 20 fsw stop the maximum bottom mix PO_2 is planned for 1.4 ATA. What mix will supply this PO_2?

$FO_2 = PO_2/p\ or\ 1.4/\ (100/33 + 1)\ or\ 4.03 = .35\ \ so\ the\ FO_2\ is\ 35\%$

The END is $\{(FN_2)\ (depth + 33)\ /.79\ \} - 33$

or $END = \{(0.65)\ (133)\ /\ .79\} - 33\ = 76.43\ fsw$

Our decompression will be planned as a 80 fsw dive for 120 minutes. According to U.S.N. air tables the decompression is 17 at 20 fsw and 56 at 10 fsw. The diver will go to oxygen at 20 fsw and O_2 will be breathed for 25 minutes followed by a five minute airbreak. During the air break ascent is made to 15 fsw and O_2 breathing is resumed. The purpose of the air break is to allow the CNS clock to drop off and to allow OTU's to slow down their accumulation. The remaining decompression will feature 25 minute oxygen breathing periods followed by five minute air breaks.

In this example, the diver used 120 minutes of the allowed exposure to 1.4 ATA O_2 leaving a safe balance of minutes allowable at 1.4 O_2 breathing. During ascent, the PO_2 was dropped due to the decreased partial pressure of the bottom mix. This relaxes the C.N.S. Clock for an undetermined amount. At 20 fsw, 25 minutes were planned on the 1.6 ATA chart and the ten foot stop (taken at 15 fsw accumulated an additional 48 minutes at a PO_2 of:

$$PO_2 = 1 \times (15/33 + 1) \; or \; 1.45 = 1.45 \, ATA$$

For convenience sake, see Maximum Operating Depths for Given FO_2's and Limiting PO_2's table on page 138, providing an excellent reference for determining the maximum depth for a given FO_2 with a limiting PO_2. This chart is an excellent reference for NITROX, Heliox and Trimix dives.

A diver plans a dive for 275 fsw. The dive will feature a bottom time of 20 minutes. It can be anticipated that a lengthy decompression is to follow, thus a limiting PO_2 of 1.5 ATA is decided on. What will be the FO_2?

Refer to Maximum Operating Depths for Given FO_2's and Limiting PO_2's table, and go down the 1.5 ATA column until 275 fsw or a close number to it is reached. Then go across the chart and find the FO_2. This should have reflected a FO_2 of 0.16 (or 16%).

This dive would require approximately 79 minutes of decompression. With the first stop at 110 fsw the diver would switch to a NITROX 50-50 at 80 fsw and then to oxygen at 20 fsw. For field use, the diver must plan out the total exposure to the CNS clock and also track the OTU's.

The above dive, like most Trimix dives, is carefully planned to avoid CNS toxicity. In addition, it, and any Trimix dive with reasonable decompression times, takes advantage of using high PO_2 for decompression. Also, it is desirable to get off the bottom mix as soon as possible to avoid inert gas, especially helium uptake. The PO_2's are kept as high as they can be to control the amount of inert gas loading as well as for efficient decompression. In Trimix dives during the deeper decompression stops, the diver is off-gassing helium from the bottom mix while on-gassing nitrogen in the decompression gas. The diver will have to carefully track all accumulated times.

It is important that when using pure O_2 or mixtures of 1.6 ATA PO_2 on decompression stops that a five minute air or lesser deco mix break take place every 25 minutes. In the above dive the breaks would have been on the NITROX 50-50. With a mix featuring a FO_2 of 16% or less the diver must begin descent on a starter or travel mix. In the above case, the diver would have descended to at least 30 fsw on the NITROX 50-50. Most custom tables will specify travel/starter gases. When planning a Trimix or Heliox dive always remember the most important aspect is maintaining a PO_2 that is safe. The total exposure times will determine the PO_2 limits. The same is true of NITROX mixes.

Many physiologists endorse the use of a PO_2 of 1.4 ATA on all working dives. In addition, it is a wise practice on Trimix dives other than "bounce" dives to keep a bottom mix of 1.4 to 1.5 ATA PO_2 with decompression gases riding the 1.6 ATA as much as possible. The use of bottom mixes with PO_2's in excess of 1.6 ATA is highly discouraged. One of the main advantages of mixed gas is the safe control of PO_2. For recreational non stop dives, a PO_2 of 1.6 is acceptable as there are no additive times to the CNS or OTU clock during ascent.

Formulas Used in Management of PO₂ in Mixed Gas Applications

1. Ideal mix FO_2 = desired PO_2/P
   - A. Short bottom times for no stop dives $FO_2 = 1.6/P$
   - B. Moderate bottom times with less than 90 minutes stop time $FO_2 = 1.5/p$
   - C. Extended bottom times and stop times in excess of 90 minutes $FO_2 = 1.4/p$
   - D. Exceptional exposures PO_2 mission identified
     Note! Limits must remain within CNS oxygen toxicity clock
2. Determining PO_2, $PO_2 = Fg \times P$
3. Finding pressure or fsw $P = PO_2/FO_2$
4. Converting fsw to ATA (depth/33 +1)
5. Converting ATA to fsw (ATA -1) x 33
6. EAD = {(1- FO_2) (depth +33) / .79} - 33
7. To determine amount of oxygen to add to a NITROX mix
   {(FO_2 -.21) /.79} x psig
8. To determine amount of oxygen to add to a Trimix
   adjusted FO_2 -.21 / .79 x balance psig
   adjusted FO_2 = total O_2 in mix/balance of air added
   balance of air to add is; total pressure - He in mix

There is another phenomenon to address when using pure oxygen. The *off phenomenon* is a condition where a person either blacks out or goes into a sudden convulsion immediately upon going off oxygen. The consensus of data indicates this is due to changes in blood flow to the brain. Oxygen is a cerebral vasoconstrictor, when an off gas shift is made there is a rapid decrease in arterial PO_2. This results in a temporary "relative hypoxia" until vasodialation occurs. During this short time span a convulsion can develop due to vasoconstriction and temporary corresponding hypoxia. By limiting time to 25 minutes with an off break of five minutes the possibility of the off phenomenon is reduced. In addition, the off gas of choice would be one of the deeper NITROX decompression mixes. Although this has been observed in chambers, it is more of a remote possibility than a probability. Yet the technical diver must be aware of its existence.

SUMMARY

While those divers involved in no stop diving who dive within the limits of the NOAA NITROX tables will not be subjected to oxygen toxicity, they must be aware of the consequences of pushing these limits. The evolving technical diver using NITROX for technical applications with longer bottom times and with use of NITROX as a decompression gas needs a through understanding of the behavior of oxygen at elevated partial pressures. The Trimix and Heliox diver must continually track and plan for avoidance of both CNS and whole body toxicity problems. Oxygen is the princess of gases but if abused she is very unforgiving.

REFERENCES

University Miami Press proceedings of the fourth symposium on underwater physiology; *The Physiology and Medicine of Diving,* Bennet and Elliott.

The NOAA Dive Manual, NOAA Publication; *The NITROX Manual,* Dick Rutkowski International Association of NITROX Divers.

Wood J. D., Watson, W. J. & Murray, G. W. (1969). Correlation between decreases in brain gamma-aminobutyric acid levels and Susceptibility to convulsions induced by hyperbaric oxygen. *J. Neurochem.* 16, 281-287.

Tolerating Exposure to High Oxygen Levels Repex and Other Methods, by Bill Hamilon.

Hamilton, Bill, personal communication

Deep Diving:An Advanced Guide to Physiology, Procedures and Systems, Bret Gilliam and Robert von Maier, Watersport Publishing, Inc.

CHAPTER 7

THEORY

Carbon Dioxide Risk Management for Divers

For every liter of oxygen (O_2) consumed, almost a liter of carbon dioxide (CO_2) is produced. This is, of course, specific to individuals and varies according to diet and can change dramatically when the diver is subjected to increased work loads or exercise. CO_2 is essentially a waste product of the metabolic process of energy production and is eliminated during the exhalation phase of respiration. Its molecular weight is 44.0103 and occurs in the natural atmosphere as approximately 0.03% of the total. In that concentration, CO_2 is colorless, odorless, tasteless and nontoxic. In greater percentages or under elevated partial pressures it has an acidic taste and be dangerously toxic.

It is the primary stimulus to breathing in man. Remember the old "Ten and Ten Rule": if the percentage of either carbon dioxide or oxygen reaches 10% in the atmosphere, unconsciousness will usually result. Low oxygen levels (hypoxia) will trigger the peripheral chemoreceptors to send impulses to the respiratory center stimulating an increase in breathing rate. However, low partial pressure of oxygen (PO_2) is far less of a stimulus than high partial pressures of carbon dioxide (PCO_2). This is why the danger of excessive hyperventilation prior to extended or deep breath hold dives is so insidious.

Hyperventilation artificially blows off the normal equilibrating level of CO_2 and lowers it thus lessening the urge to breathe and extending the diver's bottom time. Upon ascent, the partial pressure of both CO_2 and O_2 is reduced as the diver rises in the water column. This results in the potential for latent hypoxia or "shallow water blackout". Our built-in warning system, carbon dioxide, has been altered through the hyperventilation process and is incapable of alerting the diver to his immediate hypoxic crisis. Several champion free divers have fallen victim to this phenomena and it is strongly advisable for divers to refrain from prolonged or excessive hyperventilation techniques.

Symptoms of carbon dioxide retention include headache, weakness, labored breathing, a feeling of air hunger, nausea, dizziness, and confusion. Observable signs are typified by clumsiness or foolish, incoherent actions and slowing of responses. At its higher plateau, CO_2 retention will manifest in unconciousness.

Those individuals who are more susceptible to carbon dioxide may be categorized as "CO_2 retainers". Many diving physicians are sufficiently concerned about this abnormality in divers that they will recommend exclusion if a predisposition to CO_2 is detected.

Dr. Ed Lanphier published the first work and formal recognition of the CO_2 retention phenomenon in individuals in 1955. His early work specifically noted the relationship of retention to increased susceptibility to oxygen convulsions. He later noted (1959 published interview), that "perhaps CO_2 retainers are the *only* individuals who develop O_2 toxicity much more readily during exercise than at rest." The significance of this hypothesis might lead to speculation that continued cautions against working diver exposures to high PO_2 values could be re-evaluated with regard to ATA(atmospheres absolute) dose/time guidelines, but no definitive investigatory data has been pursued clinically.

Lanphier went on to observe (1975 published interview), "Whatever its etiology, the individual tendency to retain carbon dioxide during exertion appears to be the single most important factor in the problem of abnormal PA CO_2 and its potentially serious consequences." He noted

Rev. Edward Lanphier led early diving physiology research in experimental chambers. Photo by Lanphier collection

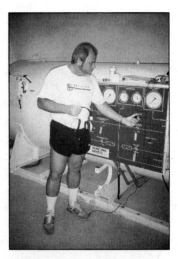

Aggressive venting will keep CO_2 build-up within comfortable limits. Here Bret Gilliam operates 54 inch field recompression chamber in Belize. With two or more occupants in inner lock, PCO_2 levels can escalate quickly.
Photo by Steve Furber

other contributory elements such as increased work of breathing, higher percentage rates of CO_2 in the inspired gas, and excessive "dead space" in breathing apparatus (helmet air volume) as important, but "their effects appear to be greatly magnified in men who do not maintain normal carbon dioxide values, even under optimal conditions of work."

The difficulty in effectively identifying the "CO_2 retainer" from a working group of diver candidates remains a problem. Hashimoto et al. (1981) conducted studies on 19 healthy divers that indicated past predisposition to some CO_2 symptoms but was unable to distinguish these individuals specifically by use of such conventional testing. His conclusions, however tentative, suggested that "identification of retainers requires an exercise test and that tethered fin-swimming is particularly suitable." *(Physiology and Medicine of Diving, 1982)*

With regard to the role of elevated CO_2 in inert gas narcosis, both clinical and anecdotal field reports all clearly identify the serious effects of high PCO_2 with narcosis symptomatically. Case, Haldane, and later, Bennett all describe this effect and subjective professional reports from experienced divers in actual dive conditions appear to confirm all speculations. One diver who was working on a pipe construction project in 190 fsw on air had no noticeable impairment in his day to day exposures across a ten day period. However, when his routine was altered to include lifting several 60 pound boxes of pipe components onto the work stage area, he became sufficiently overcome with befuddlement that he was forced to terminate the dive. Upon reaching the surface, he was unable to remember beginning work or the circumstances that caused him to abort. His dive partner, not involved in the heavy work, was unaffected. However, he was unable to note any change in behavior by his dive buddy until he abruptly dropped his tools and swam away from the work site. (Temple, Gilliam 1972)

While conducting tests on diver performance in 1963, Lanphier "rediscovered" the effects of CO_2 under pressure dramatically in an "episode of terror that has had no equal in his life". While working in a dry hyperbaric chamber at approximately 224 fsw he began testing a new bicycle ergometer at moderate exertion levels. His breathing system was modified to supply him with only about 50% of his respiratory needs. Onset of narcosis was rapid and escalated to collapse in coma. "Dyspnoea, which was very prominent before loss of consciousness, turned into a formless threat of indescribable menace when exercise ceased and aware-

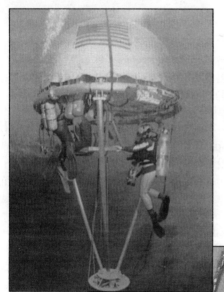

Dr. Bill Stone's CIS-LUNAR decompression habitat deployed at the 20 fsw stop. Such closed environments need to provide venting or CO_2 scrubbing techniques to ensure a safe breathing atmosphere. Photo by CIS-LUNAR

Inside view of divers entering the CIS-LUNAR decom habitat. Photo by CIS-LUNAR

Percent CO_2	Effect	CO_2 TOLERANCE RANGES
0-4%	No CNS derangement	
4-6%	Dyspnea, anxiety	
6-10%	Impaired mental capabilities	
10-15%	Severely impaired mental function	
15-20%	Loss of consciousness	
>20%	Uncoordinated muscular twitching and convulsions	

ness began to return. Had such an experience occurred in open water, survival seems improbable." *(Physiology and Medicine of Diving, 1982)*

Lanphier describes the incident in his own words: "I'm the exact opposite of a CO_2 retainer; but I discovered that I wasn't immune to serious CO_2 effects. A student and I were testing a new bike at 7.8 ATA in the dry chamber in my lab in Buffalo. Nitrogen narcosis is very evident on air at that pressure, but we were doing okay until we started breathing on the measuring circuit. That, it turned out, gave us only about half the air we needed at that work rate set on the bike. Herb tried the bike first. He stopped pedaling after about three minutes, out cold with his eyes rolled back."

"As soon as I could get Herb out of the way, I took the bike. I knew I wasn't getting near enough air, but I was too narc'd to think straight and was determined to finish the five-minute test no matter what. I pedaled myself right into oblivion, and coming around slowly afterward with a horrible feeling of suffocation was the worst experience of my entire life. Both of us surely would have drowned if such a thing had happened when we were alone underwater." *(Aquacorps 1992)*

In closed or semi-closed circuit systems, attention to proper CO_2 removal is essential. Absorbent such as lithium hydroxide, Sodasorb, or Baralyme are commonly used agents. Efficiency of such products is reduced in lowered temperatures so an awareness of thermal surroundings must be part of the diver's equation. In closed environments such as underwater saturation habitats, submersible or submarines elaborate CO_2 "scrubbers" are employed. In recompression chambers, periodic aggressive venting of the vessel interior will provide a refreshed and comfortable atmosphere.

CONCLUSION

It is extremely important for divers to consider the effects or CO_2 in planning their diving activities. Aside from the obvious problems of CO_2 toxicity itself, elevated partial pressures of CO_2 contribute to the onset and severity of both nitrogen narcosis and oxygen toxicity. Matching a high performance regulator to operational needs is vital. Breathing resistance *and* exhalation resistance must both be considered in selecting equipment. Increased gas density with depth can potentially overload the performance of many regulators in spite of glossy ad claims from manufacturers.

Proper breathing technique is equally important. Never engage in "skip breathing"; it will only contribute to CO_2 retention. Slow, deep ventilation cycles are recommended.

REFERENCES

Bennett & Elliot, *The Physiology and Medicine of Diving*, (1982) Best Publishing, Co.

Bove & Davis, *Diving Medicine*, (1990), Grove and Stratton, Inc.

Shilling, Carlston & Matthias, *The Physician's Guide to Diving Medicine*, (1984) Plenum Press

Lanphier, Ed, *The Story of CO_2 Build-up*, Aquacorps Journal, 1992

CHAPTER 8

DECOMPRESSION MANAGEMENT

Decompression Sickness

SECTION TWO

Decompression sickness (DCS) is a concern for all divers. However, it is of special concern for deep and mixed gas divers because it can strike suddenly, with serious effects and sometimes without obvious reasons.

Yet even with the threat of decompression sickness occurring on any dive, I continue to observe, over the years, a small percentage divers who "push" the tables. These divers, generally in good physical condition, deliberately omit some of the required decompression. They seem to suffer no immediate consequences for their omissions. This is regardless of the tables being used or rather the tables not being used. However, over the long run, almost to the person, each of these divers eventually took a serious neurological hit ie., developed serious DCS. Why do divers push the limits this way? Being paralyzed is a terrible price to pay for getting out of the water a few minutes earlier. Fortunately, however, each person I know to whom this occurred responded well to treatment and was able to walk away. They all continue to dive, except they new observe the rules — follow whatever decompression requirements the model they are using dictate.

Physiologists do not know what long term damage occurs to divers who have taken a "hit" even though they may have responded well to treatment. Documentation of the effects of long term pushing of the tables with omitted decompression without pronounced symptoms is still unknown. It is known that subclinical bubbles do exist on many dives and surely on dives with omitted decompression. It is theorized that long term problems such as aseptic bone necrosis (osteobaric necrosis) can be produced by this diving practice which most likely produces "asymptomatic DCS". One study of commercial divers who had not reported any DCS revealed definite scarring of the spinal cord. To this author, the risk of saving a few minutes of being cold and bored during decompression is heavily outweighed by the potential risk of immediate or latent decompression sickness.

The probability of avoiding DCS is significant if divers follow proven decompression models and complete all required decompression. The possibility of permanent damage resulting from immediate DCS or the long term affects of asymptomatic DCS is high for divers who "save time" from required decompression stops and violate specified ascent rates.

An excellent experience for divers is to observe a diver being treated at a chamber for a serious case of DCS. It is sobering to see another diver paralyzed by DCS — by tiny bubbles. It is even more sobering to learn that this diver's condition is the result of leaving the water just a little early because he was a little cold or a little bored.

I have known divers in their 30's and 40's in need of hip replacements due to DCS problems they could have easily avoided. Most of these divers simply skipped or shortened scheduled stops and reportedly they experienced no symptoms. They thought it was an "okay" decision since there were no apparent symptoms. Yet there probably were symptoms to which they gave little attention. Because when questioned they could relate mild or extreme fatigue, mild discomfort in the joints, etc. Some of these divers, who recognized their symptoms, and elected to treat themselves by breath-

SYMPTOMS OF DCS

Brain	Dizziness, blurry vision, headache, convulsions, blindness, auditory disorders, personality changes, unconsciousness
Spinal Cord	Paralysis, weakness, loss of bowel and bladder control, motor function disorders, loss of balance (staggers), abdominal pain, pins and needles sensation, inability to urinate, sexually despondent
Peripheral Nervous System	Muscle twitching, cool wooly feet, local numbness
Cranial and Spinal Nerves	Heaviness
Respiratory System	Chokes, shallow rapid breathing, burning sensation on inspiration, shock
Skeletal and Muscular Systems	Muscle pain, edema, swelling around joints, unusual feeling in muscle
Skin Bends	Itch, rash, discoloration splotchy
Delayed Symptoms Include	Degenerative Bone Disease
Misc. Symptoms	Fatigue, overall soreness/aches of body

Proper hydration is of primary importance in lessening the risk of DCS. Rob Parker has a last minute drink before descending into a Bahamian blue hole system. Photo by Rob Palmer

ing pure oxygen off and on for several days, even continued to dive between these surface treatment procedures. As is often the case, history repeats itself. One generation learns and yet the next one has to relearn the same experiences.

Decompression sickness is a disease caused by bubble formation. The bubbles are due to improper decompression on ascent. Once bubbles are formed they may or may not produce symptoms based on their eventual growth. When symptoms do occur they relate to the area the bubble has "attacked".

There are probably more divers hit on "no-decompression" dives than on "decompression" dives. This is due to a common trait of recreational diving "bad habit" — rapid ascents. Most divers assume that since they are within the safe bottom time limits for their particular dive they can exceed the recommended ascent rates with no problem. They are not remotely concerned with the possibility of getting DCS. Yet, rapid ascents is one of the most common contributing factors for DCS recognized by chamber operators. Divers must realize that all ascents even from moderate depths are a part of the decompression profile. If a given model for avoidance of DCS requires a specific ascent rate, be it 30 feet per minute or 60 feet per minute, it must be followed as it is the key element of the model and failure to observe it violates the model. Rapid ascents are a violation of any decompression model.

153

Referring back to the chapter on breathing, we traced the flow of blood and gas through the body. As you may recall, gas exchange occurs between the cells and the blood. The inert gas in the breathing mixture is transported by the blood to the tissues where it diffuses into the tissues. The amount of gas that can enter the tissues at a given moment is limited by the amount of gas dissolved in the blood. Consequently, it takes numerous rounds of circulation before tissues can become totally saturated, or in other words, when the partial pressure of the gas in the tissue equals the partial pressure of the gas in the ambient mixture. The longer one remains at a given depth, the more gas will dissolve in the tissues. Eventually the tissues will become completely saturated.

On the majority of dives, divers do not remain at depth long enough to become totally saturated. Once the tissues are partially saturated at a depth, an ascent will lower the ambient pressure of the inert gas. When the tissue partial pressure exceeds the ambient pressure of the inert gas we are said to be "supersaturated". We must eliminate this now excess gas by the same process that we acquired it. Gas must diffuse from the tissue to the blood and then be carried to the lungs where it is eliminated from the body. The same inert gas, if all factors are equal, diffuses into and out of the tissues at the same rate. However, this process is complicated by the fact that after an extended time at depth there is a large amount of gas dissolved in the tissues. This gas must be released slowly by the tissues to avoid DCS. If the relationship between the tissue gas pressure and the ambient gas pressure exceeds certain thresholds, gas will not remain in solution and gaseous bubbles will form.

The degree of supersaturation the body can tolerate during ascent without the development of bubbles of sufficient quantity or size to produce symptoms of DCS is not well understood. Ascent rates which minimize, or better yet, avoid bubble formation are best. It is for this reason that the monitoring and control of ascent rates is critical to safe diving. In deep diving or dives with long bottom times it is necessary to stop the ascent at various depths to allow a reduction in the amount of tissue supersaturation before continuing the ascent. This interruption while surfacing is called a decompression stop.

Factors Contributing to Bubble Formation

- Pressure change
- Exposure time
- Gas uptake
- Agitation
- Restricted flow areas

- Eddy currents at bifurcation of arteries and veins
- Exercise
- Fat
- Factors affecting circulation
- Drugs and alcohol
- Caffeine
- Nicotine
- Cavitation
- Gas solubility (varies with individual inert gases)
- Blood and tissue variability and composition
- Tissue vascularity
- Bio-physics of bubble formation
- Dehydration (this is one of the greatest contributors)

When bubbles form they begin as a gas phase with a nucleus. At this point the bubble may or may not attach to any surface. The bubble may grow and may break into a series of smaller bubbles. This may be followed by detachment and travel through the circulatory system. During the bubble formation phase the bubble will reach a critical mass. At this point the bubble has a high surface tension that tries to maintain the spherical shape and in doing so frequently forces the bubble back into solution. An additional insult may cause continued growth of the bubble. As the bubble grows the body reacts to it as a foreign object in the circulation and the platelets in the blood will attack and adhere to it causing further enlargement of the bubble. Excess CO_2 may also add to the size of the bubble. (helium will form bubbles faster than nitrogen). Once formed, a bubble will attract other bubbles creating a vicious cycle.

Bubbles tend to contain the same gases as the tissues in which they develop. The partial pressures of the gases inside the bubble approximate those of the surrounding tissue. By using pure oxygen and thereby reducing the partial pressure of the inert gas in the tissue, bubble tension can be overcome and the emulation of the inert gas from the bubble increased. Once formed, changes in the sizes of any bubbles is dependent upon Boyle's law. If bubbles form during ascent they will further expand while the ascent continues. If the diver is placed in a recompression chamber and pressurized to depth the bubbles will be forced smaller and circulation may be restored. This is why the treatment for DCS is immediate recompression.

As bubbles migrate they may attach to either hydrophilic (water attracting, lipid repelling) surfaces or hydrophobic (water repelling, lipid attracting) surfaces. Hydrophilic surfaces include the larger blood vessels, capillaries and the tissues. Hydrophobic surfaces include nerve tissue and lipids (fat) in the body. Bubbles on hydrophobic surfaces are said to be stable bubbles. They tend to experience continued growth and are the most difficult to treat. Gas bubbles also attach to any irregularities of the blood vessels and other surfaces. For this reason older divers may be more prone to DCS.

Bubbles may be stable at or below a critical radius. Therefore smaller bubbles may be difficult to eliminate. Some physiologists theorize that there are always some small bubbles (bubble nuclei) in the blood stream and that these develop into larger symptom producing bubbles. Symptomatic bubbles form more symptomatic bubbles. It has also been demonstrated that most bubbles originate in veins. Intravascular bubbles (bubbles within the circulatory system) block blood circulation which results tissue hypoxia. Extravascular bubbles (outside circulation) result in compression of vessels and nerves. They are found in muscle, intramuscular fascia, fatty tissues, bone marrow, and the myelin sheath of the peripheral nervous system and the spinal cord.

The overall effects of bubbles are divided into primary and secondary. It is obvious at this point that bubbles create a vicious cycle. Bubbles form, they reduce blood flow, this hampers bubble reduction causing further bubble development and all additional activity produces both bubble enlargement and the production of more bubbles.

Decompression is a precise exercise. Divers Rob Palmer and Tom Mount monitor their instruments to ensure proper depth control in the current during their 40 foot stop. Photo by Bret Gilliam

Primary Effects of Bubbles
- Distortion of tissues
- Obstruction of circulation
- Pressure on nerves

Secondary Effects of Bubbles
- Lipoprotein coating on bubbles causes platelets to adhere to bubble producing intravascular clotting
- Edema
- Spasms
- Stripping of blood vessels

As stated previously, a major contributing factor to developing DCS is fast ascents. Therefore, divers can reduce their risk for DCS by controlling their ascent rates. A dive computer or device that indicates rate of ascent is essential to monitoring and controlling one's ascent.

There are a number of factors that increase a diver's susceptibility to DCS. A major contributor is dehydration. Divers must be aware of their state of hydration and consciously take steps to hydrate themselves while diving.

Contributors to Dehydration
- Sweating
- Dry breathing gas, promotes removal of fluid via respiratory process depth intensifies loss of fluid due to density of gas in lungs
- Alcohol consumption
- Immersion diureses
- Failure to drink proper fluids such as water
- Caffeine
- Long dives and long decompressions
- Any respiratory loss of fluids

Exercise is another variable in the production of DCS symptoms. Strenuous exercise immediately before, during and following a dive is another contributor to DCS. Strenuous exercise during a decompression stop is exceptionally dangerous. However, moderate exercise and slow movement during decompression is believed to improve circulatory efficiency and aid in decompression.

Cavitation may be produced by rapid movements of the limbs. This effect is possible when one holds onto a decompression line that is bouncing with the movement of a boat. Cavitation causes local pressure change that may produce bubbles.

Alcohol, in addition to adding to the effects of dehydration, also causes an increase in blood lipids. It causes vasoconstriction of blood vessels and actually destroys brain cells. Nicotine and smoking also produce increased lipids. Smoking passes carbon monoxide into the circulatory system inhibiting effective gas transport. The carbon monoxide adds to the complexity of bubble formation. Numerous drugs may be used by divers from illegal or controlled substances to readily available over the counter drugs such as decongestants. Divers who use drugs must become educated on the drug's effects on the diver's physiology and their potential contribution to developing DCS.

Fat has been shown to increase the likelihood of DCS. Both body fat and blood fat effect the probability of taking a hit.

Temperature is a definite contributing factor to DCS. Extremes either cold or hot may induce symptoms. And often divers experience both extremes in their dive profile. Divers may become cold during their dive and especially during decompression. They may become even colder during the boat ride to shore. Once on shore they then step into a hot shower. Wham!, Symptoms develop and the divers ask why? When cold, the body reduces circulation (vasoconstriction) to the extremities to protect the core temperature. When in the hot shower the body increases circulation (vasodilation) to the extremities to help cool the core. Both cause changes in circulation and thereby increase the possibility of forming bubbles and developing symptoms.

Constrictions around the body, especially the arms and legs, may increase susceptibility to DCS. Constrictions can occur from wearing an overly tight wetsuit or other constricting pieces of equipment. Wetsuits must fit snugly but they should not constrict circulation. An exceptionally tight wetsuit is comparable to a constricting band restricting the flow of blood. When removed normal circulation is restored and possibility of bubble formation is increased. Prior injury sites present another area of possible poor circulation and are believed to make the diver more prone to DCS. And in addition, there is substantial individual variation to the susceptibility to DCS.

Preventive Actions to Reduce DCS Risk
- Ascend at rate specified by decompression model used.
- Begin hydration 12 to 24 hours prior to dive.
- Hydrate immediately before and after dive.
- Avoid strenuous exercise prior to dive.
- Control exercise level during dive.
- Avoid hard exercise at decompression.
- Perform limited movement light exercise during decompression.
- Avoid exercise immediately following dive.

Sig Sigerson using "Jon line" to stabilize his decom stop. Note oxygen bottle clipped to harness for decom gas. Photo by Robert Iannello

- Treat first 10 to 30 minutes on surface as a decompression stop.
- Maintain as high of a PO_2 on decompression as allowable within the CNS/whole body clock.
- Avoid alcohol 12 hours prior to dive and at least four hours following a dive.
- Do not smoke within one hour of a dive.
- Avoid drugs that are contradictions to diving.
- Do not eat fatty foods.
- Wear proper exposure suits for maintaining body temperature and fit.
- Allow extra decompression time for injury sites.
- Maintain good cardiovascular fitness.
- Limit degree of obesity.
- Add conservatism with age
- Remain stable on decompression stops (do not swim up and down taking photo's, sight seeing etc.).
- No hot showers, hot tubs or hot baths following dive, minimum of six hours then only hot showers.
- Allow others to assist you with excess equipment when exiting the water.
- Do not breath hold dive following a decompression stop dive.
- No flying for at least 24 hours.
- Take one aspirin every other day during diving activities.

Although physiologists debate the issue, practical considerations and experience calls for special procedures for omitted decompression. In the authors' opinion, the old U.S.N. procedure has proven itself many times. I have personally used this procedure and supervised it's use on several occasions. To me it is ill-advised to follow todays suggestions and just sit idly on the surface and await the development of symptoms.

Omitted Decompression Stop Procedure

- Descend to a depth of 40 fsw, for 1/4 of the 10 fsw stop time, plus any scheduled time remaining at the 40 fsw stop (use a EAN mix not to exceed 1.6 ATA PO_2)
- At 30 fsw remain on EAN for 1/3 of the 10 fsw time and repeat any time that may have been remaining at 30 fsw
- At 20 fsw switch to pure oxygen for 1/2 the time of the 10 stop time, plus one and a half times the original 10 fsw stop time. In other words remain at 20 fsw for twice the 10 fsw schedule. Continue to use oxygen with a NITROX or air break of five minutes following every 25 minutes of oxygen breathing.
- Upon surfacing breathe oxygen for 30 minutes, discontinue diving following ommitted decompression or treatment for 24 hours.
- Re-hydrate the body completely.
- Consider taking one aspirin.

To utilize this procedure the diver must be at 40 fsw within three to five minutes of violating the stop(s).

Version Two Omitted Decompression Stop Procedures

- Within five minutes descend to 30 fsw deeper than the first scheduled stop depth, use EAN with as close to a PO_2 of 1.6 ATA as possible.
- Add ten minutes to the original bottom time and decompress on the indicated schedule using EAN and O_2 at 20 fsw. With adequate supervision the diver may elect to use O_2 at 30 fsw.
- Breathe O_2 for 30 minutes on the surface post dive.
- Discontinue diving for 24 hours .

One other question is asked regarding DCS on EAN, Heliox and Trimix dives. How do you treat a mix diver when they have problems using these mystical gases.? Simple just like you would an air diver. The physiology is exactly the same. If they exceed their oxygen clock, they react no differently than an air diver. The possibility of oxygen problems are exceptionally slim as it would require exceptional exposure to even be close to true oxygen limits that would restrict treatment. Even on such a dive the fall off on the oxygen clock is dramatic during the time it takes to transport the diver to a chamber.

In summary avoidance of decompression sickness requires us to follow whatever "proven" decompression model we are diving on. In addition, practicing the preventive action steps discussed in this chapter should give one adequate safe guards. All divers who undertake rigorous dive activities must accept the possibility of DCS. As stated by Dr. Bill Hamilton "DCS is part of the diving equation".

There is no table, no gas and no procedure that provides zero DCS risk. This is true from no stop diving to saturation dives. Statistically, DCS is a fact of life to divers. One must be willing to accept that risk on any dive. The more complex the dive, the greater risk factors involved. With multi gas switches there is more equipment dependency and a higher potential for human error. On the other hand, custom tables with multi gas switches during decompression provide better off gassing, immeasurable additional safety due to elevated PO_2, (within safe limits) and custom tables are based on a more conservative foundation than conventional tables.

REFERENCES

The New Practical Diving; Tom Mount and Akira Ikehara; University Miami Press.

The Physiology and Medicine of Diving; Bennett and Elliott,

Deep Diving: An Advanced Guide to Physiology Procedures, and Systems; Bret Gilliam and Robert von Maier; Watersport Publishing, Inc.

Dive Computers: A Consumer's Guide to History, Theory, and Performance; Ken Loyst, Watersport Publishing, Inc.

Blood Bubble Interaction In Decompression Sickness, Symposium Defense and Civil Institute of Environmental Medicine.

John Crea

CHAPTER 9

Decompression Theory

As we are discussing the utilization of mixed-gas technology in scuba diving, we must step back and take a look at the history and theories of decompression tables, and also various strategies to minimize the length of time spent in water decompressing.

In the year 1670, Robert Boyle began experimenting in England with the recently developed vacuum pump (invented by the German scientist Von Guericke). As Boyle was deep into investigation of the principles of gas behavior, he decided to build a vacuum pump of his own. After using his vacuum pump on various non-living items, Boyle began to experiment with decreased pressures on living specimens.

While exposing a snake to lowered pressures, Boyle wrote "I once observed a Viper furiously tortured in our Exhausted Receiver... that had manifested a conspicuous Bubble in the blood juices and soft parts of the body." Thus was the first recorded case of "decompression sickness" in the world's literature. As bubble formation at decreased pressures was only a scientific curiosity at that time, it was promptly forgotten.

The first description of DCS in man was by Triger in 1841. The victims were coal miners who worked in mines dug in wet ground that required pressurization to prevent flooding. "Triger noticed that some men suffer cramps and pains in their muscles after leaving compressed air, and apparently their symptoms were treated vigorously with alcohol given both internally and rubbed on externally. We have no other report as to how they later fared." (Bove and Davis, 1991)

Pol and Watelle, in 1854, began to study the phenomenon of decompression sickness, and they noticed that this disease was always associated with leaving the compressed air environment. They wrote, "one pays only on leaving." They also noted that return to compressed air alleviated the symptoms." (Strauss, 1976)

The first scientific approach to the problem of decompression sickness was begun by the French physiologist Paul Bert, when he published his massive work (1,800 pages) La Pression Barometric. Bert showed that the causative agent in decompression sickness was nitrogen bubbles that apparently formed due to the rapid pressure reduction that caisson workers were exposed to.

"He recommended that caisson workers be brought back to surface pressure slowly, allowing nitrogen gas to escape before it formed bubbles. Furthermore, should caisson's disease occur, the victim should be recompressed, then again slowly returned to surface pressure. To assist flushing nitrogen from the body, Bert recommended that caisson workers breathe pure oxygen during their decompression. As a result of this recommendation, Bert was also the first person to discover that oxygen was toxic when breathed under pressure. In fact, the classic sign of oxygen toxicity - convulsions — has been given the formal name of the "Paul Bert effect." (Brylske, 1992)

HALDANE'S MODEL

In the early 1900's there was much controversy as to how to actually perform "safe" decompression. The English physiologist, J.S. Haldane, was commissioned by the British Admiralty to study these problems and (hopefully) come up with an approach to prevention of DCS. Haldane began his study by exposing test animals (goats) to various pressures for three hours (his theory was that a three hour exposure saturated the goats with nitrogen at the depth of exposure). After this "saturation" Haldane would rapidly bring the goats back to the surface and observe them for signs of decompression sickness.

Haldane discovered that goats that had been exposed to a pressure equivalent to 33 feet of sea water (fsw) or less could be decompressed to the surface without any signs of decompression sickness. Goats that had been exposed to depths greater than 33 fsw evidenced signs of DCS. From these observations, Haldane concluded that the goats could withstand an overpressure ratio (or "supersaturation ratio") of 2:1 without developing signs of DCS. This ratio was tested with dives to greater depths, and the goats then allowed to surface until the ambient pressure was 50% of that at the maximum depth. These goats also did not experience any signs of DCS.

Haldane postulated that a diver could be brought up immediately to any depth provided that this 2:1 ratio was not violated. Once this 2:1 ratio was achieved, the remaining portion of the ascent must proceed much more slowly to allow for elimination of the excessive nitrogen from the body.

Haldane knew that while there were literally an infinite number of gas absorption and elimination rates (based on blood flow — perfusion) it was neither possible nor necessary to attempt to consider each and every one. Instead, an accurate "overall picture" could be described by looking at several representative "compartments". This method gave rise to the "multi-compartment" model of decompression. This basic model is the basis for the vast majority of the methods in use today.

A method was needed to be able to calculate the theoretical inert gas uptake and elimination from the human body . This would allow Haldane to keep a diver at a certain depth until all the inert gas in his body tissues dropped to a level where the diver could safely move to a shallower depth and still not exceed that critical "supersaturation ratio".

However, developing workable decompression schedules was not quite as simple as determining this critical ratio. Haldane looked at data based on theoretical nitrogen uptake by the body and noticed that diffusion (gas uptake) basically followed a logarithmic curve for a constant "gradient" of concentration based on circulation "passes" through the body. As Haldane stated "We may therefore substitute minutes for rounds of circulation in the above calculation of the rate of saturation of the body with nitrogen, so that, if the assumptions made for the purposes of the calculation held good for a man exposed to compressed air, his body would be half saturated with the excess nitrogen in 23 minutes, three- fourths saturated in 46 minutes, etc."

Haldane's decompression model was based on the these studies, and included the following assumptions:

1. Tissues in the body absorb and eliminate the inert gas nitrogen at an exponential rate, with the driving force being the pressure differential between the ambient inspired nitrogen pressure and the pressure of the nitrogen dissolved in the tissues.
2. There is a continuous spectrum of "tissue groups" within the body with various rates of absorption and elimination.
3. A specific "tissue group" absorbs and eliminates nitrogen at the same rate for the same pressure gradient.
4. The spectrum of "tissue groups" can be approximated by selecting a finite number of "tissue groups" from within this spectrum.

"Haldane designated the selected tissue groups by their `half-times', or the time it would take the tissue group to reach one-half of the pressure difference between the initial tissue nitrogen pressure and the ambient nitrogen pressure. According to the half-time model a tissue group would never reach a point of equilibrium with the ambient nitrogen pressure since the exponential function would only permit saturation to occur following an infinite time at a given pressure. However, the tissue pressures are close enough to the ambient pressure after six half-times that they are considered to be saturated." (Huggins, 1987).

Haldane selected five compartments (most modern physiologists prefer to use the term COMPARTMENTS rather than tissue groups, as these compartments do not actually represent known tissue types, but are utilized to represent the human body's absorption and elimination of inert gas) for his model. These compartments had half-times of 5, 10, 20, 40, and 75 minutes. The 75-minute compartment was utilized because it would be 95% saturated after five hours, which Haldane considered to be the time it would take to equilibrate a human to a new ambient pressure. The following describes the model that Haldane used to create his tables:

a. The body can be represented by five compartments with halftimes of 5, 10, 20, 40 and 75 minutes.
b. Each of these compartments can withstand a pressure reduction ratio of 2:1.

Haldane computed a set of decompression tables utilizing his model (as defined above). The following is a short summary of Haldane's method of computation:

1. The tissue pressures for the five compartments are computed for any given exposure (depth and time).
2. The compartment with the highest pressure of nitrogen is determined.
3. The absolute pressure of that compartment is determined.
4. Using the 2:1 ratio, the shallowest depth that the 5 minute compartment could withstand is calculated. Since decompression stops are usually calculated in 10 ft. increments, if the calculated depths are not exactly divisible by 10 fsw, that depth is rounded to the next deepest 10 fsw step.
5. The diver then spends enough time at that decompression stop to allow the compartment pressures to drop to a level that will allow an ascent to a depth 10 fsw shallower.
6. Step 5 is repeated until the diver reaches the surface. All compartments are never allowed to exceed the 2:1 supersaturation ratio as set forth in the model.

As the decompression progresses, the compartment(s) that control the decompression stops changes, with the first stop controlled by the five minute compartment, and the following stops controlled by compartments with longer half-times.

"The Haldane tables were adopted by the Royal Navy in 1908 and are considered to be the first true set of decompression tables. Their use helped to reduce the incidence of DCS in caisson workers and hardhat divers." (Huggins, 1987)

The ratio of 2:1 in Haldane's model refers to the ratio of tissue pressure: ambient pressure, and refers to absolute pressure in reference to air. Another way to look at this is to look at the actual tissue nitrogen partial pressure as compared to the absolute ambient pressure. When expressed this way, the ratio becomes 1.58:1. In most subsequent work, this ratio of tissue nitrogen pressure: ambient pressure ratio is referred to as the supersaturation ratio.

Since then, the concepts proposed by Haldane have been widely adopted and accepted as a basis for the development of decompression tables, although with many modifications. One user of a Haldanean model through the years has been the U.S. Navy.

The first tables for the U.S. Navy were produced in 1915. They were based on the Haldanean model and also included the use of oxygen during decompression. These tables, called the C & R Tables (so called because they were produced for the Bureau of Construction and Repair) were used that year in the successful salvage of the submarine F-4 at a depth of 306 fsw, a remarkable accomplishment with these early tables.

"In the 1930's, the U.S. Navy researchers undertook a set of decompression experiments using human volunteers. The volunteers were exposed to raised air pressures in a chamber and then decompressed, without stops, back to surface pressure. When the results of these experiments were analyzed it became apparent that Haldane's idea that the ambient pressure could be halved without ill effect was wrong. The researchers (Hawkins, et al) concluded that each tissue half-time had its own allowable decompression ratio." (Lippmann, 1990)

In 1937, it was decided that the five minute and the 10-minute compartments could tolerate so much "overpressure" that they could be ignored. Schedules were calculated which utilized only the 20, 40, and 75-minute compartments and were issued (Yarbrough, 1937). The allowable pressure ratios were increased (made more conservative) to accommodate exercise at depth. These tables gained worldwide acceptance, but eventually were found to produce too great an incidence of DCS after long dives.

Later it was decided that the supersaturation ratio must be depth-dependent and deeper stops were introduced (Dwyer, 1956). The five minute and 10-minute compartments were reintroduced and a new compartment with a half-time of 120- minutes was added.

"In 1912, Sir Leonard Hill produced both experimental and theoretical evidence which questioned the use of staged decompression as suggested by Haldane, over continuous uniform decompression. Hill believed that bubbles form whenever the tissue gas tension exceeds the ambient pressure by a particular amount."(Lippmann, 1990) In other words bubble formation depends on a pressure differential rather than a pressure ratio. This theory has been referred to as the Critical Pressure Hypothesis. (Lippmann, 1990)

PRESENT HALDANEAN MODELS

Buhlmann Tables (Swiss Tables, ZH-L16 tables)

The Buhlmann Tables (also commonly know as the Swiss Tables) were developed at the Laboratory of Hyperbaric Physiology in Zurich. This model is also derived from the basic Haldanean concepts, developed on the concept that perfusion was the major factor controlling gas uptake and elimination. The model has undergone "adjustments" over the years to accommodate newly developing physiologic data in human decompression. This model utilizes 16 compartments, with nitrogen half-times ranging from 2.65 minutes to 635 minutes. The Buhlmann model is based on pressures rather than feet of sea water, making it easily adapted to altitude diving. The Buhlmann model is the basis for the algorithm used in most popular dive computers currently in production.

Doppler Based Haldanean Tables

In the early 1970's, Dr. Merrill Spencer (Spencer, et al, 1971, 1972, 1974) at the Institute of Applied Physiology and Medicine in Seattle, Washington observed the presence of doppler detected bubbles in divers after dives that did not produce any symptoms of DCS. Because these bubbles did not produce any symptoms, they are commonly referred to as "Silent Bubbles". "These bubbles are thought to be nitrogen bubbles that have been released from solution during ascent. They are detected with an ultrasonic probe that distinguishes gas bubbles by the reflection of the ultrasonic wave off the moving bubble surfaces. Further studies by Dr. A. Pilmanis at the Catalina Marine Science Center confirmed the presence of high degrees of VGE (venous gas emboli) following `no-decompression' dives in open water". Doppler technology currently allows researchers to detect moving bubbles in the blood stream as small as 20 microns.

This discovery has lead to much rethinking of the basic Haldanean model, as Haldane assumed that no DCS meant no bubbles were present or formed during "safe" decompression. Based on these findings of Spencer, many researchers immediately began to modify the U.S. Navy model with the intent of decreasing or eliminating the formation of these silent bubbles.

PADUA Model

Other researchers also modified the U.S. Navy model in the years following its introduction. The PADUA (Pennsylvania Analysis of Decompression for Undersea and Aerospace) model was developed by the Institute for Environmental Medicine at the University of Pennsylvania in the mid 1970's (Beckman, 1976). This model differs from the U.S. Navy model in that 10 compartments were utilized (with half-times up to 480 minutes) and with more conservative Mo and delta-M values. This model would produce tables that would be more conservative than those of the U.S. Navy, however no such tables have been produced for publication.

Huggins Model

In 1981, Karl Huggins computed a set of Repetitive Dive Tables using a model based on new no-decompression limits computed from Spencer's formula (Huggins, 1981). This model uses the same six tissue compartment half-times as the U.S. Navy model. The Mo values for the compartments were determined by computing the maximum tissue pressures produced in the compartments following exposure to the new no-decompression limits. No delta-M values were necessary since the tables were computed exclusively for no-decompression diving.

Karl Huggins has taken his model further, and developed a model that handles both no-decompression and decompression air dives by incorporated delta-M values. This model was basically the original model used in the EDGE dive computer.

NON-HALDANEAN MODELS

However, as widely accepted as the Haldanean concepts were, there were other approaches to the same problem, and they took different routes to basically the same solution.

In mixed gas diving it is important to properly observe all elements of decompression carefully. This includes ascent rates, switches from bottom mix to intermediate travel mixes, and finally to various decompression gases including pure oxygen. Note each diver is carrying two stage bottles. These contain nitrox and pure oxygen to accelerate decompression. Photo by Bret Gilliam

These researchers perceived what they felt were problems with part or all of Haldane's basic concepts, and produced models to generate decompression tables based on their concepts.

U.S. Navy E-L Algorithm

In 1980, the U.S. Navy began work on a constant PO_2 closed circuit mixed gas rebreather, and began looking at a diver carried computer to utilize with this equipment.

The U.S. Navy originally was going to utilize the U.S. Navy model in these diver carried computers, and decided to retest the U.S. Navy Model before actually incorporating it into a computer. The findings were eye opening, to say the least.

"In 1984 835 man-dives were done to test a real time computer algorithm for computing air and nitrogen-oxygen decompression profiles. Dives were wet, with divers working ($VO_2 = 1.4$ l/min) for half the bottom time and resting during decompression. Water temperature (55-65° F) was set to thoroughly chill divers who wore full wet suits. Divers had a minimum of 36 hours off between dives. Open circuit scuba was used for air breathing of the 659 schedules done breathing air only, 474 were single dives and 185 were repetitive dives. Air decompression dives done over the 50-190 fsw range showed that tripling a total decompression time for long, shallow dives (e.g. 60/180; 80/120) and near doubling for medium deep dives (e.g. 150/40; 190/30) is necessary for safe decompression. Some air schedules could not be safely dived even when total decompression time was more than tripled (e.g. 150/60; 190/40). Doing repetitive 100/60 and 150/40 air decompression dives (60 minute surface intervals) showed that DCS-free dives could not be obtained even when decompression time is doubled." (Thalmann, E.D., 1985)

Based on these findings, Thalmann and the NEDU (Navy Experimental Dive Unit) began development on a new decompression model to incorporate into the diver carried decompression computer. The algorithm that they had decided to use is the E-L Algorithm. This model assumes that nitrogen is absorbed by compartments at an Exponential rate, as in other Haldanean models. However, the nitrogen elimination is at a slower, linear rate. This lengthens most decompression times and slows the surface off-gassing rate, thus giving higher residual nitrogen levels for repetitive dives. (Thus the E-L model is referred to as an Exponential-Linear process while the classic Haldanean model is E-E or Exponential "in-gassing" and Exponential "out-gassing".)

British RNPL (Royal Navy Physiological Laboratory) Model

The model used to generate the current Royal Navy Physiological Laboratory (RNPL) tables is called a "slab diffusion" model.

"In 1958, Hempleman, a British physiologist, introduced a completely different decompression concept to those that were currently in use, and devised some decompression schedules which were based on a completely different model to that of Haldane.

Hempleman had observed that, over a particular depth range, the first symptom of decompression sickness to appear was usually pain at or near a joint. He assumed that the tissue involved (e.g. tendon) was, therefore, the tissue with the greatest overpressure of nitrogen for that depth range, and that gas elimination from that tissue must control the decompression. Hempleman pictured the body as a single tissue and believed that the quantity of gas absorbed in the body could be calculated by a simple formula relating depth and time. Unlike Haldane, who believed that gas uptake and elimination took identical times, Hempleman assumed that gas elimination was one and one-half times slower than uptake. He also utilized the theory that decompression is safe if a constant difference, between the gas tension in the tissues and the environment, of 30 ft (9 m) of sea water (fsw) is not exceeded." (Lippmann, 1990)

"This model represents the body as a single 'slab' of tissue. One end of the slab is exposed to ambient pressure. As the pressure of inert gas increases the inert gas diffuses through the 'slab' following a concentration gradient. As long as the pressure of the inert gas remains less than some specific amount (initially 30 fsw) above ambient pressure, bends should be avoided." (Lippmann, 1990) The RNPL tables are more conservative than the U.S. Navy tables and are used in modified from by the British Sub Aqua Club (the RNPL/BSAC tables) and by some research divers and clubs in the United States.

DCIEM Model and Tables

The DCIEM (Defence and Civil Institute of Environmental Medicine) model is a serial model with four tissue groups (Nishi, 1984). The previously presented Haldanean models are based on the concept of parallel compartments, which assumes all the tissue compartments in the model are exposed to the ambient pressure with no interaction between the compartments. A serial model assumes that the compartments are connected in a series with only one compartment exposed to the ambient pressure.

Each of the four compartments in the model have the same half-time of approximately 21 minutes. The allowable surfacing supersaturation ratios considered are 1.92 and 1.73 for the initial two compartments in the

171

series. The pressure levels in the last two compartments are not considered in the computation of the diver's safe ascent depth. This model approximates the British bulk diffusion slab model.

The DCIEM tables are based on thousands of man-dives that were extensively evaluated using ultrasonic Doppler detection. DCIEM's primary goal with the modifications was to upgrade the decompression model that is programed into their decompression computers. At this time the DCIEM tables are the most thoroughly tested tables in use, and are much more conservative than the U.S. Navy tables or even the Royal Navy (RNPL) or Buhlmann tables.

FREE GAS PHASE MODELS (BUBBLE MECHANICS MODELS)

"Only a handful of hard and fast conclusions about simple decompression sickness can be drawn from our present knowledge. So elementary as to be innocuous, they can be stated:
1) Bubble inception or phase separation is the primary even triggering simple decompression sickness.
2) Prevention of decompression sickness amounts to prevention (as a limit) of bubble inception or phase separation; and
3) Gradual pressure reduction minimizes bubble formation.

As pointed out by many, after the above statements, consensus usually diverges. Modelers and table designers must then supply or assume, gas exchange models, trigger points, and safe diving protocols which prevent, or at least minimize, phase inception and bubble growth." (Weinke, 1991)

Tiny Bubble Group (Varying Permeability) Model

"The Tiny Bubble Group is a group of researchers at the University of Hawaii that has developed a decompression model based on the physical properties of bubble nucleation in aqueous media. Their model, called the Varying-Permeability Model, indicates that cavication nuclei, that are to "seed" bubble formation, are `spherical gas phases that are small enough to remain in solution yet strong enough to resist collapse, their stability being provided by elastic skins or membranes consisting of surface-active molecule'. The ascent criteria for this model is based on the volume of bubbles that are formed upon decompression. Growth in size and number of gas bubbles is computed based on the physical properties of the `skins' and the surrounding environment. If the total volume of gas in the bubbles is less than a `critical volume', then the diver is within safe limits of the model." (Huggins, 1987)

"Based on laboratory results of bubble growth and nucleation in gels, Yount and Hoffman (at the University of Hawaii) developed a comprehensive set of tables and compared them to the USN and RNPL conventional tables. Decompressions, bounce diving, altitude bends, and saturation diving are all successfully described by one setting of four global parameters, replacing the usual set of critical tensions. The outcome of their studies has been the development of a varying permeability bubble model. Ordinarily, bubble skins are permeable to gas, but can become impermeable when subjected to large compressions (near 10 atm)." (Weinke, 1991)

MAXIMUM LIKELIHOOD STATISTACAL METHOD

A final method seeing much use currently is a model based on statistical analysis of the risk of DCS. This approach was originated at the Naval Medical Research Institute (NMRI). "They consider decompression sickness a probabilistic risk dependent on the 'dose' (depth/time exposure) produced from a dive profile. The model is based on a database that includes over 1,700 individual exposures from various decompression studies." (Huggins, 1987).

"The risk of decompression sickness (DCS) is assumed to increase with an increase in gas supersaturation of the body. However, it is the integrated value of the gas supersaturation that is important. Also, only the inert gas component of the inspired gas is considered; in the present analysis, the inert component is nitrogen.

The level of gas supersaturation in the body and the impact that this level has on the risk of DCS are predicted by a probabilistic model. Several different types of models have been examined in the past, but all are driven by the common variables of time and depth." (Tikuisis et al, 1988, 1991) The model configuration, selected on the basis of previous success is two compartments in parallel with different time constants for gas uptake and elimination, and different weighting factors for the contribution to the risk of DCS. A small time constant pertains to the 'fast' compartment and large value pertains to the 'slow' compartment. These time constants are the kinetic parameters of the model. Whenever a compartment's inert gas pressure exceeds ambient pressure, it contributes to the weighting factor. The extent of this contribution is determined by the gain which is the compartment's risk weighting factor. The time constants and the gain are the only parameters in the present two-parallel compartment model.

The method of maximum likelihood (Edwards, 1972) optimizes the values of the model parameters through a modified Marquardt algorithm (Marquardt, 1963) that matches as closely as possible the observed and predicted DCS outcomes." (Tikuisis and Nishi, 1991)

Tom Mount at 380 fsw swimming with stage bottles necessary for use as "travel mix" before switching to "bottom mix" for operating depth. Travel mixes keep the oxygen partial pressure in safe balance and can accelerate decompression schedules. Photo by Bret Gilliam.

Maximum likelihood analysis is currently being applied to evaluation of dive profiles, and is even being used to generate decompression profiles and tables. Utilizing this technique, a series of profiles can be generated with a pre-selected level of "risk". Depending on the type of diving being done, and the degree of support services available, different degrees of risk can be picked to match the dives. (Albin, 1991)

As we have seen from the preceding material, the history of decompression theory is still evolving. There are many remaining questions to be answered before we can state that a given "model" actually matches human physiology and physiologic response to exposure in the hyperbaric environment.

Several different approaches to decompression modeling are currently utilized, quite often with different approaches to human physiology and gas uptake and elimination. Thus, the question arises "Which one is right?" And the answer is that it is possible that all of the current models do not totally represent all aspects of human physiology.

As Dr. R.W. Hamilton likes to state: WHAT WORKS, ... WORKS!!!!

As long as a model produces tables that are reliable and reproducible, then it really does not matter how those results are obtained. A good example of this is the Maximum Likelihood Analysis Method. This "model" does not claim to be based on physiology at all, but instead is based on the statistical analysis of known dive profiles. This approach is currently being used to produce tables that are as good as any currently available.

PART II - PRACTICAL DECOMPRESSION THEORY FOR MIXED GAS DIVING

No matter what approach is taken in regards to decompression theory, the end result is that the diver using mixed gas for deep diving wants to get out of the water in as short a time as is safely possible.

Our first consideration is to chose a gas mixture that is both safe and efficient for us to use during the dive. Compressed air has depth limits based

Table A

COMPARISON OF NO-DECOMPRESSION LIMITS FROM VARIOUS MODELS

No-Decompression Limits (minutes)

Depth (fsw)	U.S. Navy	Buhlmann*	Spencer	Navy E-L**	RNPL/ BSAC	DCIEM	Tiny Bubbles
30	None	300	225	296	232	380	323
40	200	120	135	142	137	175	108
50	100	75	75	81	72	75	63
60	60	53	50	57	46	50	39
70	50	35	40	44	38	35	30
80	40	25	30	37	27	25	23
90	30	22	25	31	23	20	18
100	25	20	20	27	18	15	15
110	20	17	15	24	16	12	12
120	15	15	10	20	12	10	11
130	10	12	5	17	11	8	10

* Metric conversion to feet or next greater depth
** Approximate computations from Thalman, 1984

on both oxygen toxicity and based on nitrogen narcosis levels. If we chose a limiting partial pressure level for oxygen of 1.4 ATA, then air dives are limited to a maximum depth of 187.5 fsw. This depth also corresponds to a level of nitrogen narcosis that is near the limit of performance for the average diver.

To dive deeper will require that we reduce both the nitrogen concentration and the oxygen concentration in our breathing mixture. This can very easily be done by adding another inert gas to our mixture, one that does not contribute to our developing narcosis, and is also reasonably available. The commercial dive industry and the navies of the world have pretty much agreed that the inert gas of choice is helium. The usual way this has been accomplished has been to replace all the nitrogen with helium, and at greater depths to increase the helium concentration to produce an oxygen concentration that is within safe limits. However, recently the practice of replacing only part of the nitrogen with helium has become popular among the cave diving community, and has become almost a standard in the technical diving field.

Helium's advantages are its relatively easy availability, its lack of narcosis even at extreme depths, and its lower density when compared to nitrogen (thus making helium mixtures easier to breathe at depth and therefore less likely to promote carbon dioxide retention).

However, helium has some disadvantages that we must consider. First and foremost, is the fact that helium is much more expensive than the nitrogen that we are replacing. Replacing only part of the nitrogen with helium

Bret Gilliam prepares surface supply pure oxygen for use. A 40 foot umbilical hose will be clipped at the 20 fsw stop on the descent line. All components of the system must be oxygen cleaned. Oxygen greatly enhances the outgassing of inert gases such as nitrogen or helium making decompression more efficient and drastically reduces hang times if factored into the custom table. Photo by Kim Cochrane

makes good economic sense. Second, helium molecules diffuse approximately 2.65 times faster than nitrogen molecules, and are thus absorbed by the body faster during a dive. Helium-oxygen mixtures (Heliox) can contribute to longer decompression times when compared to comparable nitrogen-oxygen mixtures, at least for short to medium exposure times. Reducing our exposure to elevated helium partial pressures by only replacing some of the nitrogen can help keep our decompression times within acceptable levels. In fact, for short dive times, the order of decompression times is as follows:

NITROGEN-OXYGEN < TRIMIX < HELIUM-OXYGEN

This relationship holds true for short bottom times, but as bottom times begin to get longer and longer, these required decompression times begin to converge. Somewhere around a bottom time of 120 minutes, they will finally converge (all these mixtures will have approximately the same required decompression time), and then as the bottom times continue to lengthen, then the order will reverse, with helium-oxygen mixtures requiring the least decompression and a comparable nitrogen-oxygen mixture requiring the most (with Trimix falling somewhere in between, depending on the relative concentrations of helium and nitrogen.)

Third, helium's thermal conductivity makes it undesirable for use in inflating a drysuit, as the insulation of the drysuit will be much less than if the drysuit was inflated with air. In fact, many technical divers are using an even denser gas (Argon) than air for drysuit inflation, claiming better insulation properties and less loss of body heat during the long dives being performed.

Decompressions at these greater depths can run into extremely long in-water times (see Table 1 below). In most applications, these extremely long "hang times" are not desirable, so ways to increase the efficiency of our decompressions have become prominent. The major concept in "optimizing" these decompressions is the following (which is basically independent of the model used): Inert gas elimination is directly influenced by the partial pressure gradient between the tissues and the inspired breathing mixture.

We can accelerate the rate at which inert gas is eliminated from our bodies by reducing or eliminating the concentration (and the partial pressures) of the inert gas in question in our breathing mixture. Obviously, this appears simpler than it really is. If we could replace the inert gas with a gas that is not absorbed, but that is instead metabolized, then we would have the ideal situation. The only problem is that the obvious choice for the replace of our inert gas fraction, oxygen, can become toxic if we exceed partial pressure limits that are too small to allow us to use it as 100% of our

TABLE 1

Comparison of Decompression Times Bottom Mix Utilized During Entire Dive and Decompression		
Bottom Mix Used		
Decom Stop Depths / **HELIOX**	**TRIMIX**	**NITROX90**
260 1		
250 1	1	
240 1	1	
230 1	1	
220 1	1	1
210 1	1	1
200 1	1	1
190 2	1	1
180 2	1	1
170 3	2	1
160 3	2	1
150 4	2	2
140 5	3	2
130 6	3	3
120 8	5	3
110 12	6	4
100 19	7	6
90 32	10	6
80 39	15	9
70 61	23	12
60 100	39	16
50 175	54	23
40 354	91	40
30 743	176	74
20 794	421	151
10 1002	1425	851
Total Decom Times (Min) 3371	2292	1209

Heliox is 90% Helium, 10% Oxygen
Trimix is 65% Helium, 25% Nitrogen, Balance Oxygen
Nitrox90 is 90% Nitrogen, 10% Oxygen

breathing mixture at most decompression stops. However, the replacement of inert gas with oxygen, guided by allowable partial pressure limits, is one of the mainstays of our approach to optimizing our decompression. (See Table 2 below)

Another option is to replace rapidly diffusing inert gas with an inert gas that diffuses more slowly. Helium diffuses approximately 2.65 times faster than nitrogen (rate of diffusion is inversely proportional to the square root of the molecular weight of the gas in question). If we assign a relative diffusion rate of 1 to nitrogen, then helium has a value of 2.65), and we will be replacing helium with nitrogen during our decompression. And, as our depths become shallower, we will also be increasing our oxygen concentration within allowable limits (both CNS limits and "whole body" limits must be considered, and are discussed in the chapter on Oxygen Toxicity.) (see Table 3 next page)

TABLE 2

Comparison of Decompression Times 100% Oxygen Utilized at the 10 & 20 Ft Stops			
	Bottom Mix Used		
Decom Stop Depths	**HELIOX**	**TRIMIX**	**NITROX90**
260	1		
250	1	1	
240	1	1	
230	1	1	
220	1	1	1
210	1	1	1
200	1	1	1
190	2	1	1
180	2	1	1
170	3	2	1
160	3	2	1
150	4	2	2
140	5	3	2
130	6	3	3
120	8	5	3
110	12	6	4
100	19	7	6
90	32	10	6
80	39	15	9
70	61	23	12
60	100	39	16
50	175	54	23
40	354	91	40
30	743	176	74
Switch to 100% Oxygen at the 20 Ft. Stop			
20	161	78	41
10	241	218	107
Total Decom Times (Min)	1977	742	355

Heliox is 90% Helium, 10% Oxygen
Trimix is 65% Helium, 25% Nitrogen, Balance Oxygen
Nitrox90 is 90% Nitrogen, 10% Oxygen

A third option is useful when breathing mixtures containing helium are utilized. The concept behind this is that helium continues to be absorbed by the body at deeper stops, and stopping the uptake of helium can make a major change in decompressions required. (see Table 4 on page 180)

Ideally, we would switch our breathing mixture at every decompression stop, optimizing our breathing mixture to maximize the inert gas gradients for inert gas elimination. (See Table 5 on page 181)

CONCLUSION

As we have seen in this overview, selection of a single table or model for decompression management is governed by a variety of circumstances related to the diver's operational physiology and work objectives. Acceler-

TABLE 3

Comparison of Decompression Times Nitrox 50% Utilized Starting at the 70 Ft Stop 100% Oxygen Utilezed at the 10 & 20 Ft Stops			
	Bottom Mix Used		
Decom Stop Depths	**HELIOX**	**TRIMIX**	**NITROX90**
260	1		
250	1	1	
240	1	1	
230	1	1	
220	1	1	1
210	1	1	1
200	1	1	1
190	2	1	1
180	2	1	1
170	3	2	1
160	3	2	1
150	4	2	2
140	5	3	2
130	6	3	3
120	8	5	3
110	12	6	4
100	19	7	6
90	32	10	6
80	39	15	9
Switch to Nitrox 50 at the 70 Stop			
70	15	8	6
60	19	11	9
50	29	15	11
40	43	21	17
30	66	33	28
Switch to 100% Oxygen at the 20 Ft. Stop			
20	82	43	29
10	195	107	68
Total Decom Times (Min)	591	301	210

Heliox is 90% Helium, 10% Oxygen
Trimix is 65% Helium, 25% Nitrogen, Balance Oxygen
Nitrox90 is 90% Nitrogen, 10% Oxygen

ated decompression through the use of enriched oxygen mixtures is desirable to enhance the efficiency of inert gas off-loading and to reduce in-water hang times with respect to environmental considerations such as hypothermia, rough sea conditions or hazardous marine life.

Technical diving within the realm of mixed gas applications is a highly specialized science. Production and use of custom tables is common and, to a certain degree, some elements of this proprietary method is still experimental. The reliability of a decompression table or procedure is not determined by any mathematical process, but by what works in practice. "What works... is what works!"

TABLE 4

Comparison of Decompression Times Air Utilized Starting at the 180Ft Stop Nitrox 50% Utilized Starting at the 70Ft Stop, 100% Oxygen Utilized at the 10 & 20Ft Stops

Decom Stop Depths	Bottom Mix Used		
	HELIOX	TRIMIX	NITROX90
260	1		
250	1	1	
240	1	1	
230	1	1	
220	1	1	1
210	1	1	1
200	1	1	1
190	2	1	1
Switch to Air at the 180 Stop			
180	1	1	1
170	1	1	1
160	1	1	1
150	2	1	2
140	1	1	2
130	3	1	2
120	2	2	2
110	2	3	4
100	5	3	3
90	5	4	5
80	8	5	6
Switch to Nitrox 50 at the 70 Stop			
70	15	8	6
60	19	11	7
50	29	15	10
40	43	21	13
30	66	33	22
Switch to 100% Oxygen at the 20 Ft. Stop			
20	37	28	24
10	89	69	57
Total Decom Times (Min)	249	191	172

Heliox is 90% Helium, 10% Oxygen
Trimix is 65% Helium, 25% Nitrogen, Balance Oxygen
Nitrox90 is 90% Nitrogen, 10% Oxygen

REFERENCES

Bassett, Bruce, and Christopherson, Sharon, *"Calculation of Non-Standard Decompression Schedules,"* University of Southern California, 1974.

Buhlmann, A.A., *Decompression - Decompression Sickness,* New York: Springer-Verlag, 1984.

Buhlmann, A.A., *"Die Berechnung der risikoarmen Dekompression",* Schweiz. med. Wschr., 1988; 118: Nr.6.

Bennett, P.B., and Elliot, D.H., *The Physiology and Medicine of Diving,* third edition. Best Publishing Company, California, 1982.

Brylske, Alex *"New Frontiers & Beyond,"* Dive Training, Vol. 2, No. 3; March, 1992.

Brylske, Alex, *"History of the Dive Tables II: Uncle Sam's Contribution,"* Dive Training, Vol. 2, No. 2; February 1992.

TABLE 5

Comparison of Decompression Times Optimal Gas Mixtures Used at all Decompression Stops Gases are Switched at Every Stop			
	Bottom Mix Used		
Decom Stop Depths	**HELIOX**	**TRIMIX**	**NITROX90**
260	1		
250	1	1	
240	1	1	
230	1	1	
220	1	1	1
210	1	1	1
200	1	1	1
190	1	1	1
180	1	1	1
170	1	1	1
160	1	1	1
150	1	1	1
140	1	1	2
130	2	2	1
120	2	1	2
110	3	2	3
100	2	3	2
90	4	3	4
80	4	4	3
70	6	4	5
60	7	7	6
50	10	8	7
40	14	12	10
30	18	17	12
20	26	24	19
10	63	56	45
Total Decom Times (Min)	174	155	129

Brylske, Alex, *"The Genesis of Dive Tables,"* Dive Training, Vol.2, No.1; January, 1992

Des Granges, M., *Repetitive Diving Decompression Tables,* Report 6-57, Navy Experimental Diving Unit, 1957.

Dwyer, J.V., *Calculation of Air Decompression Tables,* Report 4-56, Navy Experimental Diving Unit, 1956.

Dwyer, J.V., *Calculation of Repetitive Diving Decompression Tables,* Report-57, Navy Experimental Diving Unit, 1957.

Edmonds, C., Lowry, C., and Pennefather, J., *Diving and Subaquatic Medicine.* Mosman, N.S.W., Australia: Diving Medical Centre, 1981.

Gilliam, Bret, *Deep Diving: An Advanced Guide to Physiology, Procedures and Systems;* Watersport Publishing, 1992

Hoffman, D.C., *"On the Use of a Gas-Cavitation Model to Generate Prototypical Air and Helium Decompression Schedules for Divers,"* Ph.D. dissertation, University of Hawaii, 1985.

Huggins, K.E., *"Doppler Evaluation of Multi-Level Dive Profiles,"* in Proceedings of the Fourteenth International Conference on Underwater Education, National Association of Underwater Instructors, 1983.

Huggins, K.E., *"New No-Decompression Tables Based on No-Decompression Limits Determined by Doppler Ultrasonic Bubble Detection,"* Michigan Sea Grant College Program (Report #MICHU-SG-81-205), MI, 1981.

Kidd, D.J., and Stubbs, R.A., *Analog Computer Solution of Decompression,* Defence Research Medical Laboratories, 1966.

Lauchner, G.R., and Nishi, R.Y., *Decompression Tables and Procedures for Compressed Air Diving,* Based on the DCIEM 1983 Decompression Model, Report #84-R-72. Defence and Civil Institute of Environmental Medicine, 1984.

Nishi, R.Y., and Lauchner, G.R., *Development of the DCIEM 1983 Decompression Model for Compressed Air Diving,* Report #84-R-44. Defence and Civil Institute of Environmental Medicine, 1978.

Spencer, M.P., *"Decompression Limits for Compressed Air Determined by Ultrasonically Detected Blood Bubbles,"* Journal of Applied Physiology. 40 (2) 1976, pp. 229-235.

Shilling, C.W., Werts, M.F., and Schandelmeier, N.R., *The Underwater Handbook,* Plenum Press, New York, 1976. Key Documents of the Biomedical Aspects of Deep-Sea Diving, Undersea Medical Society

Thalmann, E. *Computer Algorithms used in Computing the MK 15/16 Constant 0.7 ATA Oxygen Partial Pressure Decompression Tables,* Report 1-83, Navy Experimental Diving Unit, 1983.

Thalmann, E. *Phase II Testing of Decompression Algorithms for use in the U.S.Navy Underwater Decompression Computer,* Report 1-84, Navy Experimental Diving Unit, 1984.

Weathersby, P.K., Survanshi, S.S., Homer, L.D., Hart, B.L., Nishi, R.Y, Flynn, E.T., and Bradley, M.E., Statistically Based Decompression Tables — Analysis of Standard Air Dives; 1950-1970. Report NMRI 85-16, Naval Medical Research and Development Command, 1985.

Weathersby, P.K., Survanshi, S.S., Homer, L.D., Hart, B.L., Flynn, E.T. and Bradly, M.E., Statistically Based Decompression Tables -Equal Risk Air Diving Decompression Schedules, Report NMRI 85-17, Naval Medical Research and Development Command, 1985.

Wienke, B.R., *Basic Decompression Theory and Application,* Best Publishing Company, 1991

CHAPTER 10

Decompression Sickness Accident Management

DECOMPRESSION SICKNESS OVERVIEW

The "bends" is an occupational hazard of diving. It matters little whether the stricken diver was engaged in commercial, military or simply recreational pursuits. He's just as bent and the same rules apply. The mixed gas diver and other high tech participants have to deal with another anomaly of diving: the fact that if you're in trouble, it's generally your responsibility to get out of it without standard medical assistance.

Dick Clarke, founder of the National Association of Diver Medical Technicians, has provided this observation: "Decompression accidents are unique in that, with few exceptions, it is the layman who is responsible for patient assessment, diagnosis, early therapeutic intervention and, in some cases, even definitive care."

That's right folks, if you get bent on a dive trip the chances of having immediate medical help are slim to none. It is vital that divers, especially those involved in mixed gas diving activities have a clear and thorough understanding of decompression sickness (DCS) symptoms and predisposing conditions. Early recognition of DCS signs and symptoms and appropriate first responder care are key to the stricken diver's successful recovery. DCS is a statistical inevitability and must be accepted as an assumed risk of any diver. You can do everything exactly by the book and still get bent; hopefully, this is not news to anyone. In Gilliam's study (1989-90) of sport divers covering the customers of a large liveaboard dive/cruise ship, 71.4% of DCS cases he treated in the vessel's recompression chamber were diving within the limits of their diving tables. There is no guarantee that any table or computer is infallible.

CAUSES OF DCS

In a nutshell, improper decompression resulting in occlusive inert gas bubble formation is probably our major culprit in decompression sickness. Although some would argue to the contrary, most experts generally agree that ALL dives are decompression dives. Even ones without stage decompression obligations have ascent rates factored into their model as a means of decompression. Hopefully, divers are now routinely practicing slow ascents in the last two atmospheres (66 fsw to the surface) in conjunction with a recommended five minute "safety stop" around the 10-15 fsw level.

CONTRIBUTORY FACTORS TO DCS

Primary Direct Effects of Physics: Depth, time, rate of release (dive profile)

Secondary Effects, Inherent: Physical fitness and overall health condition, age, body fat level (obesity or extreme lean condition), height, muscular makeup, old injuries that may affect circulation etc. , theories of male versus female susceptibility.

Secondary Effects, External: Thermal conditions (cold water or excessively hot conditions), physical exertion during and after dive (elevated PCO_2 levels), constrictive equipment factors (tight wetsuit, binding straps etc.), improper hydration, smoking, alcohol use, drugs.

Equipment factors: Breathing regulators with excessive resistance, inaccuracies of depth gauges or watch, failure of dive computers.

Decompression Models: Use of invalidated tables, improper manipulation of tables for averaging or extrapolation etc., failure to compute repetitive dives correctly, improper decompression stops, compromised model or table through improper ascent rates, high altitude diving, use of extreme exposure tables, flying after diving.

Stress: Time pressure and task-loading.

There are many excellent reference texts cited in our bibliography that can provide a detailed subject treatment of the pathophysiology of decompression sickness and so only a brief review is offered in this section. We are more concerned with divers being able to recognize symptomotology effectively and react accordingly. Divers with a desire to delve deeper into the mechanisms of DCS are encouraged to access these separate materials.

At the surface, we are basically saturated with nitrogen at one atmosphere. As we descend breathing air or mixed gas in our scuba systems, pressure increases and the inert gas (nitrogen or helium) is dissolved and absorbed by the body's tissues and blood. The deeper we go, the more inert gas is "loaded". Theoretically, after a period of time (based upon the longest half-time utilized in the model) at any given depth, be it 60 fsw (18.2 m) or 600 fsw (181.8 m), we are saturated with all the inert gas we can hold and no further decompression obligation would be incurred no matter how long we stayed down. This is the basis of "saturation diving" theory where aquanauts are placed underwater in a bell or habitat to work for as much as a week or more and then decompressed when the project is finished.

As untethered free swimming-divers we do not have the luxury of saturation support equipment and we must come back to the surface. Herein lies the problem with the pesky inert gas we have absorbed (in-gassed or loaded) during our brief, by comparison, sojourn into the deep.

Remembering our diving history, we will recall that Haldane originally postulated his theory that our body could tolerate inert gas pressure up to twice that found normally at the surface. This 2:1 ratio became the basis of the earliest dive tables and accounted for the presumption that we could have unlimited bottom times at 33 fsw (10 m). However, as more research study was accomplished it became evident that his ratio theory was flawed and has since been modified to be expressed as approximately 1.58:1, a significant difference. In fact, authenticated DCS cases have been observed in divers at 18 fsw (5.5 m) after extended time periods.

Haldane offered other valuable principles of decompression that included the theory of exponential inert gas uptake that provided the basis of tissue half-times and compartment M values. We are now overwhelmed with new decompression models or algorithms that stem from Haldane's early work and go considerably farther in scope. Navy tables were developed assuming a 120 minute tissue/compartment as the slowest; we now see use of models that incorporate compartments with 689 minute half-times in dive computers and far longer in custom tables!

But all this was to serve the purpose of preventing bubble formation in the blood as pressure was decreased upon ascent. Haldane and other pioneers in DCS originally thought that no bubbles would form if their decompression models were followed. Through the use of modern Doppler devices it is now known that bubbles may exist on every dive. Such scanning is frequently employed to monitor divers during test criteria for new table development and as a benchmark of decompression stress. "Bubble trouble" as a term was first popularized by Rutkowski as a convenient catch-all for DCS and embolism manifestations. In our discussion, we are concerned with inert gas bubbles, of course, not air bubbles as would be the problem in lung overexpansion accidents typical of breath holding ascents.

Where these bubbles are located and their size will dictate the presentation of DCS symptoms.

SIGNS AND SYMPTOMS

Many texts distinguish DCS symptomotology into type I (pain only) or type II (serious symptoms, central nervous system involvement). To the layman or diver in the field, this distinction is not of great importance and requires special training in many instances to classify presentations. Most importantly we want our readers to be able to recognize any symptoms or signs of DCS and leave diagnosis and treatment selection to trained chamber staff or medical consultants. But what you do for the patient and the observations you can record and pass along to treatment personnel will be of significant aid to his ultimate hope of recovery.

Type I (Pain Only, Mild Symptoms):
- "Skin bends"- skin blotching or mottling of the skin producing a red or purplish-blue tinge.
- Itching similar to fiberglass irritation.
- Fatigue
- Indifference, personality or mood swings, irritable behavior, diver unaware of surroundings.
- Pain usually associated in or near a joint such as shoulder or knee. Onset may be gradual and may be transient (niggle).

Type II (CNS Involvement, etc.):
- CNS spinal and cranial abnormalities usually gradual in onset with initial subtle symptoms often masked by pain distractions.
- Cardiopulmonary symptoms are typically manifested by "chokes", a dry persistent non-productive cough. Cerebral symptoms may follow; all effects in this group should be considered life-threatening.
- Unusual fatigue
- Dizziness or "staggers", vertigo
- Numbness, paralysis, progressive loss of feeling in skin patches.
- Shortness of breath
- Unconsciousness, collapse, syncope
- Loss of bladder and bowel control, inability to urinate.
- Muscular weakness, poor grip, poor resistance to restraint of motion.
- Visual disturbances, inability to hear fingers rubbed close to ears etc.
- Headache
- Abdominal encircling pain or lower back pain precursor of overt spinal symptoms. Frequently this presentation is misdiagnosed as less serious Type I DCS.

- Convulsions
- Any symptoms developing while still underwater.

The alert diver will recognize that many of these symptoms are nearly identical to those of embolic event presentations. Since treatment and first aid are essentially the same, don't worry about the distinction. This list illustrates symptoms as categorized by Type I and Type II but consider all symptoms serious in the field.

One of the most frustrating aspects of sport divers and DCS is their stubborn denial of symptoms and failure to accept early treatment. This has historically led to the majority of sport diver accidents being unnecessarily delayed for treatment. Even divers that knew beyond a doubt that they were at risk from their profile and were presenting early symptoms have refused oxygen when readily available due to some perceived ego threat or for fear that fellow divers would think less of them. Others refuse to accept the possibility that DCS could be involved since "I can't be bent, I was within the limits of the tables".

Early recognition, reporting and treatment of DCS problems dramatically improves patient resolution prognosis. Bends can happen to anyone, it is no one's fault and should involve no "loss of face". Indeed, the prudent diver and his dive group should overtly encourage prompt relation of any ailment that even remotely resembles the symptoms list. Many divers may mistake DCS symptoms as muscle strains or limb numbness to sitting on it etc. **ALWAYS ERR ON THE SIDE OF CAUTION.** If you are suffering from DCS it is only going to get worse as symptoms are progressive. Don't wait to seek qualified help!

FIRST AID IN THE FIELD

Immediately give the patient oxygen for surface breathing. Many divers do not realize the importance of 100% O_2 administration and this can only be accomplished via a system incorporating a demand valve/mask (or by use of an oxygen-clean scuba system regulator connected to an oxygen cylinder). This seal should be tight fitting to insure the maximum level of O_2 delivered to the patient. Air leaks around the mask will dilute the percentage of O_2 (FO_2) inspired. Care must be taken to insure the integrity of the mask seal especially in male patients with beards or mustaches or any patient with facial wrinkles etc. As a rule of thumb, you want the mask seal to be good enough for the patient to breathe on his back underwater. Free flow oxygen systems, although still widely in use, are not recommended. Most free flow devices usually will not deliver 100% O_2 and are extremely wasteful of the gas.

Oxygen is administered primarily to help eliminate inert gas and reduce bubble size to some extent. By breathing pure O_2 at the surface, the blood's oxygen partial pressure is elevated dramatically. This provides a breathing media totally absent of the harmful inert gas, and establishes a steeper gradient across the tissue-bubble interface. This allows more efficient out-gassing of the occlusive nitrogen or helium, and also contributes to better oxygenation of the tissues where the bubble insult has occurred. Key to the outcome of this therapy is sufficient PO_2 (best accomplished by a 100% O_2 demand valve system) and adequate flow for delivery.

Many patients will relieve of symptoms simply by proper and immediate oxygen first aid techniques. Davis was a leading advocate of O_2 role's in field resolution and Gilliam's experience (1989-90) recorded 12 cases of symptomatic DCS that were completely relieved by 100% O_2 administration during transit of the patient to his chamber facility.

Training is available widely in oxygen administration. One of the first programs implemented was developed by EMT/dive instructor Jim Corry for NAUI and recently the Diver's Alert Network (DAN) has offered a similar course. Both programs are excellent and require between six and eight hours of hands on training in equipment, patient scenarios and theory. Most diving conferences and trade shows will usually offer such courses as a seminar and the benefits to divers are invaluable.

Until recently patient management included positioning the diver in either Trendelenberg (head down, legs bent at knees, left side tilted down) or Scoltetus (head down, legs straight). Recommendations from DAN in 1990 have modified this traditional advice to suggest use of simple supine positioning (patient lays flat on his back). Trendelenberg proved to be of little benefit except in the first 10-15 minutes of surfacing primarily in arterial gas embolism (AGE) cases, and the difficulty of maintaining this posture was not felt to be significantly beneficial.

Removal of the diver's wetsuit etc. is desirable but insure that he is kept warm and comfortable. Cover with blankets, towels or dry clothing. Observe for any "skin bends" symptoms. Continue administration of oxygen until delivered to medical care or supply is exhausted.

Oral fluids should be given if the patient is conscious. Regular drinking water or unsweetened apple juice in amounts of 12 to 16 ounces every 30 minutes will help keep the patient properly hydrated. This amount may require urination if transit is prolonged. This is a good sign and should be accommodated in the supine position. Inability to urinate may indicate more serious Type II manifestation. Such urinary retention will ultimately become quite painful. If the patient is unable to pass water within a reasonable time period, back off on continued administration of fluids.

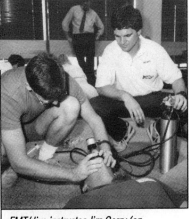

EMT/dive instructor Jim Corry (on right) developed one of the first training programs in oxygen administration. Derivatives of his original course are now taught all over the U.S. Photos by Pam Corry

Do not administer pain drugs other than two aspirin initially (aspirin has been shown to effect a decrease in platelet aggregation in the blood). Pain killers may mask other symptom development.

Be prepared to initiate CPR and rescue breathing if patient condition deteriorates. Mixed gas diving should automatically infer that the dive team as well as the surface support crew is well trained and well experienced in CPR techniques.

TRANSPORTATION

If you are shore diving, insure initial patient care and make sure victim is attended at all times. Hopefully, a properly planned dive will include a contingency list of medical professionals and the nearest recompression chamber facility. Call the chamber or hospital and advise them of the incoming patient. If they direct you to wait for an ambulance team, do so. Otherwise transport patient to the facility they designate and by their proscribed method, either vehicle or aircraft.

If at sea, call the Coast Guard via VHF radio or cellular phone. It may be necessary to relay messages through another vessel if sufficiently offshore that your radio cannot reach the mainland. Make certain that the Coast Guard knows that this emergency involves a diving accident victim and requires transportation to a recompression facility. At this point, they may direct you to proceed with your vessel to a designated port where assistance can meet you or they may decide to send an evacuation helicopter to intercept your vessel and extract the diver for faster transport (see opposite page).

It is incumbent upon divers to know what facilities are available to them in an emergency. This becomes particularly important if your trip is remotely located or out of the United States. Prior to leaving on that long-awaited dive vacation to the south Pacific or Caribbean inquire as to the availability of medical staff, chamber locations and medivac flights if required. You should also determine if the resort or liveaboard has 100% demand mask O_2 available on their boats; insist on it. If enough divers demand proper equipment it will finally be made standard practice. Most mixed gas divers will already have made facilities for both surface and underwater oxygen delivery systems. Always plan for a surplus of O_2 in case decompression needs to be extended or for post-dive therapy.

Call DAN to confirm chamber locations and readiness with listings of local addresses and phone numbers. Now is an excellent time to join DAN's diving insurance program which can cover your costs if treatment or medevac "life flight" is required. Costs of air ambulance, chamber time and medical staff can easily exceed $30,000 from a remote location. DAN's insurance is an inexpensive hedge against such a financial burden. Although not widely known by most divers in the high tech community, DAN insurance has no exclusions for either depth or breathing gases. Therefore, if you do get a DCS hit while breathing Trimix or Heliox at, say 400 fsw, your treatment is covered by their current policy as long as you are engaged in recreational diving. The key word here is "recreational". If you stray into the realm of "commercial" diving by definition, you are excluded. It is not considered commercial diving if a sport diving instructor is being paid professionally as will be the case in many mixed gas high tech operations conducted for training or simply for the personal satisfaction of exploration.

Many of the editorial commentary and published articles by DAN senior officials might appear to be "anti" high tech and mixed gas diving. In this author's opinion, the role of these professionals is to present a conservative posture that reflects their deep concern for diving safety as a whole. It's true that DAN has specifically recommended against the use of NITROX/EANx and mixed gases, but it's also nice to know that these same medical professionals are providing the best insurance available and are standing by 24 hours a day to assist in treatment should the need arise. DAN insurance should be a functional part of every diver's "equipment". If you don't have it already, sign up today. Call 919-684-8111. You simply cannot afford to be without this coverage.

HELICOPTER PROCEDURES

1. Post lookout to watch for chopper's arrival on scene.
2. Attempt to establish radio communication via VHF ch. 16
3. Maintain vessel speed at 10 to 15 knots if possible. Pilot will count on your constant speed for his approach. Do not slow down or stop.
4. Assume a course that places your vessel with the prevailing wind approximately 20 degrees on port bow. If wind is calm or insignificant, maintain course to shore.
5. Lower antennas, masts, flag staffs etc. that could interfere with chopper's deployment of uplifting device.
6. Secure all loose objects and equipment on decks. Prop wash from rotorblades can be severe.
7. Do not touch the lift device or cable until it has touched the deck of your vessel and grounded. Electric shock can result otherwise.
8. Have patient wear life jacket. If available, also give him smoke flare for day or night flare if dark. This will help find the patient if he falls out of the basket or if it is dropped. Have lookout watch patient until secure inside chopper. If patient goes into sea, follow man-overboard drill immediately. Have crew member ready to go overboard to rescue patient and establish buoyancy. Swift action and anticipation of contingencies are vital to insure patient's survival.
9. Secure patient in basket (stretcher) via provided harness or tie in with seizing line; ideally with quick release knots that patient can access if necessary.
10. If patient cannot communicate or is unconscious, fasten (duct tape, safety pin etc.) as much information about his condition, dive profile, name, age, address, next of kin, emergency phone numbers etc. as possible. If he was diving on a computer send it with him. Make note of tables utilized to acquire profile etc.
11. Advise or reconfirm that patient is diving victim and requires evacuation to recompression facility.
12. If patient dies while chopper is en route, inform flight crew or Coast Guard operator. This may prevent a needless heroic effort at rescue by the flight crew, if bad weather was a factor.

RECOMPRESSION CHAMBERS

Many divers have seen a chamber either in photographs or in real life, but very few have ever had occasion to be in one unless they were being treated. As a result a certain "mystique has developed about chambers and many divers regard them as hostile and menacing environments. Briefly, we would like to acquaint our readers with the realities of these important devices.

Generally, chambers are divided into two categories: **recompression chambers** (used for the treatment of diving related injuries and other ailments) and **decompression chambers** (used for surface or deck decompression facilities so the working diver can be removed from the water and complete decom obligation in a dry and controlled situation)

Both of these units are also properly referred to as "hyperbaric chambers", meaning that the pressure inside will be higher than normal atmospheric pressure. These elevated pressures are usually expressed in feet of seawater (fsw) just as if we were diving in the ocean. Air pressure is introduced to the chamber to raise its internal pressure and begin the "dive". We can then use these chambers to treat DCS or AGE cases, conduct "dry" surface decompression schedules, or simulate dives for research purposes.

In Hospital situations, the role of hyperbaric medicine has been recognized as a speciality wherein victims of such injuries as crush wounds, burns, skin grafts, gangrene and carbon monoxide poisoning are treated with oxygen in large climate- controlled chambers. These typically are able to accommodate as many as 18 patients at once, have hatches shaped and sized like conventional doors, are equipped with air conditioning and humidity controls and even piped in music.

In the field, things are just a little bit different. Forget the creature comforts and get prepared for close quarters. Although a well set up field chamber can provide the same therapeutic benefits to a stricken diver, they are substantially smaller in most cases.

Field chambers range in size typically from 48 inches in diameter to 72 inches and are usually made of steel. In the past, monoplace chambers were in common use in commercial diving theatres and were designed to pressurize one patient in a single cylinder. This did not allow an inside tender to attend the patient and therefore he was pretty much on his own once treatment was initiated. Rarely will these chambers be encountered today. Most will be variations on the multi-place (more than one patient or tender) multi-lock (two or more pressure compartments with sealing hatches). These allow several divers to be treated at once with an inside tender to monitor their condition. Medical equipment or relief staff can be "locked" into or

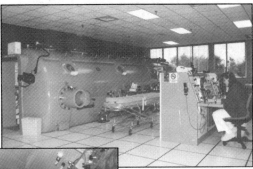

Our Lady of the Lake Hyperbaric facility is typical of large hospital-based treatment chambers. Note the "door" style entrance hatch and remote control operator panel to regulate pressure and gases within the chamber. Located in Baton Rouge, LA. Photo by Rock Palermoo

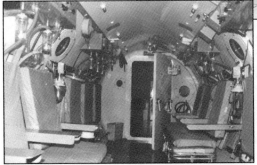

Interior of Our Lady of the Lake chamber showing spacious main treatment lock capable of handling up to a dozen patients comfortably. Photo by Rock Palermo

out of the chamber by use of the outer lock which can be pressurized to equal the treatment inner lock and subsequently depressurized to travel back to the surface pressure.

From the outside of the chamber, the supervisor can control the depth of the dive or treatment schedule and choose what gases will be supplied to the occupants. Pressurization is accomplished with standard AIR but most modern treatments call for oxygen therapy beginning at 60 fsw (18.2 m and 2.8 ATA). NITROX mixes of 50/50 (N_2/O_2) or 60/40 (N_2/O_2) are commonly used deeper than 60 fsw instead of AIR to lesson narcosis and safely keep the O_2 partial pressures within tolerance ranges. Both O_2 and NITROX therapy gases are delivered to the patient or tender via BIBS (built-in-breathing-system) masks similar to aviator oxygen masks.

The chamber supervisor monitors his gauges that are calibrated to display pressure in fsw graduations. He also has an oxygen analyzer plumbed into the chamber to monitor the inside environment's O_2 percentage. Due to fire hazards, this percentage of O_2 (FO_2) will not be allowed to exceed 25%. Most BIBS are set up with "overboard dumps" that exhaust the expired oxygen outside the chamber to prevent the rapid rise of the FO_2. However, it is common to have some leakage of masks due to improper fit etc. and O_2 will be leaking into the chamber from this source. As the supervisor sees the FO_2 approach the 25% level he will institute a chamber "vent"

Dick Rutkowski's Hyperbarics International field chamber in Key Largo, Fl used for training medical and diving staff in recompression protocols. Photo by Bret Gilliam

where the inner lock is flushed with AIR by inputting pressure and simultaneously exhausting the incoming air from an outflow valve. This scrubs the chamber of excess O_2 and also cools and refreshes the atmosphere.

The supervisor is assisted by an outside operator and a record/time keeper who logs all stages of the treatment. They can communicate with the inner occupants via a low voltage radio or sound-powered phone handset to discuss patient status or to confer on treatment procedures.

Inside the chamber, the patient will either lie in a supine position or sit up with the legs outstretched while leaning back against the chamber wall. A fire retardant mattress is usually provided or bunks may be hung from the chamber sides. Medical equipment, or fluids etc. may be passed inside via a medical lock (small hatch door compartment usually about 12 inches in diameter) or through the same outer lock that accommodates staff transfers.

A patient is cleaned of all oils such as sun tan lotions or chap sticks and he is given fire retardant clothing to wear. This further reduces the chance of fire.

Old style monoplace chamber, vintage 1958. This unit was the first chamber used on Cozumel, Mexico for treatment of divers. It used air as both compression and therapy gas and the typical treatment lasted as much as 48 hours! The occupant could not communicate with the operator except by eye contact and was unable to change his position or even move his arms comfortably. Bret Gilliam and local divemaster are shown for size comparison. Photo by Lynn Henrickson

CHAMBER DIVES

As the chamber is pressurized with AIR, the occupants will immediately sense the pressure change in their ears and the equalization techniques will be necessary. Usually the outside operator will observe through signal from the inside tender that all occupants are clearing comfortably. If problems occur and someone is slow to clear, descent is stopped until rectified. Remember that our patient needs to get down to 60 fsw as quickly as possible to begin treatment so in many cases the dive is conducted as fast as the occupants can equalize. In cases where severe DCS symptoms are present and the patient cannot clear, the ear drum may be punctured by the inside tender to allow the dive to continue, (a ruptured ear drum will heal, DCS may not).

During the dive it gets quite noisy inside as air pressure is introduced and protective ear muffs are provided for occupants. It also gets hot! Compression of the air atmosphere rapidly raises the temperature inside the inner lock to nearly 100 + degrees F. in tropical locations. Newcomers will be surprised to notice the high pitched speech caused by the increased air density. This becomes more pronounced and distracting as depth increases. In deep treatments, as in Table 6A at 165 fsw, speech even between staff members is discouraged if the chamber environment is AIR. The altered voice effects can stimulate narcosis in less experienced tenders or ones with less adaptive time at chamber depths. Once reaching treatment depth the chamber will be aggressively vented to flush out the stale, hot, humid air and replace it with fresh. The patient will be breathing O_2 via BIBS mask in 20 minute intervals with five minute "air breaks" where the mask is removed and chamber AIR is breathed.

Air breaks are provided for the patient's comfort and to allow him recovery time from breathing pure oxygen for prolonged periods. At any time during treatment if symptoms of chronic (whole body) or CNS O_2 toxicity are noted, the tender will suspend BIBS mask breathing and provide a 15 minute air break. This time is not counted as part of the treatment table. After this rest, the schedule is resumed on BIBS O_2. Standard treatment Table 5 is two hours and 15 minutes long and Table 6 is four hours and 45 minutes long. Extensions may be added to Tables at the supervisor's discretion.

Table 5 is reserved for the less serious, pain-only bends while Table 6 is used for more serious DCS involvement and pain-only bends that is not relieved in the first ten minutes of O_2 breathing at 60 fsw. Most chamber supervisors will now go directly to Table 6 in treating sport divers. This is due to the fact that upon close neurological examination of patients it has been found that pain only symptoms frequently masked or distracted from

Recompression chamber supervisor Bret Gilliam operates Ocean Tech chamber aboard diving ship. Note treatment tables and patient flow charts in rear. Photo by Lynn Hendrickson.

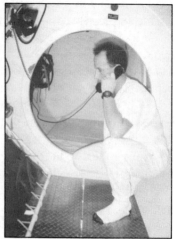

Inside patient tender communicates with chamber supervisor on "sound-powered" phone. Note that Tender wears fire retardant hospital scrubs and static free slippers. Ocean Tech 60" field chamber. Photo by Bret Gilliam.

the more severe but less compelling (in the patient's mind) Type II symptoms of numbness etc.

The more immediate treatment is instituted, the better the chances of complete recovery.

During treatment, the ascent phases will be marked by the chamber dramatically cooling as the pressure is reduced. In many instances, the air will become so humid that a dense mist is formed, almost like being in a cloud. The mist can be irritating to the throat if inhaled and cause coughing or choking so breathing is always done through the nose. If coughing etc. develops, the ascent will be stopped to avoid the hazard of embolism.

Training is available in chamber operations and medical support from several sources (see appendix). Some facilities offer seminars designed for sport divers to learn more about chambers and afford the opportunities to make actual chamber dives. The Catalina chamber sponsors such programs and Gilliam (1989-90) developed a PADI/NAUI certification program in Accident Management/Recompression Chambers that included patient handling and first aid, O_2 administration, symptom recognition and two chamber dives. Almost two thousand sport divers went through this training during that period aboard the dive/cruise ship Ocean Spirit.

Table 6

TABLE 6—MINIMAL RECOMPRESSION, OXYGEN BREATHING METHOD FOR TREATMENT OF DECOMPRESSION SICKNESS AND GAS EMBOLISM

1. Use—treatment of decompression sickness when oxygen can be used and symptoms are not relieved within 10 minutes at 60 feet. Patient breathes oxygen from the surface.

2. Descent rate—25 ft/min.

3. Ascent rate—1 ft/min. Do not compensate for slower ascent rates. Compensate for faster rates by halting the ascent.

4. Time at 60 feet—begins on arrival at 60 feet.

5. If oxygen breathing must be interrupted, allow 15 minutes after the reaction has entirely subsided and resume schedule at point of interruption.

6. Tender breathes air throughout. If treatment is a repetitive dive for the tender or tables are lengthened, tender should breathe oxygen during the last 30 minutes of ascent to the surface.

Depth (feet)	Time (minutes)	Breathing Media	Total Elapsed Time (minutes)
60	20	Oxygen	20
60	5	Air	25
60	20	Oxygen	45
60	5	Air	50
60	20	Oxygen	70
60	5	Air	75
60 to 30	30	Oxygen	105
30	15	Air	120
30	60	Oxygen	180
30	15	Air	195
30	60	Oxygen	255
30 to 0	30	Oxygen	285

TABLE 6 DEPTH/TIME PROFILE

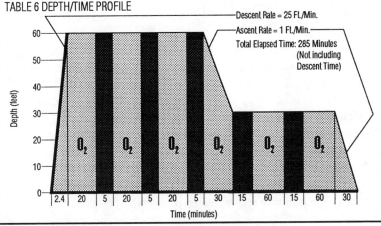

Descent Rate = 25 Ft./Min.

Ascent Rate = 1 Ft./Min.

Total Elapsed Time: 285 Minutes (Not including Descent Time)

Table 5 is reproduced graphically below for information only.

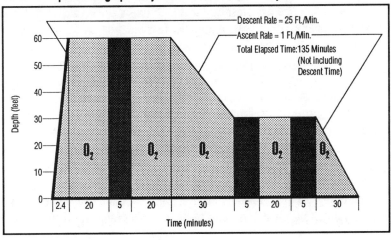

Descent Rate = 25 Ft./Min.

Ascent Rate = 1 Ft./Min.

Total Elapsed Time: 135 Minutes (Not including Descent Time)

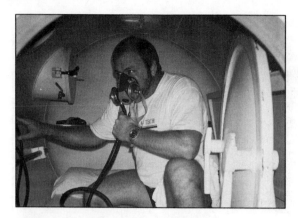

Chamber occupant
breathing on BIBS
mask in inner lock of
field chamber.
Photo by Steve Furber

QUALIFICATION OF DCS

When a patient is presented to a chamber facility, the diver medical technician (DMT) or chamber supervisor will want to perform a gross physical and neurological examination to list the diver victim's symptoms. There is a protocol for rapid neurological exams that can be done in five minutes (**see procedure in box**). In severe cases, the exam will be done in the chamber if the patient's condition precludes further delay. The DMT will note the patient's deficits and observe that many of them may fall in our symptom list. However, that alone does not qualify our patient as a confirmed DCS case.

Confirmation or qualification of DCS is accomplished by a Test of Pressure. The patient is recompressed to a depth of 60 fsw (2.8 ATA) and put on O_2 via BIBS mask for a twenty minute breathing period. If pain, paralysis, weakness etc. is relieved or improved during this Test of Pressure breathing period it is presumed that DCS exists and is the source of the patient's problems. Similarly, if no relief is noted then DCS is not considered a factor in the patient's ailment.

This distinction is important since divers can manifest symptoms that would be very similar to DCS from other problems including muscle strains from lifting gear or an idiosyncratic reaction to medication. This Test of Pressure confirms whether further recompression therapy would benefit the patient. Applying this test has proven to be nearly 100% reliable.

During the period of the Test of Pressure a determination will be made as to what the appropriate Treatment Table applies. This is determined by the time factor involved for the relief of symptoms and the seriousness of symptom presentation. Patients resolving in ten minutes or less have historically been treated on Table 5. If resolution takes longer or if any Type II symptoms were initially presented, a Table 6 is chosen. This is a judgement call and the current trend is more towards committing to a Table 6 regardless of time factor resolution. Experienced field chamber supervisors such as Rutkowski, Gilliam and Mount (1991) all suggest application of Table 6 if DCS diagnosis is made.

You may then ask: what about the patient who manifests symptoms, reports promptly and relieves after O_2 administration during transit? Opinion is divided on this issue. If the patient is unsymptomatic and a Test of Pressure does not confirm DCS at that time, can they be considered a bends case?

Unquestionably, patients have had DCS and been relieved by O_2 breathing. This only confirms the importance and validity of aggressive O_2 use in first aid. If transportation from a remote site involving significant financial cost is a consideration, we recommend close observation and suspension of diving activities. However, if a field chamber is readily available and the diver's profile would seem to have put them at risk, we recommend treatment to be administered at least to the extent of Table 5. It can't hurt the patient, and may provide a safety net for recurrent symptoms.

An interesting observation is offered here for the reader's consideration. Can you get bent free-diving (breath hold diving)? Most divers would answer no. But there is no requirement that you breathe compressed air from a scuba tank to manifest DCS. The malady is dependent on time and depth primarily and therefore expert breath hold divers can, in exceptional diving circumstances, place themselves within a window of vulnerability.

Competitive spearfishermen, South Pacific native working free-divers and Japanese ama. divers are most at risk. Typically, these divers can attain relatively deep depths (80 to 130 fsw) for up to three minutes bottom time. Their profiles reflect an average to rapid ascent followed by a "working" period at depth. Ascents are rapid, sometimes assisted by buoyant apparatus. Considerable exertion may be expended on the dive if the diver must struggle to land a large fish or to swim objects off the bottom.

Originally, little serious consideration was given to the prospects of free-divers falling victim to bends hits, but with Bob Croft's dramatic 240 fsw breath hold dive in 1968 some discussions were prompted. Dives exceeding four minutes had already been recorded and anecdotal accounts of longer breath hold dives were in circulation. A 1962 National Geographic article recounts the diving style of a South Pacific diver: "A man from the Tuamotos who at 59 years old went to 100 feet as many as 50 times a day summed up his attitude toward this skill, It is nothing... I have big lungs and a strong body. It is my work.' Two minutes, three, four... a long time if your are holding your breath, but what if you are trying to follow a fish?"

FIVE MINUTE NEUROLOGICAL EXAM (as recommended by DAN)

Examination of a victim's central nervous sustem soon after an accident may provide valuable information to the physician or chamber supervisor responsible for treatment. The Five Minute Neuro Exam is easily learned and performed by individuals with no medical experience at all.

The examination can be done step-by-step while reading from this text. Perform the steps in order, and record the time and results.

1. Orientation
- Does the diver know name and age?
- Does the diver know present location?
- Does the diver know what time, day or year it is?
- Even though a diver appears alert, the answers to these questions may reveal confusion. Do not omit them!

2. Eyes
- Have the diver count the number of fingers you display using two or three different numbers. Check each eye separately and then together. Have the diver identify a distant object.
- Tell the diver to hold head still, or you gently hold it still, while placing your other hand abouty 18 inches in front of the face. Ask the diver to follow you hand with his eyes. Then move your hand up and down, then side to side. The diver's eyes should smoothly follow your hand and should not jerk to one side and return. Check that pupils are equal in size.

3. Face
- Ask the diver to whistle. Look carefully to see that both sides of the face have the same expression while whistling. Ask the diver to grit the teeth. Feel the jaw muscles to confirm that they are contracted equally.
- Instruct the diver to close the eyes while you lightly touch your fingertips across the forehead and face to be sure sensation is present and the same everywhere.

4. Hearing
- Hearing can be evaluated by holding your hand about two feet from the diver's ear and rubbing your thumb and finger together. Check both ears, moving your hand closer until the diver hears it. Check several times and confirm with your own hearing. If the surroundings are noisy, the test is difficult to evaluate. Ask bystanders to be quiet and turn off unneeded machinery.

5. Swallowing Reflex
- Instruct the diver to swallow while you watch the "Adam's apple" to be sure that it moves up and down.

6. Tongue

• Instruct the diver to stick out the tongue. It should come out straight in the middle of the mouth without deviating to either side.

7. Muscle Strength

• Instruct the diver to shrug the shoulders while you bear down on them to observe for equal muscle strength.

• Check the diver's arms by bringing the elbows up level with the shoulders, hands level with the arms, and touching the chest. Instruct the diver to resist while you pull the arms away, push them back, up and down. The strength should be approximately equal in both arms in each direction. Check leg strength by having the diver lie flat and raise and lower the legs while you gently resist the movement.

8. Sensory Perception

• Check on both sides by touching as done on the face. Start at the top of the body and compare sides while moving downwards to cover the entire body. The diver's eyes should be closed during this procedure. The diver should confirm the sensation in each area before you move to another area.

9. Balance and Coordination

• Be prepared to protect the diver from injury when performing this test. Have the diver stand up with feet together, close eyes and stretch out arms. The diver should be able to maintain balance if the platform is stable. Your arms should be around, but not touching the diver. Be prepared to catch the diver who starts to fall.

• Check coordination by having the diver move and index finger back and forth rapidly between the diver's nose and your finger held approximately 18 inches from the diver's face. Instruct the diver to slide the heel of one foot down the shin of the other leg. The diver should be lying down when attempting this test.

• Check these tests on both right and left sides and observe carefully for unusual clumsiness on either side.

SUMMARY

• The diver's condition may prevent the perfomance of one or more of these tests. Record any omitted test and the reason. If any of the tests are not normal, injury to the nervous system should be suspected. The tests should be repeated at frequent intervals while awaiting assistance to determine if any change occurs. Report the results to the emergency medical personnel if attendance at the chamber or responding to your call.

• Good diving safety habits would include praticing this examination on normal divers to become proficient in the test.

Surprisingly, no correlation between deep breath hold dives and symptomatic DCS was made in many cases. In National Geographic's 1980 book *Exploring the Deep Frontier* the authors relate rather naively," Oxygen deprivation much longer (than four minutes)... can be damaging or fatal. In the Tuamotos, those who make successive, lengthy dives to great depths, risk a condition they call *taravana* , a sickness that includes vertigo, nausea, partial or complete paralysis, and unconsciousness." Don't these symptoms have something of a familiar ring to them? A quick glance through the DCS symptom list should provide some easy match-ups.

Competitive free-diving spearfishermen in the Virgin Islands in the early seventies experimented with wearing the old Scubapro/SOS decom meter during prolonged diving days with interesting results.

Many were able to advance the analog needle almost into the "red zone", indicating required decompression, while diving in 100+ fsw depths. During this same era, in St. Croix commercial lobster diver Sam Espinosa presented himself to Bret Gilliam for evaluation after suffering from numbness, exceptional fatigue and joint stiffness following his diving day. "I did a neurological examination on him and confirmed that his symptoms were progressively worsening. I was convinced he was bent. He told me that he had been diving since sun rise between 90 and 110 feet deep and stopped just before dark. It was only after I started to record his actual dive profiles and surface intervals, that I realized he was free-diving!" Espinosa responded well to a thirty minute breathing period on pure oxygen from a demand regulator and declined recompression treatment. When questioned further by Gilliam, he said several of his fellow lobster divers had similar episodes.

Admittedly, it takes an exceptional diver to get bent holding his breath but it obviously does happen. Readers are cautioned about deep breath hold diving following aggressive scuba diving activities. Dive instructor Scott Valerga of Virgin Gorda had made repetitive scuba dives in 1978 while taking tourist divers on scuba tours. When he was unable to free his anchor following the last dive, he made several dives to 90 feet holding his breath to break out the anchor. Within minutes after getting back on board, he was symptomatic of DCS. His previous diving schedule was within the limits of the Navy tables but with little safety margin. He was treated in the St. Croix recompression chamber operated by NOAA's *Hydrolab* facility with full recovery.

PORTABLE CHAMBERS

Recent advances in light weight low pressure designs have resulted in a practical portable field chamber that can actually be transported in two hand carried cases easily stowed in a van or dive vessel. Weighing around

160 pounds for the pressure tube and control panel, this unique package allows for a patient to be placed under pressure immediately in the field, blown down to 60 fsw with a patient O_2 BIBS mask including overboard dump, and then the entire unit evacuated to a full size field chamber of hospital based unit. Procedure for patient transfer without decompression is simple: put the portable chamber inside the treatment chamber and remove the patient after pressures are equalized.

This unit was first introduced in 1989 by SOS Ltd. of England and is called the HYPERLITE. The chamber is constructed of a remarkable seamless, flexible tube of Kevlar encapsulated in a silicone rubber matrix. Dimensions are seven feet long, 23 inches wide and weighs 88 pounds, approximately. Obviously, it was designed for one occupant but its value as a method of patient stabilization during transport is unquestionable.

End panels are placed in the tube with control pressure hoses equipped with non-return valves in the patient's foot end. Pressurization is accomplished by scuba tanks while O_2 is supplied from an included oxygen cylinder. Options include a portable O_2 analyzer and CO_2 monitor. Working chamber depth is slightly in excess of 60 fsw so it is compatible with standard Treatment Table depths.

The SOS Hyperbaric Portable field chamber showing control panel in case and scuba tank/ oxygen cylinders for pressurized and therapy gas respectively. Photo by SOS Ltd.

The SOS Hyperbaric chamber can be easily carried by four persons and used in the remotest site conditions. It can be winched aboard a helicopter for patient evacuation or can conduct an entire treatment in the field. Photo by SOS Ltd.

If a formal treatment facility is accessible, the unit can be transported via land conveyance or by boat, or even winched aboard a helicopter. If in a remote site, the HYPERLITE can effectively conduct a full Treatment Table 6 on its own assuming enough O_2 is on hand for therapy gas and enough scuba tanks are available for pressurization and venting.

This innovative product would seem to be an affordable option for remote diving in exotic locations or carried as emergency aboard a liveaboard dive vessel. Dive clubs or expedition groups should contact the manufacturer at the address below; price in mid-1991 was approximately $28,000: SOS LTD., Box 328, London NW7 3JS, England (phone: 081-959-4517)

IN-WATER RECOMPRESSION

Now we enter an area of major controversy. Ask any hyperbaric expert or chamber supervisor their feelings on in-the-water recompression and you will get an almost universal recommendation against such a practice. The logistics of attempting to manage equipment for sufficient gas supply, thermal protection for the patient, marine life considerations etc. not to mention the hazards of patient management all basically add up to a grim scenario. Most divers will not be equipped to handle even the compressed air requirements for an air Treatment Table which can last over six hours. And air is the *least* effective recompression gas; in fact such efforts could lead to worsening the patient's condition by loading him up further with nitrogen and subjecting him to debilitating cold even in tropical conditions.

A shade of gray is introduced if the dive team has access to surface supplied oxygen in adequate quantity. Rutkowski (1991) recommends that oxygen not be used deeper than 45 fsw (13.6 m) and only then in an extreme emergency. He would prefer a long "soak" at 30 fsw (9.1 m) on O_2 in 20 minute cycles with five minute air breaks. Ideally, O_2 should be delivered via a full face mask. The author emphasizes that this is not a blueprint for divers to follow, but represents a discussion of worst case scenarios where evacuation is not a practical or realistic possibility.

There are protocols for in-water recompression therapy in existence primarily with tables developed by the Australians. Missionary EMT Jack Thompson had surprisingly good results with custom therapy in-water tables in Roatan before a chamber was available and both Mount and Gilliam have successfully conducted in-water proprietary oxygen tables on patients with full resolution.

The decision must, of course, ultimately be made based upon personal circumstances and training. However, when faced with no alternative such extreme practices may present a choice. The author does not sanction or endorse in-water techniques and they are presented here for discussion purposes only. The following table outlines the procedures for in-water decompression following the Australian method.

AUSTRALIAN IN-WATER TREATMENT TABLES
(From Diving and Subaquatic Medicine)

Notes: This technique may be useful in treating cases of decompression sickness in localities remote from recompression facilities. It may also be of use while suitable transport to such a center is being arranged. In planning, it should be realized that the therapy may take up to three hours. The risks of cold, immersion and other environmental factors should be balanced against the beneficial effects. The diver must be accompanied by an attendant.

SHORT OXYGEN TABLE

DEPTH (meters)	ELAPSED TIME (in Min.) Mild	Serious	RATE OF ASCENT
9	030-060	060-090	
8	042-072	072-102	
7	054-084	084-114	
6	066-096	096-126	
5	078-108	108-138	12 Minutes
4	090-120	120-150	Per Meter
3	102-132	132-162	(4 min./ft)
2	114-144	144-174	
1	126-156	156-186	

Total Table time is 126 minutes to 156 minutes for mild cases and 156 minutes to 186 minutes for serious cases.

Equipment
1. Full face mask with demand valve and surface supply system OR helmet with free flow.
2. Adequate supply of 100% oxygen for the patient and air for the attendant.
3. Wet suit or dry suit for thermal protection.
4. Shot with at least 10 meters of rope (a seat or harness may be rigged to the shot.
5. Some form of communication system between patient, attendant and surface.

Method

1. The patient is lowered on the shot rope to nine meters breathing 100% oxygen.
2. Ascent is commenced after 30 minutes in mild cases, 60 minutes in severe cases, if improvement has occurred. These times may be extended to 60 minutes and 90 minutes respectively if there is no improvement.
3. Ascent is at the rate of one meter every 12 minutes.
4. If symptoms recur, remain at depth a further 30 minutes before continuing ascent.
5. If oxygen supply is exhausted, return to the surface rather have the patient breathe air.
6. After surfacing, the patient should be given one hour on oxygen, one hour off, for a further 12 hours.

U.S. NAVY METHOD

The U.S. Navy has another alternative protocol as detailed below:

"If the command has 100% oxygen-rebreathers available and individuals at the dive site trained in their use, the following in-water recompression procedure may be used instead of Table 1A:

1. Put the stricken diver on the rebreather and have him purge the apparatus at least three times with oxygen.
2. Descend to a depth of 30 feet with a stand-by diver.
3. Remain at 30 feet, at rest, for 60 minutes for Type I symptoms and 90 minutes for Type II symptoms. Ascend to 20 feet after 90 minutes even if symptoms are still present.
4. Decompress to the surface by taking 60 minute stops at 20 feet and 10 feet.
5. After surfacing, continue breathing 100% oxygen for an additional three hours."

(U.S. Navy Diving Manual, Vol. One, Section 8.11.2, D)

This method can be easily adapted to full facemask diving systems or surface supplied oxygen. However, it requires a substantial amount of oxygen to be available, both for the in-water treatment and subsequent surface breathing period. If either the Australian or U.S. Navy method is considered as a "last resort" procedure, take care to provide the diver with appropriate thermal protection (dry suit preferred, wet suit with hot water hose etc.), safety diver in attendance at all times, and track the OTU/UPTD count from the prior dives and treatment period. Seek protected water location before beginning treatment. Diver should be supplied regular drinking water for hydration during treatment; this may be accommodated simply by flexible containers with integral "straws" with removable stoppers.

Air in-water recompression treatment tables are not discussed in this text for two reasons: the very strong possibility that a diver's condition could be worsened, and the requirements for available gas to conduct such treatments is probably beyond the operational and logistical planning capabilities of the dive team.

SUMMARY

With good diving practices and some luck you may never need to see the inside of a recompression chamber. But it is more than likely that you will encounter a DCS incident during your career for another diver. Remember, prompt treatment is vital. Administer oxygen by demand valve mask, if conscious provide oral fluids, do not give pain killing drugs and transport victim by fastest available method to a recompression chamber facility.

We strongly encourage signing up for a dive insurance program, like DAN, as well.

Help promote recognition of DCS symptoms and prompt reporting. Denial of DCS problems is not macho, it is foolish. As elaborated throughout this text, proper training and education are vital factors in any dive planning. A conscious effort by all divers, not just those who push the envelope, will ultimately improve our sport and help to lay the foundation of greater adventures for future generations.

REFERENCES

Waite, Charles; *Case Histories of Diving and Hyperbaric Accidents*, UHMS

DAN Underwater Diving Accident Manual, Divers Alert Network (1985)

Gilliam, Bret; *Diving Accident Management Field Guide: O2 Ad ministration and Recompression Therapy*, Ocean Tech Publications

Bove & Davis; *Diving Medicine*, Grove and Stratton, Inc.

Edmonds, Lowery, Pennegather; *Diving and Subaquactic Medicine*, Best Publishing, Co.

Corry, James; *Emergency Oxygen Administration and Field Management of Scuba Diving Accidents*, NAUI Publications

Daugherty, Gordon C.; *Field Guide For the Diver Medic*, Best Publishing, Co.

Rutkowski, Richard; *Recompression Chamber Life Support Manual*, Hyperbarics Int'l.

Shilling, Carlston, and Mathias; *The Physician's Guide to Diving Medicine*, Plenum Press

Gilliam, Bret; *Deep Diving: An Advanced Guide to Physiology, Procedures and Systems*, Watersport Publishing

Gilliam, Bret; *Evaluation of Decompression Sickness Incidence in Multi-day Repetitive Diving for 77,680 Sport Dives*, Proceedings of the 1991 Repetitive Diving Conference, American Academy of Underwater Sciences

U.S. Navy Diving Manual, Volume One, revision 1, June 1985, NAVSEA 0994-LP-001-9010

CHAPTER 11

DECOMPRESSION MANAGEMENT
Dealing With DCS Denial

Decompression sickness (DCS) or "bends" is a statistical inevitability in diving. It has no conscience and rarely abides by any set rules. Although we can identify certain predisposing factors to DCS in divers generically, it is still impossible to explain the exact mechanisms of physiology that allows one diver to be bent while his partner escapes unscathed. It is best that divers, particularly those in the high-tech community, accept that DCS hits will eventually occur and take steps to deal with treatment responsibly.

What concerns many of us in the business of treating divers is the unfortunate mindset that somehow has developed with the sport diving population that consistently denies the possibility of DCS. Indeed, a certain stigma to reporting symptoms has developed and this trend flies in the face of all common sense and logic. Why would any intelligent adult ignore symptoms with the knowledge that DCS manifestations are progressive in nature... they get worse with time. Further, any delays in reporting symptoms and seeking treatment only contribute to a poorer prognosis for recovery.

Historically, denial of symptoms and treatment delays are the rule in sport diver DCS injuries rather than the exception. The emerging high-tech diver community hopefully will be pivotal in reversing this "head in the sand" mentality. We have to remove the stigma of "blame" that is so improperly associated with DCS reporting. It is no one's fault that they got bent; a diver can play everything in his dive plan precisely by the book and still get hit. Likewise, a deliberately high risk dive profile may not produce

Dive partners should realistically evaluate actual depth/time profiles following diving in conjunction with assessing even minor symptoms of DCS. It's best to err on the side of caution. Photo by Bret Gilliam

symptoms. The point here is diving leaders have to stop pointing fingers and using antiquated analogies ("he screwed up and he got bent, the idiot!") or continued reluctance to report symptoms will prevail.

Almost all of us know individuals who have surfaced after a dive and exhibited various DCS symptoms but steadfastly refused further evaluation or even basic first aid such as surface oxygen by demand valve/mask. It's not macho to attempt to "tough-out" shoulder pain or progressive numbness: it's just plain stupid.

In the working and commercial diver ranks an entirely different attitude prevails. Divers are trained to report symptoms as soon as possible and the attitude of diving supervisors is one of accident "containment" not accident "crisis" as in many sport diving situations. Bends is regarded as an occupational hazard that will occasionally take place and commercial operators and the more progressive sport diving facilities regard DCS as a manageable scenario. For the best outcome, divers and chamber supervisors work in a partnership of honest reporting of even slight symptoms with prompt evaluation and treatment.

Until recently, there were few operational recompression chambers in remote resort sites and divers who manifested DCS symptoms were faced with expensive medivac transportation and significant delays even in the best of circumstances. Possibly as a result of this, many so-called "experts" were prone to overly broad condemnations of sport divers who got bent and this attitude only contributed to diver denial. Negative peer pressure and professional loss of face proved to be powerful influences on divers to ignore DCS symptoms in the mistaken hope that they would somehow get better without treatment. Rarely was this the case, however.

Most chamber supervisors that I have known in my career feel that if DCS is promptly reported and evaluated with ensuing on-site treatment, then the prognosis for complete resolution is excellent. The attitude of many commercial diver medics and chamber operators is "No matter what the problem, if reported and treated quickly, we can clean the diver up". Type I DCS (mild symptoms, pain only) affords less risk than Type II DCS (serious symptoms, central nervous system involvement) but in either presentation aggressive oxygen therapy and prompt recompression has produced nearly a 98% success record. Many academicians find fault with the commercial operators' confidence in resolution of symptoms but their track record is enviable.

In March of 1991, I was an invited speaker at the joint DAN/AAUS/ NOAA Multi-day Repetitive Diving Workshop held at Duke University. For the first time, this conference included representatives from the sport, commercial, scientific and "high tech" diving communities assembled to compare notes on actual DCS incidence rates in the field. Some interesting statistical patterns developed as the workshop unfolded. The overall incidence of DCS for commercial divers was (approximately) 1 in 1000 dives, for the sport divers it was one in 10,000 dives and the scientific diving community rated an extreme low of one in 100,000 dives. Sampling from the "high tech" segment was too low to be realistically tallied.

With this rather startling multiplier of 10 between groups, it would be tempting to draw the too obvious conclusion that the scientific diving group is 100 times safer than the commercial diving group. Actually, the incidence rates are interesting for discussion purposes but do not reflect much data to produce true comparisons of relative dive safety vis-a-vis DCS risk. Rather, a clearer pattern of diving "attitude" was defined. Discussion of what an acceptable rate of DCS would be provided the best indication of how several schools of thought can basically approach a complex problem from entirely different angles.

Most scientific diving projects are planned from inception at eliminating as much risk as possible in all phases of the diving operation. This is accomplished by strict supervision and training of divers and a markedly conservative discipline in dive profiling. In short, every possible precaution is taken to reduce the possibility of a DCS occurrence. At the other end of the spectrum, the commercial diving community must deal with a job performance/task completion goal motivated by economics. Therefore, the concept of "acceptable risk" comes into play for both groups but each deals with risk differently.

By extremes of discipline, supervision and training the scientific community hope to prevent DCS incidence. With the use of highly trained supervisors, diver medical technicians and on-site recompression facilities, the commercial companies aim to effectively manage any accidents that may occur. It is difficult to quantifiable gauge the "end user" effectiveness of either group since DCS still occurs in scientific and commercial divers; the distinction being that if a commercial diver gets hit he is benefited by immediate and state-of-the-art medical treatment which may not be available to a science diver in a remote situation. Per capita DCS rates may or may not reflect the effectiveness of either approach to accident management, but the commercial operators are steadfast in their opinion that immediate evaluation and treatment are an acceptable alternative to a lesser statistical incidence rate.

All would agree that no bends hit is a good one, especially if you are on the receiving end. Terry Overland of Oceaneering International made this point at the conference: "While most sport and scientific dive operations would like to reach a goal of zero per cent DCS incidence, in commercial diving this is simply unrealistic. Ideally, we would like to reach a zero rate on Type II hits, but we still feel that our protocols allow us to treat DCS effectively enough that Type I hits are essentially manageable. I guess what I'm saying is that we accept the fact that if we give a worker a hammer, he will eventually hit his thumb and when he does we'll treat it. If we put a diver in the water to work, eventually he will get bent and we'll treat that as well. That's the simple facts. We have the technology to handle such hits and we feel that this is a more responsible outlook than attempting to unrealistically eliminate the malady. It's going to happen; we all know that. Let's be prepared to treat it. Importantly, our divers feel that our system works and it's their butts on the firing line, of course."

Further distinctions are sometimes made between "deserved" and "undeserved" DCS hits. Simply put, hits following a dive profile that would suggest the high-risk of DCS exposure such as clear Table limits violations or deep repetitive or reverse profile dives can be categorized as "deserved". Hits following dives that were within accepted limits are considered "undeserved". This is not to say that as chamber supervisors we sit back and blithely pass judgement on patients; categorizations of DCS hits using such terms merely allows a perspective on reasons for the presentation.

First and foremost, we have to encourage reporting of symptoms at the earliest observation. Second, the importance of surface oxygen by demand valve/mask cannot be overemphasized. Dr. Jefferson Davis was one of the earliest advocates of aggressive 100% O_2 delivery in the field and his pioneering work has resulted in the now accepted practice of oxygen therapy as a first line of treatment en route to the chamber. A significant percentage of symptomatic DCS patients will relieve following a 30 to 45 minute oxygen breathing period if delivered by demand valve/mask. During a one year period while vice president of Diving Operations for Ocean Quest International, I observed nearly a dozen cases of symptomatic DCS clear completely following demand system O_2 during transit to our chamber on the ship. Free-flow systems are far less effective and are wasteful of the gas.

I ran the Ocean Quest diving program along similar guidelines to a large commercial operation: expect the worst and be prepared to deal with it. We were very successful in encouraging divers to report any symptoms and had a 100% resolution rate on every one of the DCS cases we treated. Our overall incidence rate came out to be approximately one case in 12,000 dives; this is significant since we allowed an unlimited diving program with respect to depth and numbers of repetitive dives daily. In the space of one year we conducted almost 80,000 dives!

Thankfully, we are seeing more and more fully operable field chambers coming into use. Grand Cayman, Cozumel, Roatan and even some live-aboard vessels all feature state-of-the-art treatment facilities that would have been unthinkable only a decade ago. But remember, the chamber is only an effective tool if used (hopefully as soon as the diver notes a problem). It's incumbent on all divers to take responsibility for themselves and

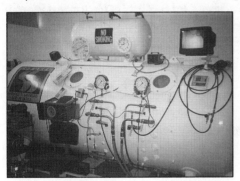

Modern field chambers such as this 60 inch unit in Cozumel is staffed 24 hours a day by qualified medical and operational staff. The reluctance of reporting symptoms due to the considerable costs of air evacuations, is now virtually eliminated in most popular Caribbean resort areas. This facility, owned by Subaquatic Safety Systems, is completely funded by contributions: $1/day per diver. Photo by Bret Gilliam

Education is the key to DCS recognition and reporting. Subaquatic Safety Systems, which operates chambers in Cancun, Cozumel, and Belize. Recently brought in hyperbaric expert Bret Gilliam to run extensive seminars for staff and local dive operators on dive accident management and prevention protocols. Here the graduates in Cozumel gather outside the chamber facility. Photo by Lynn Hendrickson

report any abnormality that could even be remotely linked to DCS. Use 100% O_2 at once and seek professional evaluation and a test of pressure if the possibility of DCS is suspected.

All divers should have a complete and detailed contingency plan for DCS management. For higher risk dive profiles, more attention to detail will be required and should include the provision for on-site recompression either in a properly staffed and set-up field chamber or through use of an evacuation chamber such as SOS's Hyperlite.

With the advent of affordable medical insurance such as available through DAN, the financial deterrent to admitting DCS and seeking help should be removed. There is nothing "macho" or "cool" about denial of DSC symptoms that could result in lasting injury such as paralysis or worse. It's time divers woke up to the fact that bends is an injury like any other and common sense dictates its treatment. Finally, the encouragement of prompt reporting with no associated peer or professional blame will vastly improve the safety of a sport infamous for symptom denial.

REFERENCES

Gilliam, Bret, *"Evaluation of DCS Incidence in Multi-day Repetitive Diving for 77,680 Sport Dives"*, Proceedings of the American Academy of Underwater Sciences Repetitive Diving Workshop 1991

Overland, Terry, *"Oceaneering International"*, Proceedings of the American Academy of Underwater Sciences Repetitive Diving Workshop 1991

Rutkowski, Richard, personal communication 11-91

Gilliam, Bret, *"DEEP DIVING: An Advanced Guide to Physiology, Procedures and Systems"*, Watersport Publishing 1992

CHAPTER 12

OPERATIONAL PRACTICES

Dive Planning and Gas Management

SECTION THREE

Dive planning is the key to a safe mixed gas dive. A well organized dive plan covers a wide variety of information and, on paper, appears time consuming. In reality, the dive plan, once practiced, is fulfilled quickly. A dive plan defines the maximums and minimums of the dive. Dive plans are readily adjustable for changes in the anticipated performance of the dive. They are not fixed and rigid except where violations compromise safety. Dive plans specify objectives not fixed goals that, in themselves, can create stress to complete.

A Well Structured Dive Plan Includes Four Primary Points:
1) Information gathering; 2) Group/team planning; 3) Personal planning; 4) In-water (update) planning.

Each of the objectives of a dive plan may be broken down and better defined in steps. The true intent is to "cover all the bases" especially the "what if's" and "how to's". Failure to fulfill all steps of this simplified format of dive planning has resulted in accidents and/or bad experiences on a dive.

INFORMATION GATHERING

Information gathering is the first step in preparing for a dive. Information gathering includes the abilities and goals of the team members towards a specific project. It encompasses gaining all pertinent knowledge about the dive site, the equipment needed to full fill the dive, risk analysis, and the establishment of maximums and minimums.

SKILL ONE

Sit quietly in front of a clock with a second hand, take three to five breaths slowly and deeply to relax the body and mind. Look at and concentrate on the second hand, allowing no other thoughts to enter your mind. A short term goal is one minute. The first thought, other than the second hand, that enters your mind terminates the exercise. A reasonable and practical long term goal is five minutes. A person who can concentrate this intensely is beginning to develop thought discipline and the ability to focus. Being able to focus allows us to mentally attack the source of a problem and solve it. False messages or meaningless distractions are eliminated. Being focused speeds up the thinking when under duress. This single ability is why some succeed or survive when others with equal physical competence, experience and mental capability fail in the same situation.

SKILL TWO

This skill is a deep meditation or self hypnosis exercise. First, take three deep slow breaths, carefully inhaling and exhaling fully each breath. Then repeat: "I'm calm and relaxed. My pulse is slow and relaxed. My breathing is slow and relaxed. All the muscles of my body are relaxed and at ease". As you feel gradual relaxation tell yourself (while counting backward from five) "I'm becoming more deeply relaxed"; then count five, My arms are becoming heavier; then count four, a warm glow of peace is filling me; then count three, I am relaxed and at peace; then count two, I am in total harmony with myself; then count one, I am totally open to my innerself. Relax for a moment, then mentally picture a red ball (such as a float) on the surface of the water. Now make this ball submerge and surface it over and over again without any other thoughts for 90 seconds. After 90 seconds, relax and allow the mind to drift and listen to your innerself or drift in quietness. After a reasonable time, take your breath, visualize and feel your breathe travel the length of your spinal cord as you inhale and exhale. Then shift the breath and allow it to enter the base of the spine, travel up through the brain and exit the mouth. Once comfortable, count yourself back to normal awareness by counting one, I am returning to my present position; 2, feel the energy flow of breath throughout your body; 3, begin to lightly move your arms and legs; 4, return to awakening consciousness; 5, become fully awake and alert. For those who take the time, this is one of the best concentration and relaxation exercise one can practice. With repeated practice, the ball can be in focused activity for five minutes to an hour. Why is this focus ability important for mixed gas divers or anyone who ventures beyond the norm? Because it conditions the mind to take one thought, isolate it, and block all other distractions. Concentration ability is the first and most important step to survival in life. Another side benefit of this exercise is it develops our intuition to a fine and reliable edge.

SKILL THREE

Take a cup, fill it with water, then select a straight pin and cover it with mineral oil to produce a surface tension enabling it to float. Place the pin in the water. Take three relaxing breaths and begin to focus and concentrate on the pen. Once all other thoughts are blocked, use the electrical energy from your hand to guide and point the pin. This is done by holding one's hand about three to six inches above the cup and directing the pen with your finger tips. Once mastered, quit using the hands. At this point with your face six inches to one foot from the cup concentrate on the pin and its direction. This is an advanced mental exercise but with practice you will achieve it. This should be practiced after becoming proficient in the first two skill levels. Mastery of this represents a high degree of concentration and thought control. If truly interested in furthering your mind control abilities, there are numerous tapes and programs available at metaphysical book stores. True mastery will come with personal effort and practice. Just as diving skills must be learned one step at a time, so does the path to full mind focus. As a mentally fit and physically fit diver your abilities are greatly extended. The diver possessing both physical and mental fitness is extremely aware and intuitive about his surroundings and his dive partners.

One can be a good diver with either physical or mental strength, but one cannot be his personal best without both. In survival situations the diver who is lacking in either physical or mental fitness has a reduced capacity to succeed. The more a diver wishes to push the "envelope", the greater the need to be physically and mentally fit. It is also true the more success in life, or in overcoming injury and disease, the greater the demand on both physical and mental fitness. Focus your thoughts and life is a more rewarding experience. Tune your body to mental and physical fitness and fully experience life.

Team member abilities are the first considerations to be addressed in information gathering. The dive objective must consider the experience level of each diver. In mixed gas and other technical diving applications, a dive frequently utilizes multiple dive teams with differing responsibilities. As the plan unfolds, these responsibilities are specified. However as part of information gathering, the experience level or perhaps more exactly, the capability of each diver must be understood. Divers should not be expected to or be depended upon to perform skills or meet objectives beyond their expertise. Indeed, the least proficient divers should be assigned support tasks that enable them to confidently develop skills and build a foundation to gain confidence to grow. Physical and mental fitness are required of mixed gas and technical divers.

The Physical Demands Include:

1) caring for all of the support equipment, 2) the ability to handle equipment changes, 3) the endurance to complete long swims, 4) the ability to pull one self down a descent line in strong currents and 5) the ability to remain on a decompression line in a current or during wave action.

Dive planning must include the acceptance of personal risk. The demands of deep wreck diving have to be within the risk/benefit balance for the dive team and its individuals.
Photo by Bob Cunningham

Mixed gas divers should participate in some form of physical training. The training programs selected must emphasize endurance more than strength. It is also recommended that the same muscle groups used in diving be exercised vigorously during the training. A physically unfit diver in mixed gas diving environments is an accident waiting to happen.

Mental fitness is a special prerequisite to mixed gas diving. Just as a person does not survive on bread alone, they will not survive or develop their full potential on physical prowess alone. Mental fitness and mental toughness are the key to survival. The mentally fit diver has discipline, and is able to control himself under adverse conditions. This control is gained via the exercises described in the chapter on stress. Another need for mental fitness is the ability to concentrate. There are a variety of means to develop concentration abilities. I would like to share a couple of these with you as this aptitude is paramount to safe diving and the mastering of survival skills.

RISK ANALYSIS AND ACCEPTANCE

A key component in the dive plan is the ability of each diver to analyze all the risks involved. On a given dive one must be willing to accept these risks. If a risk is beyond the diver's frame of mind or physical ability then the diver must disqualify himself from the dive. Risk is a variable factor based on numerous considerations: 1) The experience level of the diver, 2) The goals of the diver, 3) The level of discomfort a diver is willing to encounter (such as six or more hours of decompression, or carrying multiple scuba bottles, etc.), 4) A balance between what is enjoyable and pleasurable versus the discomfort the diver is willing to accept.

Risk acceptance and diver skill are not directly related. Many highly skilled and intensely focused divers reject numerous risks simply because they are out of their personal "comfort zone". A diver who does accept incredible risk must be totally mentally and physically in tune with himself. "envelope divers", like extreme mountain climbers, high altitude sky divers and race car drivers, in order to be successful and achieve their objective, must recognize the risks to their life. These risks are then balanced with the individual's worth of the goal. This approach enables a diver to overcome and survive obstacles beyond those of one not willing to pay the "ultimate price". Even the most serious of divers is not always up to total acceptance, and usually this is reflected through the divers intuition. Those in tune to themselves take a breather when the little voice inside tells them to do so.

The majority of mixed gas divers are not extreme envelope divers. These mixed gas divers accept some calculated risk for the reward of seeing and being where few other divers venture. They do this without having to achieve the extreme accomplishments of envelope divers. They limit their decompression risk, penetration risk, equipment dependency risk, and personal risk to well within acceptable limits. Their dives are equally, if not more satisfying, than the envelope dives. To evaluate your personal risk analysis and acceptance, answer the following questions for determining risk acceptance: 1) Is the objective of the dive within my comfort zone? 2) Is the dive one I would enjoy doing? 3) Do I have the experience/abilities to complete this dive? 4) Am I willing to take the decompression risk required to do this dive? 5) Is the equipment dependency risk within my personal acceptance ranges? 6) Is the penetration and or depth requirements of this dive acceptable to me? 7) Do I have confidence in the dive team? 8) Are the gas management rules being practiced safe? 9) Are the "what if's" addressed sufficiently? 10) Is the risk of injury or death on this dive acceptable to me?

"What If's"

A. Physical loss of a gas bottle for decompression or regulator malfunction, burst disc, tank valve o-ring etc.
B. The boat is not on station, anchoring failure and drifts away, or the boat departs to rescue another diver etc.
C. A malfunction of penetration stage bottle
D. A silt out in a cave or wreck environment
E. Dive team becomes separated.

Rob Parker covers the question of "what if?" by carrying a "bailout bottle" with his rebreather system. Photo by Rob Palmer

These "what if's" could and do continue on, but now you have the idea for establishing a protocol for "what if's".

Lastly, ask yourself, "if my part of the dive has a risk of serious personal bodily injury or even death am I willing to balance this risk against the pleasure of accomplishing the objective?" Divers seeking records or achieving extreme accomplishments must consider all risks and seriously address the above statement before undertaking any such adventure.

COMPATIBILITY

On complex dives or dives employing multiple dive teams, one must be able to function with all members of the dive teams. Be sure each person is mentally compatible with the other and that a working relationship is achievable. The team members should before and during the dive be friends with mutual respect and trust for each other.

A diver's awareness of what is going on around him is a key consideration when putting a team of divers together. Mixed gas environments demand self, buddy and environmental awareness. Awareness is being both consciously aware and subconsciously in tune to all that is taking place during a dive. Many physically competent divers measure up short on the awareness scale. A diver who continually becomes separated from a buddy is unaware. A buddy who is not knowledgeable of a problem to another member of the dive team is not an aware diver. Unaware divers have no place on a mixed gas dive team. Aware divers seem to have a sixth sense and respond immediately to situations that occur during a dive. The aware diver turns a "what if" situation into an almost unnoticeable experience.

Awareness is a key component in diver compatibility. It is a learned trait for most. To develop this skill, practice concentration "play" with identifying the breathing patterns of other divers, mentally study body language and dive posture in one's dive partners, recognize subtle changes in diver performance. These skills will help you develop total awareness. There is nothing more pleasurable than to dive with someone who can feel and share your thoughts. Jim Lockwood and Bret Gilliam, two of my regular dive partners, rarely communicate formally with me as we dive. We simply sense each others thoughts during the dive. With team skills of this intensity a precision dive is guaranteed.

THE DIVE SITE

The dive site to be explored needs to be understood in order to develop a safe plan. The type of dive site will dictate the equipment, gas management rules, and dive techniques to be utilized. Physical characteristics such as currents, wave action, sea conditions, depth, bottom type and overall access are prime considerations to making a working dive plan.

If the dive is an overhead environment such as a cave or wreck, special consideration must be given to it. First, all members of the dive team must be certified in either wreck penetration diving or cave diving, whichever is to be explored. Each diver must be properly equipped for overhead diving with safety reels, lights, correct tank configurations, etc.

If strong currents are anticipated, one should set up the dive using the most hassle-free techniques. The type of current — a steady consistent current, a tidal current, reversing currents, etc., must be analyzed and plugged into the dive plan. There are numerous ways to set up boats and dive sites to accomplish easier diving. As the means to do so varies from location to location we will not get into specifics in this chapter.

Depth along with the dive objectives play a major role in preparing the gas mix to be used and determining the available bottom time (dive time) and required decompression time. On dives between 50 and 190 feet the diver will most likely plan to use a "NITROX" (enriched air) mixture. Although below 150 feet, many divers elect to use a Trimix gas supply such as N_2 (65%), he (12%) and O_2 (23%). Trimix is recommended in cold, low visibility water between 150 and 190 feet. In warm tropical climates NITROX is often preferred to depths down to 190 feet. Regardless of the mixture the maximum PO_2 of 1.6 ATA should be maintained with PO_2's between 1.4 ATA and 1.5 ATA for long duration working dives. Below 200 feet, the use of Trimix is the logical choice.

For bolder divers, the risk factors published by Miles and McKay in Underwater Medicine should provide a good guide line. Basically, it concluded that dives on air between 180 fsw and 240 fsw are in a physiological risk zone due to narcosis and oxygen toxicity with dives below 240 fsw being dangerous for the same physiological reasons. Historically, this material (it was first published in 1961) has been field validated by analysis of deep air diving accidents.

Yes, many of us have dived to great depths on air, with no accidents. However, most of us that have made excessive deep bounces or long duration deep dives have experienced or witnessed "close calls". Personally, i have had two tough bouts with oxygen poisoning. One, a rescue dive to 400 fsw, where exertion at the start of the ascent with the diver being rescued resulted in collapsed vision consisting of a red field decorated with black dots. I was well above 300 fsw before normal vision returned. A second experience with oxygen poisoning was on a long duration dive in eagle's nest cave at a depth of 290 ffw. On this occasion I experienced pronounced muscle twitching in my forearm. The chapters on narcosis and oxygen, other experiences with the effects of deep air diving.

With the state of the art in mixed gas diving today, it is advisable to use NITROX from 50 fsw to between 150 and 190 fsw. Trimix becomes a desired gas on dives below 130 feet when extreme concentration such as on a research dive is needed. Dives below 200 fsw are best accomplished on Trimix. Wall dives are perhaps the most enjoyable gas dives to plan and to perform. However, special care must be taken to carry decompression gases with the diver. In the event that all decompression gases cannot be carried, the dive boat must be set up with in-water gas bottles staged on a line for the divers' decompression. In this event, the diver still should carry a decompression "bailout " bottle. This gas should be a mix to help reduce the possibility of DCS. The bailout bottle is used in the event of an emergency or separation from the boat and ascent line.

Deep reefs are also explored with mixed gas dives. The complexity of a reef dive site must be considered whether it be a complex cave, wreck, a wall with variable currents or even a reef that is difficult to navigate on. Of course, accessibility of a dive site influences the gas chosen, the amount of equipment to be used, and the approach. To gain local knowledge, talk to divers and residents who are familiar with the dive site. On many occasions, local knowledge will not extend to the planned depths. However, one can discover information about currents, marine life, sea states, road access and all the other needed supporting data to formulate a dependable dive plan.

On boat dives be sure to communicate the dive needs to the captain and crew and to personally verify that the decompression gases, etc., Are set up as needed. Do not leave anything to chance when making decompression gas shifts. Also, verify backup gases are staged to cover a gas failure. My personal "fail safe" recommendation is one complete extra decompression system for every three divers. In addition, each diver is supplied with more than enough gas for a safe return to the surface. In an emergency some of this extra gas may be shared. However, gas is only to be shared to the point that it allows the donor to safely exit the water.

EQUIPMENT

The dive plan should insure each diver is properly and completely equipped for the type dive to be performed. Each member of the team must be familiar with the equipment and the equipment configuration of each other member. Specialized equipment must be clearly understood by all and its capabilities specified. Divers need to pre-dive check the equipment on land and in the water before descending. Once in the water, each team member is to complete a functional check and verify the performance status of there equipment. It is important that regulators, alternate regulators, stage-decompression regulators and all gas bottles be checked for performance and verified leak-free. Each team member must know how to operate each others' equipment. An equipment check list should be provided and utilized. As in flying, it is recommended that this list be checked off during pre-dive. The in-water checks should be verbally stated by one's buddy.

MAXIMUMS AND MINIMUMS

The maximums and minimums establish the parameters within which the dive shall be conducted. They must be understood by all dive team members. Gas turn-around points must be agreed on by all. The type dive will influence the exact gas rule incorporated. In overhead environments, the "one third" rule is the starting point. A one third rule specifies that divers will begin to return to the exit or surface when they have used one third of the gas supply. Two thirds of the gas supply is then available for the divers personal use on exit and in transit, plus any emergencies that may take place. "adjusted thirds" are sometimes used when conditions warrant changes. This concept will be addressed in detail later in this chapter.

Other rules used on gas dives include the "one half plus 200 psig" rule. This is more common when there is not an overhead environment and a direct ascent to the decompression bottles is possible.

Unfortunately, many divers use "play it by the ear" gas rules which can and has lead to diving accidents. Solo divers frequently incorporate an "exact halves" approach thus planning for and anticipating the perfect dive — no environmental problems, perfect equipment reliability and performance as well as 100% diver performance. As a solo diver, this may be individually acceptable but in a dive team other members are at risk. Be aware that a one half rule leaves zero margin of error and is truly placing one's health and well being on the line.

It is mandatory that the maximum depth and bottom time be anticipated in order to plan for gas usage on the dive and adequate gases for decompression. The maximum time at depth is usually based upon the longest swim distance to be made on the dive. On long dives, support personnel will place stage bottles at critical points along the way to enable the primary divers to explore far away regions. Dives of this nature require precision gas planning, time management and team coordination. It is important that the maximum objective of any part of a dive profile is not to exceed the abilities of the least capable member of the team.

GROUP OR TEAM PLANNING

At this stage of the dive plan each person must agree and understand the objectives and backup objectives of the dive plan. All contingencies will be discussed and agreed on. Communications are reviewed and timing considerations are addressed.

The gas supply of all divers is totaled and gas rules are modified so that in the event of an emergency the diver who has the least available gas supply will still be able to safely complete the dive. This may be due to less gas capacity or higher gas usage during the dive. Gas matching allows the gas available to all divers to be within the selected gas rules. Thus a diver who breathes twice as much gas as another team member will force the diver using less gas to modify his gas consumption rate turn-around point to allow the heavier gas user to be within the gas rules on his tank. In other words the diver with the lower consumption rate will be forced to turn around earlier than his consumption rate dictates. This is an important "what if" part of a dive plan and provides adequate reserve gas for unexpected gas failure during a dive.

The team members at this time review and agree on the responsibilities each is charged with. The number of divers is established and each diver confirms willingness and ability to complete their responsibilities. Flexibility is maintained and divers are cautioned to avoid ego threat. Buddy assist and buddy rescue procedures are included in the plan. Upon completion, a unified dive team has been formed.

PERSONAL PLANNING

It is important for each diver to determine for himself "am I diving within a comfort zone that is acceptable to me?" Are there any questions that need to be rehashed? Do my personal limits allow me to participate on this dive? Can I be depended on yet not be dependent upon others? Do I have the discipline to assist a buddy or to terminate the dive if I feel uneasy? Remember, if the dive really feels good and you are comfortable, you will be turned-on and it will be a great dive experience. The next step is to allow three to 20 minutes to visualize a fun, safe and rewarding dive. To me the pre-dive visualization is the critical and most important function of a dive plan. When visualization of a dive takes place all the senses are activated and mental preparation is completed. Should you experience a forbidding feeling during a visualization, do not make the dive. In fact, influence the

Tom Mount is a proponent of positive pre-dive visualization as a method of dive preparation. Photo by Bret Gilliam

other team members to postpone the dive. On the other hand, it is almost a certainty if the visualization is good the dive will be outstanding.

IN-WATER PLANNING

Mother nature can be confusing at times and flexibility must allow for in-water modifications to a dive plan. The anticipated conditions may actually be improved or the prevailing state may be totally deplorable and unsafe. Thus, once in the water, the team must be able to modify, within safe parameters, the dive plan accordingly. Do not let a rigid surface plan dictate an objective planned in anticipation of circumstances other than those being experienced in the water.

GAS MANAGEMENT

The type dive will dictate the gas management rules to be followed. However, one must remember that if using mixtures containing helium, more gas is used during a specific time interval than would be on air. In this discussion, we will begin with rules designed for overhead environment diving.

The most accepted and time proven rule is the "rule of thirds" for overhead environment dives. On this rule in a static condition, one third of the gas is used exploring and two thirds are reserved for a safe exit. In the theory of thirds, exiting allows one third for the diver and one third for emergencies and decompression. At first, many divers feel the rule of thirds is overly conservative and in some instances it may be. Even with the conservative edge though, when a worse case scenario is encountered at maximum penetration with one diver having a gas failure the rule of thirds is just barely safe.

For discussion's sake, let's depict a scene with two divers who each breathe six psig a minute on the surface in their double 100's. Now let's examine an "out of air" situation. For benefit of the doubt we will even allow for some current to assist with the exit. So the givens are: 1) tank volumes are double 100 cubic foot tanks at 3000 psig (200 cubic feet of available air), 2) the divers swim at a pace of 45 feet per minute going into the cave, 3) the pace exiting the cave is 60 feet per minute and 4) depth is 99 feet or four ATA.

From the above we can determine: 1) 1/3 of the gas is used (1000 psig), 2) gas use per minute 4 ATA X 6 psig/min. = 24 psig/minute, 3) turn around time -1000 psig divided by 24 = 41.67 minutes and 4) distance covered is 41.67 minute x 45 feet/min = 1,875 feet. At turn around point.

By sharing gas on exit, from maximum penetration point: 1) the combined gas consumption (disregarding stress, etc.) Is 48 psig/minute (2 x 24), 2) exiting is made from 1875 feet divided by 60 feet /minute =31.25 minutes, 3) gas used on exit is 31.25 minutes x 48 psig/minute =1,500 psig for safe exit and 4) total exit gas used is 1500 psig leaving 500 psig for emergencies and/or decompression depending on gas mix used.

This example reflects a perfect dive performance. The stress testing exercises in the psychological aspects section was developed to enable divers to execute such a dive. Now let's look at two likely scenarios in the above situation.

Scenario #1. The exit is made at same rate as penetration but there was no current flow to assist the divers. The time element would have been 41.67 minutes for exiting, assuming the divers are calm, the gas used is (41.67 minutes x 48 psig a minute) 2,000.16 psig to exit cave. In this case, the divers would have exited the cave or wreck as they drew their last breath.

Scenario #2. As happens in many cases, divers actually slow their swim pace (again this is the reason for the drills reflected in the psychological aspects chapter) so that they exit at 30 feet per minute (instead of the 45 fpm during penetration). Exiting would then take (1,875 feet divided by 30 feet per minute) 62.5 minutes. The exit gas use would be (62.5 minutes exit time x 48 psig a minute) 3,000 psig for exiting. The divers would have needed an additional 1,000 psig (3000 psi required versus 2000 psi available) to exit the cave. In this case, we most likely had a double drowning and for certain a single drowning.

Dives in which gas matching between divers and their gas supply or breathing rate has not been made can prove disastrous. As an example; use the same dive as above but assume the diver with the gas source failure had been diving larger tanks allowing this person to travel equal distance to the gas donor. For the sake of comparison, let's assume this diver uses 12 psig per minute on the surface thus 48 psig/minute at four ATA. Now when sharing gas, the combined gas usage is 72 psig/minute. Assume the divers are quite experienced and retain a normal exit pace (in this instance 60 feet per minute) to exit the cave. The exit time will take 31.25 minutes (as determined in first part of problem with current assist). The gas needed for this swim is (31.25 x 72 psig/minute) 2,250 psig. These divers would also not be able to safely complete the dive. From this example, it should be clear why gas matching must be made when planning a dive for the gas management rules to be effective. When viewed in the above light, the rule of thirds does not seem to be overly conservative.

"Adjusted Thirds" is a modification to the one third rule by compensating for current and different diving conditions. This is a means of gas planning that allows for longer duration dives. However when applying the adjusted thirds rule, one must be familiar with the dive location and make gradual adjustments, insuring that the exit time still reflects the equivalent of two thirds of the available gas supply. As an example in dives with a strong outflow I use a one third minus 300 psig rule. On practical comparisons, the exiting gas is still effective when adjusted to two thirds. Conversely, if there is a strong inflow current so that a diver returns against the current, the rule must be adjusted the other way.

Also, many divers in adverse conditions use "one quarter" and "one sixth" rules. "one half plus 200 psig" is a common rule for deep open water dives and some divers employ it with the use of stage bottles. In the latter instance, the divers use the one third rule on their primary gas source. When anticipating long decompressions using either NITROX or Trimix, no rule less conservative than the "one half plus 200 psig" should be followed in open water. Bear in mind, ascent does not begin at the gas cutoff limit. Rather a return to the ascent line is commenced at this point. On NITROX or air dives involving no stops and without use of staged or bailout reserve gas, a good general rule is to turn at no less than one half plus 200 of the gas supply and begin ascent as follows; (remember ascent gas must allow for emergencies thus the safety factors)

DEPTHS (FSW)	ASCENT PSIG
60-80	800 psig
80-100	1,000 psig
100-120	1,100 psig
120-140	1,200 psig
use 1/2 plus 200 rule below	140 fsw

On decompression dives, the stated gas management rules (one thirds, adjusted thirds and one half plus 200) must be incorporated. The catch is that in addition to bottom mix, the gas needed for decompression must also be calculated and feature a built-in safety factor. Thus, all gas at all depths must be computed, including the various mixes for decompression on a Trimix or Heliox dive. Absolutely nothing can be left to chance.

For clarity of gas planning, lets plan a dive and the gas usage from point of water entry to stepping back on board the boat. The parameters of the dive are: 1) surface breathing rate at one ATA is .75 cubic feet minute, 2) depth 297 fsw 10 ATA, 3) bottom time 20 minutes, 4) gas mix is N_2 (44 %), He (40 %) and O_2 (16%), 5) ascent is at 30 feet/minute and 6) the stops on bottom mix begin at 110 fsw and continue through the 90 fsw stop for a total of six minutes, 7) a mix of N_2 (50%) and O_2(50%) is used at the 80, 70, 60, 50 , 40, and 30 fsw stops for a total time of 28 minutes, 8) oxygen is used at the 20 and 10 fsw stops for a total of 42 minutes.

Therefore, on the above dives 1) the gas needs are (.75 ft^3/min x 10 ATA) 7.5 ft^3 / min at 297 feet. The amount of gas used on the bottom is (20 minute x 7.5 ft^3/min) 150 cubic feet. To allow for safety you must calculate ascent gas at bottom consumption rate thus ascent of a) 300 fsw - 110' = 190 fsw travelled, b) 190 / 30 feet/min = 6.3 minutes of ascent time, c) 6.3 x 7.5 ft^3 = 47.25 ft^3. Bottom mix stop gas is computed at breathing rate of deepest stop a) 110 (110/33 +1)= 4.3 ATA, B) gas needed is 4.3 $ft.^3$/min x .75 = 5.05 $ft.^3$ gas/minute, c) total gas = 5.05 x 6 = 30.3 $ft.^3$. The total bottom mix needed is (150 $ft.^3$ + 47.25 $ft.^3$ + 30.3 $ft.^3$) 227.55 $ft.^3$. To determine the 50-50 decompression stop gas needs compute at 80 fsw breathing rate (80/33 +1) = 3.42 ATA x .75 = 2.56 $ft.^3$/minute. There for the total 50-50 is (2.56 x 28 minutes) 71.68 $ft.^3$.

The oxygen is planned as if used fully at 20 fsw, thus (20/33 +1) = 1.6 ATA x .75 breathing rate/minute = 1.2 $ft.^3$/minute O_2 use at 20 fsw. The total O_2 needed is (1.2 x 42) 50.4 $ft.^3$.

Most experienced divers will actually use less gas on a dive than the above example. However this is the model that should be used on gas man-

Constant awareness of depth and remaining gas volumes is crucial to in-water dive planning. Tom Mount at 240 feet on Florida wreck. Photo by Bret Gilliam

agement. Adjust the gas use to your personal consumption. Always plan in additional safety to allow for unexpected "what if's".

Another consideration is what happens if the O_2 system fails. A general guide line is to go back onto the NITROX mix and double the remaining stop time using the EAN mix. On the surface breathe oxygen at rest for 30 minutes. To cover loss of NITROX for decompression each diver should carry twice as much NITROX as needed. In this event adequate EAN is available to safely complete the NITROX stops.

Ideally, a diver in open water should transport all gas, both bottom mix and decompression gases, on their person. This is accomplished by rigging them as stage bottles. The procedures for this will be discussed in the equipment chapter. The simplest gas dive is a EAN NITROX (oxygen enriched air) dive. Most divers elect to do the decompression on the bottom mix, thus, less bottles to carry. Indeed, just the tanks for the dive are usually adequate. On longer dives or NITROX dives to or below 150 feet, it is a good policy to carry a 13 to 40 cubic foot tank of oxygen to use at the 20 foot stop. Some divers prefer to use a 50-50 mix (N_2P_2) and start using it at 70 feet on ascent. Either 50-50 or O_2 is ideal as a decompression gas.

Decompression gas mixes can be used to shorten decompression or to increase the physiological safety. NITROX and Trimix tables with decompression gases are available for standard and custom mixes.

Custom tables frequently use O_2 or 50-50 ($N_2 O_2$) to shorten and increase decompression effectiveness and safety. Once the decision is made to use Trimix or Heliox specialized tables must be followed. In most practical applications of Trimix or Heliox, long decompressions can be anticipated. This is due to greater depths, longer bottom times, and the use of blends in the divers gas. Helium is a fast gas and thus requires exacting detail in decompression procedures. However, helium is also termed a "friendlier" gas than nitrogen. Substantial time can be deducted from decompression by using multiple gas changes on ascent. The complication is how to carry a sufficient number of gas bottles. It is for this reason many divers employ tables that call for from one to three gas exchanges. The decompression is a little longer than more gas exchanges require, but the dive is more manageable.

When planning a mix dive the choice is yours as to what mix, how complicated, and what ascent profile to use etc. On my dives, I prefer to use NITROX to 180 fsw. I supplement decompression with a 30 cubic foot bottle of oxygen for use at the 20 and 10 foot stops. From 180 feet to approximately 220 feet I'm an air diver if in open water. In caves or inside large or complex wrecks, I switch to Trimix at 200 feet. Below 220 fsw, I recommend the use of Trimix on all dives. For a general recommendation, it would be prudent to use Trimix on all dives below 180 fsw with NITROX being the gas of choice to that depth. For those who are highly sensitive to narcosis use of Trimix beginning at 130 fsw is practical.

The dive plan procedures in this chapter are intended as a safe guide for field implementation. Use them and be rewarded with hassle-free diving.

REFERENCES

The New Practical Diving; Tom Mount and Akira Ikahara; University Miami Press;

Safe Cave Diving; Tom Mount; NACD (out of print)

CHAPTER 13

OPERATIONAL PRACTICES

Equipment Configurations

The equipment used with breathing gases other than air varies from the conventional to the exotic. The type gas, the depth, and the objectives of a dive will define the complexity of diving paraphernalia required. The most important ingredient in life support systems is a responsible and reliable diver. In all recommended equipment configurations a few basics are agreed on by all technical divers.

Responsible Diver
* Well informed
* Assiduously trained
* Aware of and accepts risk
* Appropriately equipped for dive
* Logical thinker
* Psychologically fit
* Physically fit

Basic Structure of Equipment for Technical Diving
* Streamlined
* Redundant
* Dependable
* User friendly
* Low drag profile
* As simple as possible for a given dive

- Easy access by dive buddy
- Provides self rescue ability for diver

Life support systems for technical diving begin with the single tank with conventional valve, regulator with octopus or other alternate gas source and other "normal" equipment worn by the recreational diver using EAN NITROX to increase his safety. For increased performance this diver only need streamline his equipment to avoid sloppiness and drag. Gauges should be tucked or attached so they do not dangle. The alternate gas supply second stage should be attached to a 0-ring or holder. As a diver ventures into more technical diving with the application of new skills, the equipment will be altered to suit new demands. Generally the first equipment modifications are made to meet the needs of decompression diving. At first glance this is a rather simple step. Yet, in reality, it is a critical first

Bill Gardner demonstrates a balanced configuration in a deep diving set. Note long hose octopus regulator is secured in surgical tubing along right cylinder for easy pull-away deployment. Stage bottle is clipped inside right shoulder harness. Photo by Bret Gilliam

step. For in decompression diving there is diminished allowance for mistakes. The diver must modify existing systems to provide increased dependability and redundancy. For stage decompression diving the traditional octopus is not recommended. A "y" or "h" valve or a pony bottle of a minimum of 30 cubic feet should be utilized. Should an octopus free flow or the regulator have a first stage shutdown in a conventional system, it would completely eliminate breathing availability gas for the diver. The "y" or "h" valve or separate pony bottle systems provide redundant safety for the diver. For instance, should a regulator malfunction, that side of the valve is shut down and the diver simply switches to the second regulator. In the case of

Bill Gardner's system consisting of redundant Dive Rite back-mounted BC's, regulators, and Sherwood isolation double manifold. Photo by Bret Gilliam

a pony bottle, the diver may switch to it for bailing out of the dive. If a diver insists on using a standard valve and no pony bottle, then he should use an alternate second stage such as the Scubapro Air II, Sherwood Shadow, etc. However, even with these systems there is no redundancy for the diver and therefore a substantial risk factor in the event of valve or regulator failure. Additional equipment modification is needed for the diver entering the world of stage decompression diving. In addition to two regulators, one of these regulators should use a five to seven foot hose between the first and the second stage. The purpose of the long hose is to allow easier gas sharing while maintaining normal swimming pace and safe ascending up a line. Also in restricted areas such as companionways on shipwrecks, caves, etc., It is impossible to share gas side to side. It may also prove difficult for divers to remain in contact with a guide or ascent line without a long hose. Standard hose lengths almost always create confusion and awkwardness in gas sharing situations. A suitable means of storing the long hose must be developed and utilized by the diving buddy team. This will be discussed later.

It is highly advised that all decompression dives use EAN or oxygen for decompression. On Trimix dives, one will most likely use both making a switch to EAN at some depth, followed by use of oxygen at 20 and 10 fsw. Therefor divers making decompression dives need to carry additional gas bottles. Common terminology for these extra cylinder systems is "stage bottles". These should be easily removable during a dive by the diver. On wreck and cave dives they will most likely be dropped off or "staged" at

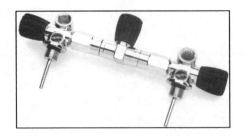

The Sherwood DIN double manifold valve which allows divers to "isolate" a malfunctioning regulator or valve while still utilizing the gas in that cylinder. Photo by Sherwood

some location for retrieval and use later. In staging, the diver removes the bottles and fastens them to a secure structure. This allows the diver to continue the dive with reduced swim drag. These bottles are not to be secured to the anchor line as the anchor may break free and the decompression gases would be lost. In some instances stage bottles for extending dive time or distance will be used in addition to the decompression stage bottles.

As direct ascent to the surface is not an option on decompression stop dives, a diver must have a means of being found should he lose access to or

For dives requiring only minimal decompression, some divers prefer to mount the stage bottle between their doubles. Photo by Peter Nawrocky

become separated from the dive boat. To provide this safety, a diver will use a lift bag or inflatable sausage. A safety reel such as a cave or cavern reel attached to the float (lift bag or sausage) which is sent to the surface. In some parts of the country "up" lines are commonly used in decompression diving.

With the surface float deployed and using the reel line as a down line, a diver drifts during decompression. The dive boat tracks the diver by following the float on the surface. When "up" lines are used they are attached to the wreck or bottom and the diver ascends up the line. A surface float should still be sent up to mark the diver's location and presence in the water. The float also makes the "up" line more stable. In heavy currents such as in south Florida "up" lines will not work. Divers should be informed by local divers of regional practice and adjust their approach to be locally compatible. A sonic alert whistle is also desirable. This is a loud whistle generally attached to the low pressure B.C. inflator hose. The purpose of the whistle is to get attention once on the surface.

Submersible dive tables or specialized dive computers must be used to determine stage decompression depths and stop times. On standard EAN mixes, either air or NITROX computers may be utilized. There are a num-

Richard Bull carries his oxygen stage bottle clipped to his shoulder harness.
Photo by Bret Gilliam

Bill Gardner with double stage bottles for nitrox and oxygen. Photo by Bret Gilliam

ber of air dive computers. NITROX computers include the Diverite Bridge, the Quatek Profinder, the Orca Delphi and the Cis Lunar computer. It is rumored that Beuchat, Oceanic and Scubapro may be planning production of NITROX computers based on market performance. In Trimix and Heliox diving, the diver will most likely use submersible proprietary (custom) tables. Dive computers capable of processing a combination of NITROX, Trimix, and Heliox are available through Cis-Lunar and Quatek . A slate and pencil must also be carried by the diver.

Submersible gas (tank) pressure gauges are attached to at least one regulator of the primary gas supply. Stage bottles should also have their own submersible gas pressure gauges. These gauges should use short high pres-

Bret Gilliam programming the Quatek Pro-File ACE nitrox computer. Note size comparison to Aladin Pro. Photo by Richard Bull

sure hoses of roughly six inches in length. Some divers do not use pressure gauges on the decompression bottles as they feel it adds additional confusion and drag. They check tank pressures prior to entering the water. On stage bottles for extending dive duration, gas pressure gauges are mandatory.

Exposure suits need to be matched to the environment being dived. When Trimix or Heliox is the breathing gas, allow for an additional loss of body heat. Thus a dive that is marginal on requiring a thick wetsuit or a drysuit, will demand the drysuit if using Trimix or Heliox. With dry suits it is recommended that suit inflation be with either argon or air, not Trimix or Heliox.

A diver's watch or other precise bottom timing device is needed for mixed gas diving. Integrated depth gages (depth capability must be considered) with bottom timers and dive computers also provide this function. When ascending on Trimix or Heliox, ascent rate and time to and at stops is critical. Thus precision is needed to maintain a continuous run time. Two timing devices are suggested. A depth gauge that is highly accurate is also demanded on all decompression stop dives. This is true regardless of the bottom mix (air, EAN, Trimix, Heliox). The instrumentation must be capable of functioning of the planned diving depths.

A buoyancy compensator is also needed. In fact, a backup compensator is highly desirable and should always be used in double tank diving. The back up B.C. may be another B.C.. or even a dry suit. A backmounted B.C. (biu or wings) is the choice of most "gas divers". When double tanks are used, it is the only logical system that provides proper lift and trim features for stabilizing and balancing double tank systems. "Stabilizing" or jacket style B.C.'s simply do not function as well with double tanks. Another consideration is the need to fasten gauges, and stage bottles to the diver. To provide this ability, a backplate and harness is mandated unless numerous modifications are made to standard BC jackets.

Other desirable equipment includes, lights (where applicable), a compass, a dive knife (usually small and sharp) is mandatory, and, of course, properly selected mask and fins. Snorkels in technical diving are not recommended. In fact, the snorkel identifies one as inexperienced in technical diving applications. "If you don't need it, don't use it". This avoids the confusion that may develop from one more piece of unnecessary equipment.

As the dive becomes more complex double tanks are the order of the day. Factors that necessitate doubles are increased depth and the need for extended bottom times. At the same time, care should be taken not to over load or overburden a diver with unnecessary equipment. For example, a diver with a low breathing rate plans a dive to 150 fsw for 20 minutes on an EAN 25 or Trimix 23:12 (a mix that can be safely decompressed on with-

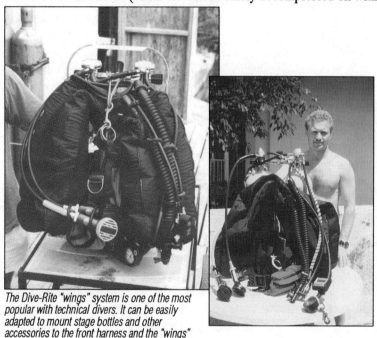

The Dive-Rite "wings" system is one of the most popular with technical divers. It can be easily adapted to mount stage bottles and other accessories to the front harness and the "wings" can be be sized for the diver's physique and desired buoyancy capability.   Photos by Bret Gilliam

out gas changes). The diver can complete the dive within accepted gas management rules on a single 100 cubic foot tank equipped with a "y" valve. In this instance, the additional drag and weight of double tanks is not mandated. It is noted though that oxygen should still be used at the 20 and 10 fsw stop.

This author is a firm believer that too much equipment is equally detrimental to dive performance and safety as is too little equipment.

To cover the "what if's", most gas divers switch to doubles if diving below 180 to 200 fsw. Doubles are a must when extending bottom times on dives. Double tanks should incorporate dual valve outlets. This allows for shutting a valve and regulator down in the event of malfunction. It also allows redundancy in regulators. Many divers like to use double manifolds that feature an isolation valve. This enables the diver to shut off or "isolate" a tank that has a gas failure problem such as blown burst disc, o-ring, etc. It is an added step in the CYB (cover your butt) concept. Valve protectors have become popular in both cave and wreck diving applications. These are essential if diving using diver propulsion vehicles (DPV's) in overhead environments.

In discussing tanks, the type of valves are worthy of mention. Two choices are available: standard o-ring and DIN. Standard o-ring valves where the regulator attaches to the tank with the customary yoke assembly are widely used and still acceptable. However, with increased pressures the din fitting becomes mandatory. DIN fittings allow regulator attachment by screwing the regulator first stage directly into the tank valve. The DIN affords a more dependable system with less possibility of o-ring failure.

When using o-ring valves, accidental bumping can and has caused o-rings to blow creating gas failure emergencies at depth. I personally have experienced two failures of this nature. Both occurred while cave diving. The first instance was on a dive in *Devils Eye* at a distance of 2,700 feet into the cave while using a DPV. The valve brushed an outcropping and "whoosh" - a blown o-ring. Within the time it took me to shut down the DPV and my buddy Bill Mee to turn the valve off (he had the valve under control faster than I could reach it), 700 psig was lost. (of course, this could have been avoided by placing a cage over the tank valves.) In the second instance, an o-ring blew for no apparent reason during a dive. The o-ring was okay during pre-dive checks. It was this scenario that persuaded me to begin converting all of my tanks to DIN fittings.

EQUIPMENT CONFIGURATIONS

There are a number of ways to configure a divers equipment for deep, mixed gas and technical diving. In this section we will provide several examples and discuss three generic systems approaches. From these three, a diver can adequately review the other systems and develop a personal compatible equipment style. The reader should take specialized training in deep, mixed gas or other technical diving modes before attempting to modify his personal equipment or make such dives. During these training programs the instructor will guide you through an appropriate equipment operating system for the diving mode you are learning. The system used in these courses may or may not be identical to configurations discussed in this chapter. However, the systems should incorporate the common points outlined below.

Concepts for Equipment Configuration
- Keep it clean
- No dangling hoses
- No dangling equipment
- Easy identification by touch systems
- Easy reflex access to equipment
- Balance for easy diving
- Valves free and within reach
- Know your own and your buddies' configurations
- Easy to trim
- Redundancy without awkwardness
- Your configuration is your insurance for safe gas diving!

Double 120 cubic foot cylinders with valve "cage" protector. Photo by Bret Gilliam

The first equipment system to be covered is the holgarthian system. This system incorporates all the essentials of an acceptable gas diving configuration. It is specifically designed for cave diving. The developer of this style is Bill Main. For gas diving, we have modified the system explanation for carrying of decompression gases, lift bags, etc., And for the open water environment.

Method One - Holgarthian Component System
- Long hose for use in gas sharing emergencies is wrapped under primary light case on side of diver up to and around the divers neck. This is the regulator used by the out- of-air buddy.
- Safety lights are attached to shoulder harness by hooks and tubing to keep them in a low drag profile
- The short hose second stage is worn on the neck attached by a neck strap
- B.C. inflator hoses are bunged to the harness
- Gauges are attached to "D" rings on harness
- Decompression stage bottles are mounted side by side and attached into the divers harness. (Some divers in open water add a pony or bailout bottle mounted between the tanks when wearing doubles. In singles, the pony bottle is attached on the opposite side from the stage bottles

- Reels are placed in tight with low drag
- Lift bags are bunged around the tanks

The primary advantage of this system is that it minimizes the drag profile in the water. It provides ease of access to all system components. In emergencies it is a fast reaction configuration. One controversial issue with this and within all systems is the practice of breathing from the long hose and using it to hand off in an out-of-air emergency. This is easily modified by the personal dictates of a diver. The issue will always be debated with strong feelings both ways.

Pros / Cons

- Diver goes for regulator in mouth.
- Diver can be trained to take any trade off regulator.
- If a problem exists with the second regulator it is best that the control diver deal with the stress. If the control diver is stressed, the chances of survival is reduced with increased probability of a double drowning.
- There is some reduction of gas through a long hose.

In the author's opinion the first rule of life saving is assistance that will not result in a double drowning. The worst case situation is a double drowning. In most activities other than diving, the accepted rule is to maintain a stress-free mind set by the person(s) effecting the assist or rescue. Do not do rescues that will place you at a greater psychological and physical disadvantage than the person being rescued. Numerous in-water gas sharing rescues have been successful. The reason for the success was the ability to remain calm and in control.

I refuse to hand off the regulator in my mouth as a first choice. In some emergencies, a diver may get that regulator initially. We then exchange once the person has calmed. In any gas sharing incident the first step to survival is to stop! Exhale! Breathe at absolute rest for three breaths! Think! Solve problem!

Almost always the stressed diver will take an offered regulator from any position and it is rare (but in some instances does happen) that they grab the regulator in the mouth. Most often divers who take the regulator from the mouth were trained in that way.

In my opinion, the worst possible action is to place the assisting diver in a stressed condition. If overly stressed he may become incapacitated during the rescue effort. A calm diver may successfully enact a rescue.

It is like the instructor who pursues a panicked student to the surface at a high rate of ascent. On reaching the surface the student may need help but the instructor is paralyzed due to DCS and now both are in trouble. Had the instructor come up more slowly a rescue would have taken place. The same is true in out-of-gas situations. Fellow diver and highly experienced cave explorer Bill Gavin offers the following counter argument in the book, *The Art of Cave Diving*, "a stressed diver will grab the regulator from the mouth and thus in doing so receives the correct regulator. When handing off the extra second stage if it has a problem it will heighten the stress of the diver. The donor should be the one to subject themselves to this increased stress as they are in a more calm state of mind". He goes on to question, "how do you feel about diving with a person who by their equipment configuration, has blatantly expressed they would not give you the regulator they are breathing from?"

The above points of view express the diversity in thinking on gas management in emergency gas sharing scenarios. Both Bill and myself have been in gas sharing incidents. Both our opinions are based on experience. Yet our experiences and recommendations are vastly different. These same recommendations are debated throughout diving circles. Most arguments, beliefs and recommendations are based upon real life personal experiences of the individuals involved. Thus, the choice is really yours. There really isn't a right or wrong protocol. It becomes a matter of belief, experience, training, and value judgments. In answer to Bill's question, I'm comfortable diving with anyone who has taken the precaution to plan for gas to share with me in event of a failure. This is true regardless of where it comes from. In final analysis, both schools of thought are based on survival of the dive team. Historically, both have been proven successful.

This method of organizing equipment is common to many cave, deep and wreck divers.

Method Two
- Long intermediate hose tucked around the space by the tank valves, utilizing surgical tubing
- Long intermediate hose is attached to shoulder harness (some divers use it as a primary)
- Lights are butt mounted on (tanks bottom(s) or side mounted
- Safety lights are attached to the shoulder straps
- Pony bottle mounted between tanks. This is usually a back-up EAN decompression mix that can also function as a bail-out gas supply
- Decompression stage bottles are mounted on alternate sides
- Safety reels are attached to O-rings on tanks
- Lift bags are snapped to D-rings or bunged to tanks
- Tools are in a carry-all bag and clipped to the harness
- Gauges are clipped to the harness

In this system, one discovers the agreed upon elements of common gas needs. It varies slightly from the first style of configuration. Within this system the debate over which regulator to breathe from is still an issue. The disadvantage of this system, according to those opposed to it, is that the hose tucked in by the valves is in a busy location. Also the attachment to d-rings on the tanks is not considered the best.

METHOD THREE

This is my personal system. It is equally as debatable as the others. It is however the system to which I have evolved. It works for me. Each diver should work with each system. In the field, there are almost as many variations as dive groups. The goal you must strive towards is to comply with the mutual equipment configuration goals, and evolve to the system that is comfortable for you and your partner. We all are built slightly different, use different types of equipment, and apply various modifications to meet our individual dive style and beliefs.

The eventual ideal system for a diver will be obtained by trial and error. However, the three systems showcased in this chapter reflect time-proven operational configurations. It is advised that the diver start with one of these set systems and then begin to experiment until the most natural personal equipment set up is developed. Each of these systems can be applied to single tank and double tank setups. Remember that the users of these systems are still evolving in their quest for the perfect system. Thus their set-ups change from time to time just as yours will change with time and experience.

Method Three (author's system)
- Long hose is tucked under surgical tubing; three bands on right side of tank(s).
- Second stage of long hose regulator attached to around neck with quick release mouth piece retainer.
- Double back mounted flotation systems.
- Primary light is butt mounted on tanks.
- Safety lights are snapped to left side of waist strap at point it enters backplate.
- Safety reel(s) are on right side of waist strap at point where the strap enters waist strap.
- Primary regulator has neck retaining ring on it attached to hose so it can drop free when using stage bottles.
- Lift bag is tucked under surgical tubing on left side of tanks (removed when cave diving).

- Stage bottles are carried on each side to balance configuration (on DPV dives stage bottles are carried on left side. This is a recent adaptation that I employed after watching its application on video by cave/deep/wreck diver George Irvine).
- BC hoses bunged in over left shoulder on harness.
- As in the other systems all gauges are attached to d-rings on the harness and a pocket carries dive tables, back up knife etc.
- Diver alert, sonic alarm is attached to B.C. Inflator hose.
- Note some modifications are employed when cave diving.

The above listed configurations represent a small sampling of the equipment setups used in mixed gas diving. It is important that we all continue to evolve, modify and update our equipment. The day we establish a "this is the ultimate system configuration" is the day all progress and evolution stops. There is no one way — no perfect way, as stated by Bill Gavin in *The Art of Safe Cave Diving.* "He (the diver) must put aside ego, impatience, and excuses and settle for nothing less than perfection". As we all know, the search for perfection is a life long and ever evolving process.

In the words of Lamar Hires, "Each day one sees a new modification in existing equipment design and utilization". High-tech manufacturers such as Mark Leonard, of *Dive Rite,* are plagued by the rapid evolution of and new developments in technical diving techniques and equipment. Although they are responsible for much of this evolution, each new creation makes the previous creation obsolete forcing new challenges upon themselves. Such is the world of progressive manufacturers. The recreational dive industry customarily follows the high-tech field with about a five year lag time. This has been true in alternate second stages, dual valve manifolds, buoyancy compensation devices, lighting technology, EAN use, Trimix and most advanced concepts of diving and equipment design and configuration. It is still happening in the use of back plates and back mounted flotation systems which provide lower drag, higher efficiency, better buoyancy control and more convenience.

Equipment selection must be a well thought-out process. Your choice of a regulator must be by deliberate action and investigation not random chance. Most manufacturers produce regulators capable of supplying gas flow needs to divers. However, the choices of suitable high performance units for deep and mixed gas diving are very limited. You must investigate these and other pieces of equipment thoroughly before choosing.

Choosing a Regulator

- Adequate gas flow abilities
- User friendly
- Reliability
- Low maintenance
- Compatible with gas to be used (at the time of publishing mixed gas, a one manufacturer invalidates warranties if there equipment is used in mixed gas diving applications, users should check this out).
- Maintenance/warranty response time of manufacturer or pro dive store.
- For second decompression regulators different style, size or color second stages.
- For O_2, green second stage cover.
- Stage regulator second stages should be adjustable so they can be modified in-water not to freeflow (the deco gas tanks are in off position until ready for use)

Rob Parker using the side-mount system popular with some cave divers. In this configuration, the primary cylinders are carried like stage stage bottles and none are worn on the diver's back. Photo by Rob Palmer

The most recent advance in the recreational "gas diving" community is the rebreather. Although these units have been around for dozens of years their popularity and availability in the gas diving community is recent. The author has been privileged to dive on numerous systems including the Bio Marine CCR1000, GE MK 10, Electrolung, MK VI, MK VIII, and some "home made" or "home brew" systems. The "home brew" systems even include a cryogenic unit developed by Jim Woodbury back in the 60's. There are now two systems being developed that are within reasonable cost for the gas diver. The application of rebreathers is discussed elsewhere in this text.

Mixed gas rebreathers are the most efficient means to explore greater depths or to make longer dives. With these rebreathers bottom times from six to nine hours regardless of depth are a reality. These systems are able to maintain a given PO_2 for the dive and an increased PO_2 for the decompression. Oxygen partial pressure regulation is built into the system. As the reader will discover in the chapter on "the future", rebreathers are the ideal equipment for gas diving and exploration of deeper depths, wrecks and caves.

DPV's have become a key component for exploration and energy conservation on deeper dives. Basically there are two types. The tow DPV where the diver is towed by the DPV. *(See photo)*. The mounted DPV where the diver rides the DPV like a motorcycle. The desirability of each type varies among dive groups and what they are trying to accomplish. As in all life support systems for technical diving redundancy is a key factor. Some DPV's being developed feature inherent back up systems. With most current models it is recommended that divers either stage a safety DPV or stage additional "what if" gas bottles for emergency use in case the DPV fails. On tow DPV's use a harness configuration to allow the unit to pull

Billy Deans of Key West Diver and his Aqua-Zepp DPV. Photo by Bret Gilliam

Photo by Gary Gentile

you. (With mounted systems a kill switch is desirable. Also a diver is well advised to wear a helmet when DPV diving.

When using DPV's, reliability is a key issue. Due to the diver's extended range when using one of these vehicles an unaware diver may travel to a point that is beyond his ability to swim back to safety. In caves, this presents a serious problem. Thus, careful gas management is a must for safe use of DPV's. Redundancy is desirable in these as in all exploratory systems. Bailout gas must be considered. In event of failure, each DPV team should carry a tow line to assist a diver with a disabled system. Some divers also stage a "safety" DPV along with additional gas bottles.

For practical, long penetration exploration of caves DPV's are a must. They are also highly desirable for traveling to a desired location on a wreck. DPV's offer the most efficient means of surveying deep reefs and walls. In addition to speed and distance, DPV's also extend the gas duration of a dive by reducing the workload of swimming. However, this savings in gas consumption is also a double edge sword if a DPV fails. Divers not equipped to cope with system failures could be placed in jeopardy. The author highly advises all who wish to take advantage of DPV's to seek out specialized training in the use of these devices.

Apply logical reasoning as you chose wetsuits, drysuits, tank valves, B.C.'s, rebreathers, DPV's and even knives. Gas diving beyond the use of recreational EAN is demanding and deserves attention to every detail of equipment selection. Remember you, the diver, and your reasoning processes are the most critical part of a life support system. You are the life being supported.

REFERENCE

The New Practical Diving; Tom Mount and Akira Ikehara; University Miami Press;
Safe Cave Diving; Tom Mount; NACD (out of print)

CHAPTER 14

Diving Techniques

The key to a relaxed safe dive is good technique. In fact, the most critical part of your enjoyment of innerspace is proper dive technique including buoyancy control. In the 60's, there was a common statement "if you are going to be a diver, look like a diver". This statement has much merit. Not only does it address appearance, but safety as well. A diver who is lacking on technique can not be as comfortable or as safe as a diver who has mastered good technique. Immediate advantages of technique are less fatigue on a dive, longer dive durations and less stress. It is much easier to breathe properly with streamlined body movements and low drag profiles in the water.

The first step to good technique is to streamline one's profile in the water. This will present the lowest drag profile to the water while swimming. The first step to a streamlined profile is to attach or secure all gauges and equipment in such a manner that they are not dangling. The reader is referred to the equipment configurations chapter for examples of this process. The second step is to understand the importance of proper swim attitude. The third step is developing perfection in buoyancy control. The fourth and final stage is incorporating efficient propulsion skills. Once these steps have been mastered a confident, competent and safe diver will emerge.

Swim attitude is evasive to even those who do use good buoyancy control. A proper swim attitude reflects a diver totally level in the water. In theory, a straight line could extend on a horizontal level throughout a diver with correct swim posture/attitude.

To develop excellent swim attitudes much discipline is needed to position the body. In fact, initially most divers will feel the posture is slightly unnatural. It is difficult on the first few tries to maintain a level body attitude. To do so requires arching the shoulders and lifting the neck. If, when applying these principles, you experience sore back and neck muscles then you are most likely on the right path. Once accustomed to this attitude, it becomes comfortable and sore muscles become a part of the past. Normally, even with good buoyancy control, divers tend to swim with their body at a slight feet down angle. This is because it is a lazy way to see where we are going. Some divers slightly overcompensate and maintain a feet high posture. This attitude is useful in some environmental conditions, but creates more drag than a level profile.

An evolving gas diver must be aware of all factors concerning work while moving through the water column. The recreational NITROX diver needs good technique for watermanship. The NITROX technical diver and the Trimix diver carry significantly more equipment than recreational divers. With the added drag of the equipment it is imperative that these divers exhibit near perfection in body attitudes.

Looking at our well postured diver, note that on the swimming down stroke nothing is extended more than 10° below the midline of the body. Equipment such as stage bottles should likewise remain as close to this tolerance as possible.

To summarize posture/attitude, the body is straight, neck lifted for forward vision, shoulders arched. No part of the body, including attached equipment, varies more than 10 ° below the midline of a person.

Buoyancy control is a key ingredient to being able to implement correct body attitude/posture. Exceptional buoyancy control is gained by a balance in correct use of the B.C., proper weight adjustment and distribution of the diver, and breathing correctly. One of the biggest "no no's" to combining good body attitude and buoyancy control is initial over-weighting. Even though a B.C. can compensate for too much lead being carried by the diver it still leaves the diver with bad posture. The first step then is too forget the "bull" about 10% of your body weight somehow giving you the amount of lead weight to wear for diving. Once a diver evolves beyond open water certification, this is not even in the ball park. Instead, personalize the actual amount of weight you need. Factors affecting weighting will be the type exposure suit, such as a wetsuit and its thickness, or a dry suit. Seawater vs. freshwater is another factor in the equation. Degree of relaxation effects breathing patterns, thus as divers gain experience and develop good breathing habits they tend to need less weight.

In weighting yourself for gas diving be comfortable at the end of the dive hovering at 10 feet on a decompression stop. If, at this depth, excessive flotation is needed to maintain neutral buoyancy, then remove some of the lead. On the other hand, do not become so buoyant that it is a struggle to stay at 10 feet without swimming downwards or hanging onto something. In my basic equipment, with a 1/4 inch suit, I plan a dive to be slightly negative at the beginning of the dive. In fact, with most double steel tanks I'm quite negative (as are most divers at the beginning of the dive). When using steel tanks other than the Farber double 70's, I use no weights. With the Farber tanks, six pounds is the magic number for me. Double eighties require 10 pounds due to the tremendous buoyancy change as gas is used. I allow 10 pounds for my drysuit. In steel 100's, 104's and 120's no weight is carried. When using a dry suit, I only put enough gas in it to maintain warmth. All buoyancy control is with the B.C. You will require different adjustments than I. Some folks will be more buoyant while others will require less weight. Individual experimentation is the only method to gain the right weight combinations. It is critical for comfort, proper swim attitude and gas consumption that we are correctly weighted. An over-weighted diver creates more drag due to the volume of the inflated B.C., uses more air, has difficulty maintaining adequate body attitude and is more fatigued at the end of a dive. Plus, heaven forbid, the over-weighted diver should have the "up" button on a B.C. fail.

Once the right amount of weight is derived, it is important that it be placed properly. It is a sad state that with over 40 years of recreational diving, that the weight placement is still the same obsolete overall style. Innovative technical divers devise methods of redistributing weight to enhance, rather than distract, from gaining better body attitude control. A heavy weight about the middle of the body (waist) makes it quite difficult to maintain a level posture regardless of perfection in buoyancy control. Once a diver has adjusted the weight system, it is time to fine tune buoyancy control. First, be efficient in use of the B.C. To maintain any posture totally at ease. Be able to be motionless (other than a foot up and down on inhalation and exhalation) in vertical and horizontal attitudes.

When swimming is commenced, if the head is in an upright position, it will create more lift and thus a slight adjustment to buoyancy is needed. As a matter of fact, a good practice session is to swim and change buoyancy simply by the placement of the head. As you change head angle you also change the direction of thrust. Being aware of use of the head for additional buoyancy control is valuable as in a critical buoyancy problem. This knowledge/ability can be the difference in lack of control and maintaining posture.

The location of buoyancy is also important. In single tank diving, most divers are more secure with a B.C. Jacket. However, back flotation is most likely a better body attitude control point. In double tanks, most technical divers agree back flotation systems are the only efficient means of buoyancy control combined with stability. In addition, with back flotation, a back plate may be worn affording ease of attachment of added dive tanks etc.

Propulsion skills are the key to efficacious movement through the water column. When using techniques, they all remain within the practice of streamlined profiles in the water. Propulsion skills include finning techniques, hand techniques, sculling applications and a combination of skills.

The modified flutter kick is one of the most commonly employed propulsion skills. A modified flutter kick is similar to a standard flutter kick. The primary difference is that the down stroke does not continue beyond the mid line of the diver. A maximum extension of 10 degrees is tolerated in strong currents.

The heel toe kick is a technique used in silty areas. In this kick ,the feet are bent upwards as far from the bottom as possible. Propulsion is derived by flexing of the foot along the line of the heel and toe. The foot is pointed upwards and flexed downward. Normally the leg does not move. However, a modification that is between this technique and the modified flutter allows for a short kick that travels almost half way down to the body.

The shuffle kick is also designed to use in silty areas or when a leg cramp exists. On this technique a resting leg extends along the midline of the body. This leg is centered and acts as a shield to diffuse fin action by the kicking leg. The kicking leg is arched high and kicked down to rest on the fin on the resting leg. At this point a slight glide is taken advantage of.

Two versions of the frog kick are used for efficient propulsion. The strongest of these is performed by bringing the heels together with slightly bent knees. The fins are at a 30 degree angle to the water. A outward kick is used to extend the legs to full extension followed by a inward thrust bringing the legs together. At this point, a glide for a count of five is taken, and the kick is restarted.

The second method is common in cave diving. In this application the feet are extended in a flat position, outwards to full extension. The fins are then dipped to a 30 to 45 degree angle and a strong inward thrust is made.

A modified dolphin kick rounds out the common fin propulsion skills. On this kick, both legs with ankles and knees touching are raised together and a down thrust is made to the mid line of the body. Unlike the standard dolphin kick, a diver does not hyperextend the body on a modified dolphin.

Tom Mount uses a descent line and hand pulls his way down to a deep wreck. This saves exertion in fighting the swift current in the area. Photo by Bret Gilliam

Hand propulsion skills add to the range of technique. Hands are used to pull along a sea floor (without disturbing marine life, corals etc.), Along a wreck, and along cave walls in current. The hands are also used to pull on tag lines to the anchor line on boats anchored in current. Combined hand and fin propulsion skills afford the ability to pull and glide, and to conserve gas.

Hands are not for free swimming when in scuba, and "wavy hands" are a misuse of technique. Hand sculling is beneficial in placing a diver in a given position.

Each environment a diver visits will have specific techniques to be applied. It is for this reason that the reader is advised to seek local knowledge and practice when traveling to a different locality. As a diver, we are only as efficient as the technique we have developed.

REFERENCE

The New Practical Diving; Tom Mount and Akira Ikehara; University Miami Press;

Safe Cave Diving; Tom Mount; NACD; (out of print)

C. Randy Bohrer

CHAPTER 15

PRODUCTION OF MIXED GAS
Mixing

More and more technical diving facilities are appearing each year, offering various breathing gases premixed and ready to use. These facilities allow the diver to forego the logistics and complexities of procuring, mixing, and pumping gases, and to concentrate on the objectives of the dive. Although the diver can now be insulated from these often painstaking, time-consuming processes, the knowledge of how these gases are prepared, and the limitations of the preparation and analysis equipment is still useful. There is also a segment of the diving population that prefers to be involved in all phases of the diving operation. It is to these groups, as well as to those setting up mixing and pumping facilities, that this chapter is directed.

AN INTRODUCTION TO GAS MIXING AND ANALYSIS

A complete, but simple definition of gas mixing is the combination of two or more pure gases or gas mixtures to form a final mixture of some desired composition. For example, two pure gases, nitrogen and oxygen, can be combined to form the diver's breathing gas known as NITROX. A pure gas and a mixture, such as oxygen and air, can be combined to form the same mixture. Three component mixtures, such as the helium-nitrogen-oxygen combination known as Trimix, can be prepared in a similar manner.

The techniques for mixing and pumping various gases depend upon the constituent gases, the desired final mixture, the equipment available, the skill levels of the personnel involved, and logistics. The general techniques for mixing gases are (1) mixing by partial pressure, where only the pressures of the constituent gases are considered in determining their percentages in the final mix, (2) continuous-flow mixing, where the appropriate amount of each gas is metered and injected into a gas flow stream, which is then delivered to a common mixing chamber, or inlet of a compressor, (3) mixing by volume, where known volumes of each gas are delivered to a container near atmospheric pressure, then compressed into high pressure cylinders, and (4) mixing by weight, where the gases are proportioned in the final mixture by the weight that each gas adds to the initial weight of the container.

Determination of the type and amount of various constituents in the breathing gas is important, since variations from the prescribed composition may cause adverse physiological reactions. Confidence in the composition and quality of the breathing gas is important in both air diving and mixed gas diving.

In air diving, since nitrogen and oxygen percentages are fixed, concern is centered on maintaining equipment to ensure the lack of contaminates such as carbon monoxide and oil vapor. Gas analysis is employed only occasionally, such as for periodic inspections and tests, or when the quality of the air from the compressor and storage system is in question.

In mixed gas diving, analysis of gas mixtures is performed routinely. Because of the potential hazards caused by hypoxia and oxygen toxicity, it is important that the oxygen percentage of each gas cylinder be measured before each dive. Oxygen analysis is the most common measurement performed, and although oxygen is not the only gas of interest, this measurement can be used to determine the proportions of other gases in the mixture.

DESCRIPTIONS OF VARIOUS MIXING TECHNIQUES

Mixing by Partial Pressure, Ideal and Real Gas Considerations

This method is probably the most common among technical divers. Required equipment is relatively inexpensive, simple, and portable, making it suitable for field operations. Although the accuracy of the technique is sometimes questioned, it provides for repeatability, meaning that a given procedure will yield the same final mixture time after time.

Mixing by partial pressure is usually based upon the assumption that the volume of a constituent gas in a mixture is directly related to the partial pressure of that gas. For example, if 1000 psi of oxygen is placed in an empty cylinder, then helium is added until the pressure reaches 5000 psi, the resultant oxygen percentage by volume, will equal the oxygen percentage by partial pressure, 1000 psi / 5000 psi, or 20%. This "ideal gas" assumption does not account for differences in compressibilities of various gases.

The accuracy of ideal-gas partial pressure mixing is limited to conditions where the compressibilities of the constituent gases are the same. For example, helium is not as compressible as oxygen. At pressures less than a few hundred psi, this difference is not noticeable to the technical diver. As the pressure increases, the compressibility difference also increases. At two to three thousand psi, the compressibility of helium is over ten percent greater than the compressibility of oxygen.

The U.S. Navy Diving Gas Manual (June, 1971) describes partial pressure mixing techniques which take into account the true behavior of the constituent gases. The procedures require accurate pressure readings and non-trivial computations. The demonstrative problems given often yield oxygen percentages that differ from those obtained using ideal gas methods by one percent or less, barely a difference detectable with most high-tech divers' analysis equipment.

A brief survey of high-tech pumping facilities and individuals who are active in mixing gases indicated a subjective use of real gas properties. That is, most mixers who were making an adjustment to compensate for the compressibility differences between the various gases, were applying an arbitrary "fudge-factor" which was based on experience. Others made no compensation at all, but still obtained acceptable gas mixtures.

There are several reasons that different methods for compensating for real gases yield acceptable results. First, errors introduced by gauge accu-

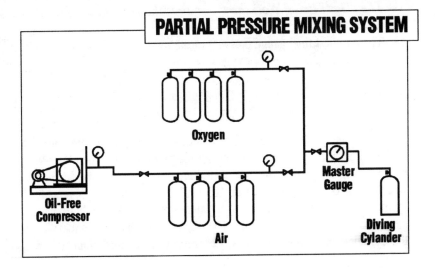

PARTIAL PRESSURE MIXING SYSTEM

racy, gauge resolution, and temperature changes during mixing may tend to cancel the real gas effects. Second, the typical oxygen analyzer in use by technical divers and pumping facilities is accurate to only one percent, which is often not sufficient to detect changes caused by real gas effects. Finally, the characteristics of the gases themselves may tend to minimize any differences that would occur. For example, Trimix is often prepared by mixing helium and air. Helium and nitrogen have similar compressibilities, (my definition of "similar" is < 5% difference between compressibility factor, Z) at diving cylinder pressures, and since air is 79% nitrogen, the compressibility of both components of the mix is similar. Although practical experience and available equipment tends to decrease the importance of real-gas considerations, these techniques are useful. Careful application of the real-gas techniques will yield more certain results, but ideal gas methods can yield acceptable results within certain limits.

CALCULATING MIXING PRESSURES USING IDEAL GAS ASSUMPTIONS

The procedures for combining various combinations of oxygen, helium, and air to produce Heliox, Trimix, and NITROX are similar but become involved and prone to error if considered on a case by case basis. Instead of attempting to describe a mixing procedure for each case here, a general worksheet has been developed which applies to all cases. The worksheet (see end of chapter for examples) removes much of the human error associated with analyzing each special case, saves time, and forces detailed recording of information.

The "Gas Mixing Worksheet" requires the entry of the following four values:
1. The required final gauge pressure of the mixture
2. The required fractions of oxygen, helium, and nitrogen in the final mixture
3. The gauge pressure of any residual gas remaining in the cylinder
4. The fractions of oxygen, helium, and nitrogen of this residual mixture.

The technique of considering the residual gas allows the mixer to "top off" a partially full cylinder without draining the cylinder, thereby saving time and avoiding gas waste. The technique also applies to the distinction which must be made between an "empty" cylinder and an "evacuated" cylinder. An "empty" cylinder has a gauge pressure of zero, but contains some gas at atmospheric pressure. This gas is either the last gas that was in the cylinder, or, if the valve has been removed and sufficient time has

Compressed air and mixed gas rack at Key West Divers High Tech Training Centers. Photo by Bret Gilliam.

elapsed for diffusion to occur, air. An "evacuated" cylinder has no residual gas in it; the gauge pressure is -14.7 psi (a perfect vacuum). This condition is not possible to achieve in practice, however, if the residual gas contains undesirable components, it can be removed by "purging". Purging involves adding a gas to a pressure of several times ambient (50 to 100 psi), draining the gas, then repeating this procedure several times. Purging can also be accomplished by flowing the gas through the container at ambient pressure for a period of several minutes. The cylinder will then contain only the purge gas.

PARTIAL PRESSURE MIXING - EQUIPMENT AND PRACTICE

The preceding discussions involve the methods used for determining how much of which gases to add to an empty or partially filled cylinder. It is easy to state that a certain amount of a certain gas is to be added to a storage or diving cylinder, but accomplishing this operation requires a variety of equipment and involves factors beyond those associated with compressing breathing air for diving.

Compressing breathing air for standard diving requires a compressor, a filtration system, and transfer hoses with appropriate fittings. Dive stores typically add a storage bank system, to store high pressure air for quicker fills and to manage compressor operation. Once operating, the compressor simply uses ambient air to manufacture high pressure air and deliver it to the diving cylinder. While technical diving mixtures often use air as a component in the mix, other gases such as helium and oxygen are also used and must be transferred from their storage cylinders to the cylinders for mixing. Additional equipment includes special transfer hoses, gas booster pumps, and special compressors or filter systems. Since higher than normal concentrations of oxygen are often used during the gas transfer or mixing process, this equipment must be cleaned and maintained accordingly.

TECHNIQUES AND EQUIPMENT FOR PARTIAL PRESSURE NITROX MIXING

NITROX can be mixed by combining oxygen and nitrogen, oxygen and air, or various combinations of oxygen, air, and other NITROX mixtures. NITROX can also be purchased pre-mixed and pumped into the diving cylinders. Most technical divers and pumping facilities produce the mixture by combining oxygen and air.

Combining oxygen and air has several advantages. First, if the oxygen is added to an empty cylinder, the required pressure is generally less than 600 psi (refer to the mixing examples at the end of this section to this section). This low pressure requirement allows the oxygen to transferred with minimal waste if several oxygen cylinders are cascaded. Also, handling oxygen at lower pressures reduces the risk of fire or explosion. Finally, the other component in the mixture, air, is inexpensive to produce.

The primary danger of combining air and oxygen involves oxygen compatibility. Most air compressors are lubricated with oil which contaminates the outlet air. Depending upon the efficiency of the filter system, some of this oil may remain in the outlet air. Even if the amount is within acceptable limits, the oil can accumulate in the mixing cylinders and possibly cause a fire or explosion when exposed to pure oxygen. Small carbon particles from the filters are also a source of contamination.

An oil-free compressor can be used to avoid these dangers. Alternatively, a standard breathing air compressor equipped with special filters or serviced with oxygen compatible compressor oil can be used. It is important to note that such compressor systems, while suitable for producing oxygen compatible, or clean air, are not oxygen compatible themselves. Oxygen compatibility depends not only on the materials to which oxygen will be exposed, but on gas flow paths, pressurization rates, and other mechanical factors. Only a compressor specifically designed or approved by the manufacturer should be used for pumping oxygen or NITROX. Cylinders and valves should be cleaned often to avoid an accumulation of incompatible materials regardless of the pumping system used.

TECHNIQUES AND EQUIPMENT FOR TRIMIX AND HELIOX PARTIAL PRESSURE MIXING:

Trimix can be prepared by combining helium with oxygen and air or various NITROX mixtures. It is also possible, but not common in technical diving to prepare Trimix by mixing the three pure gases, oxygen, helium, and nitrogen. Heliox is prepared by mixing oxygen and helium. Both gases can be purchase pre-mixed, and while pre-mixed Heliox is very economical, pre-mixed Trimix, is quite expensive by comparison.

Preparing these gas mixtures requires much of the same equipment that is used in preparing NITROX. Additional equipment required usually includes a gas booster pump. Due to the cost of helium, and the higher pressures required during the mixing process, this machine is almost essential. Returning an oxygen cylinder with 500 psi remaining does not represent a substantial loss of value, but returning a helium cylinder with the same amount of gas, increases this loss of value three to four-fold. In most cases 750 to 1000 psi of helium is required in the mixtures, meaning that the supply cylinder becomes unusable when its pressure drops below these values. A gas booster allows most of the helium in the supply cylinder to be utilized.

GENERAL PARTIAL PRESSURE MIXING PROCEDURE:

A typical mixing procedure begins with the transfer of the appropriate amount of oxygen from the oxygen supply cylinder into the mixing cylinder. This transfer is accomplished by attaching a fill hose assembly to the valves of the supply and mixing cylinders. This hose assembly should be equipped with a suitable gauge to monitor the pressure, and a regulator and valve to control the gas transfer. The pressurization rate should not exceed 70 psi per minute. This slow transfer rate aids in maintaining mixing cylinder temperature and reduces the risk of flashing caused by rapid compression of gas lines, or high gas velocities through passages. After the desired pressure has been reached, the supply cylinder is allowed to cool to initial temperature, and then the pressure is adjusted if necessary.

After the oxygen has been transferred, other gases are then added to the cylinder. For Trimix or Heliox, helium is pumped with a booster or other gas compressor. For Trimix or NITROX, the cylinder fill is completed by adding air from a compressor or air storage system. Trimix and heliox is allowed to stand for six hours, or agitated, by rolling or some similar means for one hour to allow the gases to homogenize. NITROX mixtures require less time to homogenize. An oxygen analyzer is then used to verify the composition of the mixture. Several checks should be made to ensure that the gases are sufficiently mixed, evidenced by consistent values over more than one analysis. Any necessary adjustments can then be made.

Allowing sufficient time or providing agitation for mixing is important because helium does not mix easily with oxygen and other gases. Some mixers report large variations in analyzer readings as the orientation of the mixing cylinder is changed. One mixer experienced so much difficulty in getting a consistent analyzer reading that the cylinder was drained and a new mix prepared. There is some speculation that these gas mixtures are prone to "stratify", or separate in the cylinder into oxygen rich and oxygen deficient zones. Although such lack of mixing exists when the gases are first added to the cylinder, experience has shown that after successful mixing, stratification will not occur. There is also a belief that the composition of a helium mixture can change over time as pure helium leaks from the cylinder, leaving other gases behind. Given the fact that helium is difficult to contain under pressure, this phenomenon seems likely. However, experience has shown that such changes in mixture composition do not occur.

During the mixing or adjustment process it may be necessary to add oxygen at higher pressures than a few hundred psi. Gas boosters or compressors used for this purpose must be specifically designed for use with oxygen. Compressing oxygen to pressures over 3000 psi should not be attempted.

CONTINUOUS FLOW MIXING (ATMOSPHERIC ENTRAINMENT METHOD)

Continuous flow mixing systems are usually employed for mixing NITROX, although these systems can be used to mix other gases. In the typical NITROX system, oxygen is metered and injected into an air flow stream at atmospheric pressure. This gas is then passed through coils of tubing or baffles to provide sufficient mixing before delivery to a compressor. The compressor either delivers the gas to high pressure storage containers, or directly to a surface-supplied diver. The compressor output is sampled and analyzed for proper oxygen percentage. If the oxygen percentage is incorrect, the operator can adjust the metering device. Some systems are equipped with high and low oxygen alarms, and feedback loops for automatic adjustment of the metering device.

This method avoids the problems associated with handling high pressure oxygen, and allows all of the gas in the gas supplier cylinder to be utilized. Also, since high pressure oxygen is not required, containers of liquid

ATMOSPHERIC ENTRAINMENT SYSTEM

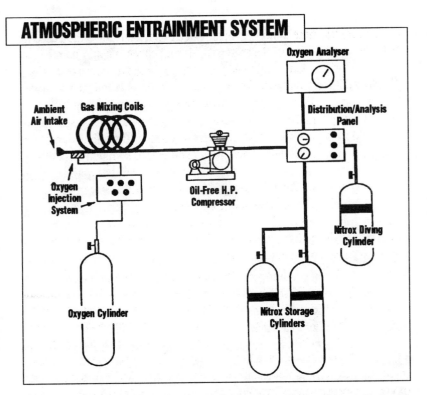

oxygen can be used, decreasing both the cost of the gas and required storage space.

It is easier to obtain accuracy with this system, since the gases are mixed at low pressure, where real gas effects are not significant. Also, in most systems, oxygen analysis is performed continuously during mixing, so that adjustments can be made before mixing is completed.

Continuous flow mixing equipment includes gas mixing controls, distribution and analysis controls, and a compressor suitable for pumping the gas. If the gas mixture is NITROX, the compressor should be specifically designed or approved by the manufacturer for this purpose. As previously stated, cleaning a standard compressor for oxygen service and replacing its lubricant with oxygen compatible oil does not necessarily make it suitable for pumping oxygen and NITROX. Rix manufactures compressors that are suitable for these mixtures.

A typical mixing procedure involves simply pressurizing the system, starting the compressor, adjusting the oxygen metering device, observing the oxygen analyzer reading and making any necessary adjustments. The system allows for relatively large volumes of gas to be prepared easily and efficiently.

Ed Betts, president of American NITROX Divers, Inc. (ANDI) with NITROX filling station and gas analyzer. Photo by Bret Gilleam

MIXING BY VOLUME

Mixing by volume is very similar to continuous flow mixing in that the volume of the constituent gases is considered and mixing occurs at low pressure. The primary difference is that a large volume of gas is mixed and analyzed at low pressure first, then pumped into storage cylinders or delivered to a surface supplied diver.

The gas can be mixed in a large flexible bag at atmospheric pressure or in a decompression chamber at a pressure of around 100 psi. The mixing chamber used must be large enough to hold the amount of gas required. For example, if a 240 cubic foot high pressure cylinder is to be filled with a mixture prepared in a flexible bag, then the capacity of that bag must be 240 cubic feet, or about the same as that of several small closets. Since the decompression chamber method contains gas under pressure, the size requirement is only a fraction of that required for the flexible bag.

This method is not currently in use by technical divers but may be useful since it is accurate, and equipment is relatively simple and inexpensive. The size of the required mixing container however, precludes its application to most field operations.

MIXING BY WEIGHT

Mixing gases by weight requires the application of the real gas techniques described in the U.S. Navy Diving Gas Manual (1971). Given the required volume of each constituent gas in the mixture, the weight of each gas is calculated. The mixing cylinder is weighed, and gas is added until the required amount by weight is reached. After mixing, the gas is allowed to homogenize, then analyzed. Adjustments are made as necessary. This method requires relatively complex calculations and accurate scales.

Mixing by weight is not suitable for field operations and is not currently in use by technical divers.

GAS ANALYSIS

Analyzing the diving gases in technical diving is essential to ensure that the mixture is as required and expected. Gas analysis is used after and during mixing to ensure that the mixture is prepared properly. It is also performed before each dive to ensure that each cylinder contains the proper gas mixture and was not inadvertently interchanged with a cylinder containing a different mixture.

Although the percentages of helium and nitrogen in a mixture are of interest, most technical divers and gas mixers do

Dick Rutkowski with examples of two oxygen analyzers: the Teledyne analog unit and the Mini-Ox portable digital model. Photo by Bret Gilliam

not have analysis equipment capable of measuring these gases. Therefore, oxygen analysis is normally the only measurement performed. The determination of the oxygen percentage is of primary importance for evaluating the risk of oxygen toxicity and the application of decompression schedules. A five percent variation in the nitrogen and helium percentages has no effect on the oxygen toxicity risk, as long as the oxygen percentage is correct. The same variation is also tolerable with respect to the validity of most decompression schedules. However, if the oxygen percentage varies by as little as two percent, both the oxygen toxicity risk and decompression schedule are affected.

Given the components of a gas mixture and its oxygen percentage, the percentages of the other gases in the mixture can be determined. For example, if a NITROX mixture is known to contain 32% oxygen, then the nitrogen percentage is 68%. A similar technique can be applied to determine the helium and nitrogen percentages in a Trimix. In addition to the oxygen percentage, the component gases must be known, and the mixture must contain only two component gases, such as helium and NITROX or helium and air.

As an example of determining helium and nitrogen percentages in Trimix, consider a Trimix prepared by mixing helium and air. If the oxygen analyzer reads 16%, then the percentage of air in the mixture is 16/21 =

76. Therefore the helium percentage is 100 - 76 = 24%, and the nitrogen percentage is the balance, 100 - (24+16) = 60%.

It is interesting to include the accuracy of the oxygen analysis in this problem. If the analyzer is accurate to 1%, the true oxygen percentage can be as low as 15% or as high as 17%. Then the air percentage can range from 15/21 = 71 to 17/21 = 81, causing the helium percentage to range from 100-71=29 to 100-81=19. The resultant nitrogen percentage range is then 100-(29+15) = 56, to 100-(19+17)=64. Note that although the oxygen percentage only varies 1% from the required 16%, that the helium percentage varies 5%, and the nitrogen percentage varies 4%. These variations indicate that special care must be used when mixing three components to produce Trimix or when mixing in a partially full cylinder, and that adjustments to such mixtures should not be attempted.

SPECIFIC EQUIPMENT DESCRIPTIONS

Haskel Gas Booster

The Haskel pump is a small, lightweight, one or two cylinder compressor type piston machine. Unlike a compressor which takes ambient pressure gas, usually air, as the input, this machine takes high pressure gas and compresses it further. It is commonly used by dive shops and fire departments to boost storage gas pressure to diving and SCBA cylinder pressures. It is also used by commercial dive contractors to boost gases such as helium and oxygen which are purchased in 2400 psi cylinders to the required pressure.

This booster does not have a fuel or electric drive motor; it is driven by low pressure (100 psi) air, much like a garage or auto body shop's air tools. In the dive shop, the high pressure storage air is separated into two paths. One path is regulated down to low pressure to drive the booster, while the other is compressed to higher pressure. Therefore, only a portion of the air put into the pump ends up in the scuba tank; the rest is used to power the machine. When boosting an expensive gas such as helium, a separate drive gas, often from a low pressure compressor is used to power the booster while the helium is transferred without waste. When boosting gases such as oxygen or NITROX, the a separate drive gas must be used, as the drive section of the booster is not compatible with higher than normal concentrations of oxygen.

Boosters are available for pumping to a variety of pressures and for a variety of gases, including oxygen. The dive shop model is known as the Scuba Amp and is effective for generating 3000 psi or more output with an input of 1500-2000 psi. Others are capable of generating pressures of 5000 psi or higher with an input of only a few hundred psi. The greater the difference between the input and the output pressure, the more air that is required to drive the booster. As an example, the AGT-15/30 booster compressing 500 psi to 3000 psi uses about eight cubic feet of drive air for each cubic foot of gas pumped. The Scuba Amp is not capable of this degree of compression, but is much more efficient with respect to drive air in its normal operating range, boosting 2000 psi to 3000 psi.

Sierra Precision Gas Booster

The Sierra Precision gas booster is a compressor type machine that takes high pressure gas as its source and compresses it further. It is normally used by dive shops and fire departments to boost storage bank air to diving and SCBA cylinder pressures. Unlike the Haskel pump which depends upon compressed air for power, the Sierra booster is electrically driven, therefore all of the source gas is compressed.

The booster utilizes dry seals which add no contamination to the gas transferred, making it ideal for pumping breathing gases. The manufacturer does not recommend using this machine for pumping NITROX, oxygen, or other gases with higher than normal concentrations of oxygen. Depending upon the efficiency of the seals, however, the booster may be useful for pumping helium or premixed Heliox.

The primary disadvantage is the required minimum inlet pressure of 1000 psi. The pumping system requires this pressure to function properly and operating this booster with a lower inlet pressure results in gas transfer that is very inefficient.

Other Gas Boosters

Other machines for compressing various gases include hydraulically actuated pumps and oxygen compressors. The hydraulic machines use oil which acts upon flexible diaphragms that in turn compress gas. The oxygen compressor is often used by industrial gas suppliers and is available to the technical diver through manufacturers such as Rix. While these machines are useful for mixing technical diving gases, they are not commonly used for this purpose at this time.

Reimers Engineering Oxygen Enriched Air Blending Unit

This system provides mixing and analysis equipment for continuous flow mixing of NITROX gas mixtures. Controls for oxygen flow, indicators for oxygen pressure, storage bank pressure, compressor pressure, and oxygen percentage are provided, as well as warnings for high and low oxygen percentage, and other operating conditions. The system includes an Analox oxygen monitor for oxygen analysis and high/low oxygen detection and alarm control.

Incorporated with an oil-free compressor, NITROX mixtures containing up to 50% oxygen can be delivered at flow rates from five to 30 scfm to storage banks or diving cylinders. This mixing system is contained in one neat, easy to use package that helps minimize errors in mixing. It is also suitable for pumping air, making it an ideal candidate for air system upgrades or new installations.

HIGH PRESSURE GAS CYLINDERS:

Oxygen, helium, and other gases are normally purchased from the gas supplier in high pressure cylinders. The same type of cylinder is commonly used for gas storage at dive shops and mixed gas pumping facilities. The cylinders are available in a variety of sizes; the particular sizes and their designations depend on the gas supplier.

Not included in this list are aluminum cylinders, cylinders with rated pressures less than 2000 psi, and various odd sizes. Based upon this list, there appears to be no standard for cylinder designation, capacity, and rated pressure. Generally, the common designations and sizes are the H or K, containing from 240 cf to 290 cf at 2015 to 2400 psi, and the J or T, containing 337 cf at 2640 psi. These cubic foot capacities are usually the amount of ideal gas that will be in the cylinder at the stated pressure. Due to compressibility effects, the cylinder will contain approximately this amount of oxygen, but less helium or nitrogen.

Since dive shops usually compress gases to 3000 psi and more, a storage cylinder with a pressure rating higher than the 2000 to 2600 psi ratings of the common industrial gas cylinders is favored. Cylinders of similar physical size, with pressure ratings of 3600 psi and 4500 psi are available.

Gas mixing cylinders which are exposed to pure oxygen must be cleaned for oxygen service. This requirement is usually not a problem, since industrial gas cylinders for oxygen are readily available.

TRANSFER HOSES

In order to add a gas from an industrial gas cylinder to a diving cylinder, some form of transfer hose is required. A large variety of hoses of different materials, sizes, and pressure ratings are available. The hose must be equipped with appropriate fittings or adapters to allow connection between the gas source and destination.

Hose material and rated pressure depend upon the gases transferred and the pressure that the hose is likely to encounter. For transferring oxygen from 2400 psi storage bottles, SAE100R7 specification hose in 1/4" inside diameter, such as Parker Parflex 550H is normally used. For trans-

CYLINDER DESIGNATIONS AND CAPACITIES

The following is a list of common industrial steel gas cylinder designations and capacities:

Designation	Gas Supplier	Cubic Ft	Pressure	Height (in.)	Weight (lbs.)
A, 1C	Scott	214	2015	56	114
B	All-Gas	6	2015	17	6
B	Air Products	7.4	2015	16	5
C	Scott	33	2015	24	27
D	All-Gas	12	2015	19-3/4	9
D	Air Products	15	2015	20	11
D	Scott	11	2015	18	12
DEY	Linde	124	2200	48	82
E	All-Gas	25	2015	28-3/4	12
E	Air Products	25	2015	30	14
M	All-Gas	122	2015	47	72
M	Air Products	125	2217	47	63
G	Air Products	251	2217	51	97
H	All-Gas	244	2015	55	111
H	Air Products	282	2492	51	119
HC-500	Linde	504	4500	56	145
HH	All-Gas	300	2400	59	144
J	Air Products	337	2640	55	140
K, 1D	Scott	289	2400	60	135
K	Linde	249	2200	56	133
Q	Linde	83	2200	35	65
R	Linde	20	2200	19	12
S	Linde	154	2200	51	80
T	Linde	337	2640	60	143
XHP	All-Gas	360	3600	55	182
XL	Linde	70	2200	41	49
XXXHP	All-Gas	480	6000	55	304

ferring helium or air to pressures up to 5000 psi, SAE100R8 in 1/4" diameter, such as Parflex 520N or Synflex 3R80 are used. When in doubt as to the gas compatibility of the particular hose, always contact the distributor or manufacturer.

It is common practice among "backyard mixers" to transfer gases, including oxygen, by attaching a hose with appropriate fittings between the supply cylinder and the scuba cylinder and using the supply cylinder valve to control the gas flow. This method causes excessive wear to the supply cylinder valve seat, and when pure oxygen is transferred, can cause possible ignition and failure of the valve seat. It is recommended to equip the fill hose with a regulator or variable restrictor designed for this purpose.

This equipment not only makes the gas transfer safer, but more controllable, resulting in easier and more accurate gas mixing.

GAUGES

Accurate gauges with resolution sufficient to ascertain the pressure within required limits are necessary for efficient gas mixing. Unfortunately, the typical 2-1/2" face 3000 or 4000 psi gauge has graduations only to the nearest 100 psi and accuracy from plus and minus 30 psi to plus and minus 80 psi or more. When a few hundred psi of oxygen needs to be added to a cylinder, the amount of variance allowed by such gauges can affect the oxygen percentage of the final mix by two percent or more. These gauges can be used if the mixer is willing to make adjustments each time the mix is found to be incorrect.

A low pressure gauge can be used for metering small amounts of gas that are added to an empty cylinder. A 2-1/2" face 300 or 500 psi gauge typically offers resolution to the nearest 10 psi. A mixer with a good eye can read to the nearest five psi or better. This technique provides an inexpensive means to prepare certain gas mixtures, but is rather limited.

Manufacturers such as Ashcroft and US Gauge offer gauges with face sizes up to 12", and accuracies of 0.25%. The large, accurate gauges can be quite expensive, on the order of hundreds of dollars, compared to the ten to fifteen dollar price tags of the small common gauges.

Electronic digital gauges are also available which offer accuracies of 0.25% and readings to the nearest psi. Some technical diving suppliers are also designing digital pressure gauges for gas mixing.

OXYGEN ANALYZERS

Principles used by oxygen analysis equipment include galvanic action, which utilizes a "fuel cell" as the oxygen sensor, colorimetric detection, where gas is passed through color indicating tubes, magnetic susceptibility, where the effect of a gas on a magnetic field is considered, thermal conductivity, where the heat transfer capacity of a gas is measured, and light refraction techniques such as ultraviolet spectrophotometry, infrared spectrophotometry, and gas chromatography.

Analyzers using the galvanic fuel cell process are the most common in technical diving applications. The galvanic fuel cell contains a chemical which generates an electrical current as it oxidizes. The faster the oxidation, the greater the current. The current depends upon the oxygen partial pressure, therefore, the oxygen percentage can be determined. Sensor accuracy varies from less than 0.5% to over 2%, depending on the type. Be-

Teledyne oxygen analyzer indicating normal oxygen per centage at 21% during calibration test. Photo by Bret Gilliam

cause changes in pressure, temperature, and humidity affect the current from the sensor, it is important to calibrate the sensor each time that the instrument is used, to ensure that these conditions are identical between the time of calibration and actual analysis. Since the sensor oxidizes with exposure to oxygen, it will eventually be exhausted. Depending on the type, sensor life varies from three months to four years in normal use.

When selecting an oxygen analyzer, durability, sensor accuracy, sensor life, portability, and price are considerations. Care should be used when evaluating specification sheets as some manufacturers site instrument accuracy as well as sensor accuracy. Many digital electronic instruments offer accuracies of plus or minus 0.01% of their full scale reading. This statement does not imply that oxygen analysis can be accomplished with this degree of accuracy. The sensor accuracy, which for galvanic fuel cells is usually around plus or minus 1%, is the figure of interest.

OTHER GAS ANALYSIS SYSTEMS

While helium and nitrogen analysis is generally not done, due to the cost and availability of measurement equipment, analysis of toxic gases, such as carbon monoxide can be accomplished with inexpensive electronic analyzers or by using color indicating tubes, such as the Draeger tube. Testing for these gases may have a place in technical diving, especially since the toxicity of these contaminants increases with depth.

MARKING OF CYLINDERS

It is important to mark mixing and diving cylinders in a manner that clearly indicates the cylinder contents. Conspicuous tags or labels should be attached to alert users or handlers that the cylinder contains gas other than what is normally expected.

The Compressed Gas Association (CGA) designates standards for color coding of industrial and medical gas cylinders. The standard colors

Nitrox cylinder showing green color band and labeling. The top portion (or cylinder neck) is "oxygen green" and the cylinder body is yellow. Note the DIN fitting valve and clip harness for attachment to diver or stage line. Cylinder contents tag or label will reveal exact mixture. Photo by Bret Gilliam

for medical gases are green for oxygen, yellow for air, black for nitrogen, brown for helium, and brown and green for Heliox. Sometimes cylinders are used for mixing and storing various diving gases without regard to their color code. This practice is unacceptable and clearly in violation of accepted standards. However, recognizing that the color code is not always observed, the importance of conspicuously tagging or labeling the cylinder to indicate its contents cannot be understated.

Diving cylinders do not necessarily follow the CGA standards for color coding, but many technical divers are attempting to observe the standards or establish new ones to meet unique requirements. A NITROX diving cylinder is yellow with a four inch wide green band near the top of the cylinder. In addition, large letters stating "NITROX ONLY" are printed in green under the green band. A tag or label is also affixed indicating the particular gas mixture. Oxygen cylinders are normally entirely green. In addition to color coding and labels indicating gas composition, many technical divers also attach a removable tag stating "DANGER DO NOT OPERATE", as a warning that the cylinder contains a gas mixture other than air.

OTHER CONSIDERATIONS FOR GAS MIXING

A question that is often asked regarding transferring helium or oxygen into diving cylinder is, "How many fills can you get without a booster pump?" The answer to this question is not a simple one, but if the internal volume and initial pressure of both the supply and diving cylinder is known, then the final pressure in each cylinder can be determined after any amount of gas has been transferred.

Using an ideal gas approach, the sum of the pressure-volume products before mixing and after mixing is equal. In the case of two cylinders, a supply cylinder and a diving cylinder, the equation is:

Pi (supply) x V(supply) + Pi(diving) x V(diving) =

Pf(supply) x V(supply) + Pf(diving) x V(diving) where Pi is the initial pressure of the supply or diving cylinder, Pf is the final pressure of the supply or diving cylinder, and V is the internal volume of the supply or diving cylinder. The internal volume is actual volume, not the standard cubic foot capacity that is normally quoted. The internal volume of a standard aluminum 80 cubic foot cylinder is approximately 0.4 cubic feet. The internal volume of an industrial "K" cylinder is approximately 1.6 cubic feet.

To illustrate these points and explain the use of the equation, consider a series of gas transfers from a "K" cylinder containing 2400 psi. The requirement is to add 750 psi of helium to an empty aluminum 80 cubic foot cylinder. For the first transfer:

Pi(supply)	= 2400
V(supply)	= 1.6
Pi(diving)	= 0
V(diving)	= 0.4
Pf(supply)	= unknown
Pf(diving)	= 750
2400 x 1.6 + 0	= Pf x 1.6 + 750 x 0.4
3840 - 300	= Pf x 1.6
2212	= Pf

For the second transfer:

Pi(supply)	= 2212 and all other values are the same.
2212 x 1.6	= Pf x 1.6 + 750 x 0.4
3539.2 - 300	= Pf x 1.6
2024.5	= Pf

This process can continue until the supply pressure becomes (according to the formula) less than the diving cylinder pressure. In this example, the aluminum 80 can be filled eight times. After this last fill, the supply pressure is 900 psi. The highest pressure that can be achieved without a booster is about 720 psi.

More efficiency and higher pressures can be obtained by using several supply cylinders and cascading. Cascading is a process where as the pressure in one supply cylinder becomes too low to transfer the desired pressure, the next supply cylinder is used until its pressure becomes too low, and the process can continue. As few as two or three supply cylinders can be used very effectively in this manner. The same equation is used to calculate final pressures, except that the diving cylinder pressure will not always be zero as in the previous example.

The equation presented can also be used to calculate the final pressures in the supply and diving cylinders after using a booster pump, provided that none of the gas transferred is used to power the booster. The final supply cylinder pressure will be less than the diving cylinder pressure, but not less than zero. A negative number indicates that the gas supply was exhausted before the required pressure in the diving cylinder was reached.

SUMMARY

Of the available gas mixing methods, the two most common are mixing in high pressure cylinders by partial pressure, and continuous flow mixing. Each has advantages and disadvantages, and the selection of the method depends upon the objectives of the mixer.

Mixing by partial pressure does not require expensive, complex, or bulky equipment, making it suitable for the weekend mixer or for field operations. This method requires complex calculations, but the risk of error can be removed by utilizing pre-printed worksheets, computer or calculator programs, or other tools that use consistent calculation techniques. Most mixing is performed using ideal gas laws which are sometimes not sufficient to achieve the required accuracy. In these cases, real gas techniques can be used to compensate for the inadequacies of the ideal gas laws, or adjustments can be made to the final mixture.

Continuous flow mixing is favored for mixing NITROX, but may be applied to other gases. Mixing is accomplished at low pressure, where real gas effects are insignificant. The composition of the final mixture is monitored throughout the mixing process, allowing adjustments to be made instantly to ensure a proper mix. Pumping and transfer of high pressure oxygen is not necessary, since the oxygen is added at low pressure, decreasing associated risks and allowing the use of liquid oxygen. The method requires special equipment for metering and mixing the gases before delivery to a compressor, but for the mixer interested in producing larger volumes of gas without a proportional increase in work, is relatively simple and efficient.

Mixing by volume in a large inflatable bag or decompression chamber is not commonly performed in technical diving but may be useful since it offers many of the advantages of both partial pressure and continuous flow mixing. Mixing by weight seems to combine the disadvantages of the other methods, but offers greater accuracy. It is not used in technical diving and seems more suited to research related applications.

Preparing gas mixtures for technical diving requires special equipment that is not normally used at air pumping facilities. Examples include oil-free compressors, oxygen booster pumps, accurate gauges, and oxygen analyzers. Any equipment exposed to higher than normal concentrations of oxygen must be cleaned and maintained accordingly. Much of the typical dive shop equipment can be adapted or prepared for gas mixing. An example is the cleaning of Haskel gas boosters for oxygen service. Also, a conventional oil lubricated compressor can be cleaned and refilled with oxygen compatible oil, making it suitable for producing air for partial pressure gas mixing.

Gas mixing, analysis, and dispensing requires equipment and effort beyond that which most divers and dive stores are accustomed. There will always be groups and individuals who will not follow accepted procedures because of ignorance, or unwillingness to obtain the necessary equipment and training. Accidents will undoubtedly follow this portion of the mixed gas diving community, as is the case in the sport diving community. However, if responsibility, patience, and care are applied to preparing technical diving gas mixtures, the objectives of the diver and the mixer can be realized both efficiently and safely.

REFERENCES

Van Wylen, Gordon J. and Sonntag, Richard E. *Fundamentals of Classical Thermodynamics.* John Wiley and Sons, Inc., New York, 1978.

U.S. Department of the Navy, *U.S. Navy Diving Manual,* Volume 2, Revision 3, NAVSEA 0994-LP-001-9020, 15 May 1991.

U.S. Department of the Navy, *US Navy Diving Gas Manual,* Second Edition, NAVSHIPS 0994-003-7010, June 30, 1971.

Rutkowski, Dick. *NITROX Manual.* Hyperbarics International. Key Largo, FL, 1989.

Betts, Edward A., *The Application of Enriched Air Mixtures,* American NITROX Divers, Inc., 1992.

U.S. Deep Caving Team, The Wakulla Springs Project, Edited by W. H. Stone, 1989.

Halliday, David and Resnick, Robert. *Physics - Parts I and II,* Third Edition. John Wiley and Sons, Inc., New York, 1978.

Haskel, Inc. *AG Series Gas Boosters Rapid Reference Performance DATA Book,* Haskel, Inc., Burbank, CA, 1990.

Sierra Precision, *Booster Air Compressor Model 9000 Specification,* Sierra Precision, Cucamonga, CA.

National Draeger, *Detector Tube Products and Specifications,* 1990, National Draeger, Inc., Pittsburgh, PA.

Butler, Glenn J., *Technical Diver,* Issue No. 1, Winter 1991, AquaCorp, Key West, FL

INSTRUCTIONS AND EXAMPLES

The following section is included for the purposes of example and to show what the typical steps are in a gas mixing process for a qualified professionally trained dispenser. It is not intended that the reader use these examples to attempt to mix his own gases. Gas blending and mixing is a highly technical process that requires specialized training and equipment. It is recommended that the reader procure gases from a professional facility.

Row A. Enter the required final gauge pressure (psi) of the mixture.

Row B. As indicated, add 14.7 to Item A.

Row C. Enter the required final fractions of oxygen, helium, and nitrogen. *For example,* 0.32, 0, and 0.68 for 32% O_2 NITROX.

Row D. Multiply the items in Row C by the pressure in Item B.

Row E. Enter the gauge pressure (psi) of the residual gas. If the cylinder is "empty" or has been purged, enter 0.

Row F. As indicated, add 14.7 to Item E.

Row G. Enter the residual fractions of oxygen, helium, and nitrogen. If the cylinder is empty, enter composition of the previous mixture, if the cylinder has been purged, enter the composition of the purge gas.

Row H. Multiply the items in Row G by the pressure in Item F.

Row I. Subtract the items in Row H from the items in Row D. If any of these entries are negative, then it will not be possible to achieve the desired gas mixture without first draining some or all of the residual gas.

Row J. Item J2 is the same as Item I2. Divide Item I3 by 0.79 to find the pressure of air to add. Finally, Item J1 is the difference between the final pressure (B) and the sum of the residual pressure (F), helium pressure (J2), and Air pressure (J3). The items in this row are the respective increases in gauge pressures required for each gas. If any of these items are negative, then it will not be possible to achieve the desired gas mixture without first draining some or all of the residual gas.

Check: Add the oxygen pressure due to residual gas (H), due to pure oxygen added (J1) and due to air added (multiply J3 by 0.21). This sum should equal the final oxygen pressure in item C1 within a few PSI (tolerance for rounding errors).

#1 SAMPLE GAS MIXING WORKSHEET

Instructions: Enter final (desired) and residual (remaining in tank from previous mix) gauge pressures and fraction of oxygen (FO_2), helium (FHe), and nitrogen (FN_2) in the spaces indicated. Perform calculations and checks as indicated. If Item I1, I2, or I3 is less than zero, then some of the residual gas must be drained from the cylinder. Items J1, J2, and J3 are the respective increases in pressures for each gas added to the cylinder.

REQUIRED FINAL MIX

A. PSIG _____

B. PSI
(A + 14.7) _____

C1. FO_2 _____   C2. FHe _____   C3. FN_2 _____

D1. PPO_2 _____   D2. PPHe _____   D3. PPN_2 _____
(BXC1) _____   (BXC$_2$) _____   (BXC3) _____

RESIDUAL GAS

Note: If an empty cylinder is to be purged (emptied of any residual gas by flushing with a pure gas), enter 0 for PSIg and the composition of the flush gas in row G. If the cylinder contains a residual gas at ambient pressure (usually air), enter 0 here and the composition of that gas in row G.

E. PSIg _____

F. PSIa _____
(E+14.7)

G1. FO_2 _____   G2. FHe _____   G3. FN_2 _____

H1. PPO_2 _____   H2. PPHe _____   H3. PPN_2 _____
(FxG1)   (FxG$_2$)   (FxG3)

GAS PRESSURES FOR MIXING

I1. $dPPO_2$ I2. dPPHe   I3. $dPPN_2$
(D1-H1) _____   (D2-H2) _____   (D3-H3) _____

J1. PSI O_2 _____   J2. PSI He _____   J3. PSI Air _____
to add   to add   to add
B- (F+J2+J3)   (I2)   (I3/0.79)

Check: The partial pressure of oxygen (PPO_2) due to residual gas (H1) plus PPO_2 due to oxygen added (J1) plus PPO_2 due to air added (J3 x 0.21) should equal the final PPO_2 (D1).

H1. _____ + J1. _____ + J3x0.21 _____ = D1. _____

EXAMPLE #1

Prepare a 10% oxygen, 90% helium mixture by adding pure oxygen and pure helium, for a final pressure of 3000 psig, to an empty cylinder. The cylinder previously contained air.

Since the cylinder previously contained a nitrogen mixture, this mixture must be purged from the cylinder. For convenience, oxygen will be added first, and is a good choice for a purge gas. Add oxygen to 50 psi, drain, and repeat at least three times. Less than one percent of the residual air will then remain. The residual gas is now 0 psi and its composition is between 99 and 100% oxygen.

Enter the eight known values in Rows A, C, E, and G as shown.

Perform the calculations on the worksheet as indicated. J1 and J2 are the pressures of oxygen and helium to add. Add 296.77 psi oxygen (gauge pressure will read 0 + 296.77 = 296.77 psi). Then add 2713.23

psi helium (gauge pressure reads 296.77 + 2713.23 = 3000 psi).

Due to the differences in compressibility of helium and oxygen, this ideal gas method will cause the actual oxygen percentage to be about 11%. This difference is barely detectable by most analysis equipment in use.

#1 GAS MIXING WORKSHEET CONCLUSION

Instructions: Enter final (desired) and residual (remaining in tank from previous mix) gauge pressures and fraction of oxygen (FO_2), helium (FHe), and nitrogen (FN_2) in the spaces indicated. Perform calculations and checks as indicated. If Item I1, I2, or I3 is less than zero, then some of the residual gas must be drained from the cylinder. Items J1, J2, and J3 are the respective increases in pressures for each gas added to the cylinder.

REQUIRED FINAL MIX

A. PSIG   __3000__

B. PSIA
   (A + 14.7)   __3014.7__

C1. FO_2 __.10__	C2. FHe __.90__	C3. FN_2 __0__
D1. PPO_2	D2. PPHe	D3. PPN_2
(BXC1) __301.47__	(BXC2) __2713.23__	(BXC3) __0__

RESIDUAL GAS

Note: If an empty cylinder is to be purged (emptied of any residual gas by flushing with a pure gas), enter 0 for PSIg and the composition of the flush gas in row G. If the cylinder contains a residual gas at ambient pressure (usually air), enter 0 here and the composition of that gas in row G.

E. PSIg   __0__

F. PSIa   __14.7__
   (E+14.7)

G1. FO_2 __1__	G2. FHe __0__	G3. FN_2 __0__
H1. PPO_2 __14.7__	H2. PPHe __0__	H3. PPN_2 __0__
(FxG1)	(FxG2)	(FxG3)

GAS PRESSURES FOR MIXING

I1. $dPPO_2$	I2. dPPHe	I3. $dPPN_2$
(D1-H1) __286.77__	(D2-H2) __2713.23__	(D3-H3) __0__
J1. PSI O_2 __286.77__	J2. PSI He __2713.23__	J3. PSI Air __0__
to add	to add	to add
B- (F+J2+J3)	(I2)	(I3/0.79)

Check: The partial pressure of oxygen (PPO_2) due to residual gas (H1) plus PPO_2 due to oxygen added (J1) plus PPO_2 due to air added (J3 x 0.21) should equal the final PPO_2 (D1).

H1. __14.7__ + J1. __286.77__ + J3x0.21 __0__ = D1. __301.47__

EXAMPLE #2

Prepare a 36% oxygen, 64% nitrogen mixture by adding oxygen and air for a final pressure of 3000 psi to an empty cylinder. The cylinder has just been tested and cleaned.

Since the cylinder has recently been serviced and is empty, the ambient pressure gas is air. Air is one of the gases which will be used in the final mix, therefore there is no need to purge the cylinder. The residual gas is air at 0 psig.

Enter the eight known values in Rows A, C, E, and G as shown. Perform the calculations on the worksheet as indicated. J1, is the pressure of oxygen to add, J3, is the pressure of air to add.

#2 GAS MIXING WORKSHEET CONCLUSION

Instructions: Enter final (desired) and residual (remaining in tank from previous mix) gauge pressures and fraction of oxygen (FO_2), helium (FHe), and nitrogen (FN_2) in the spaces indicated. Perform calculations and checks as indicated. If Item I1, I2, or I3 is less than zero, then some of the residual gas must be drained from the cylinder. Items J1, J2, and J3 are the respective increases in pressures for each gas added to the cylinder.

REQUIRED FINAL MIX

A. PSIG __3000__		
B. PSIA (A + 14.7) __3014.7__		
C1. FO_2 __.36__	C2. FHe __0__	C3. FN_2 __.64__
D1. PPO_2 (BXC1) __1085.3__	D2. PPHe (BXC2) __0__	D3. PPN_2 (BXC3) __1929.4__

RESIDUAL GAS

Note: If an empty cylinder is to be purged (emptied of any residual gas by flushing with a pure gas), enter 0 for psig at E and the composition of the flush gas in row G. If the cylinder contains a residual gas at ambient pressure (usually air), enter 0 here and the composition of that gas in row G.

E. PSIg __0__		
F. PSIa (E+14.7) __14.7__		
G1. FO_2 __.21__	G2. FHe __0__	G3. FN_2 __.79__
H1. PPO_2 (FxG1) __3.1__	H2. PPHe (FxG2) __0__	H3. PPN_2 (FxG3) __11.6__

GAS PRESSURES FOR MIXING

I1. $dPPO_2$ (D1-H1) __1082.2__	I2. dPPHe (D2-H2) __0__	I3. $dPPN_2$ (D3-H3) __1917.8__
J1. PSI O_2 to add B- (F+J2+J3) __572.4__	J2. PSI He to add (I2) __0__	J3. PSI Air to add (I3/0.79) __2427.6__

Check:

H1. __3.1__ + J1. __572.4__ + J3x0.21 __509.8__ = D1. __1085.3__

EXAMPLE #3

Prepare a 16% oxygen, 50% helium, 34% nitrogen mixture by adding oxygen, helium, and air, for a final pressure of 3000 psi, to a cylinder containing 16% oxygen, 25% helium, 59% nitrogen at 1000 psi.

The composition of the residual gas is similar to the required final mixture and the pressure at 1000 psi is low enough that we can probably accomplish the mixture change without draining any of the residual gas. If any of the values in row J are negative, however, at least some of the residual gas will need to be drained.

Enter the eight known values in Rows A, C, E, and G as shown. Perform the calculations on the worksheet as indicated. J1, 206.7 psi, J2, 1253.7 psi, and J3, 539.7 psi, are the pressures of oxygen, helium, and nitrogen to add. Add 206.7 psi oxygen (gauge pressure will read 1000 + 206.7 = 1206.7 psi). Add 1253.7 psi helium (gauge pressure will read 1206.7 + 1253.7 = 2460.4 psi). Finally add 539.7 psi air (gauge pressure will read 2460.4 + 539.7 = 3000.1 psi)

#3 GAS MIXING WORKSHEET CONCLUSION

Instructions: Enter final (desired) and residual (remaining in tank from previous mix) gauge pressures and fraction of oxygen (FO_2), helium (FHe), and nitrogen (FN_2) in the spaces indicated. Perform calculations and checks as indicated. If Item I1, I2, or I3 is less than zero, then some of the residual gas must be drained from the cylinder. Items J1, J2, and J3 are the respective increases in pressures for each gas added to the cylinder.

REQUIRED FINAL MIX

A.	PSIG	**3000**					
B.	PSIA (A + 14.7)	**3014.7**					
C1.	FO_2	**.16**	C2. FHe	**.50**	C3. FN_2	**.34**	
D1.	PPO_2 (BXC1)	**482.4**	D2. PPHe (BXC2)	**1507.3**	D3. PPN_2 (BXC3)	**1024.0**	

RESIDUAL GAS

Note: If an empty cylinder is to be purged (emptied of any residual gas by flushing with a pure gas), enter 0 for psig at E and the composition of the flush gas in row G. If the cylinder contains a residual gas at ambient pressure (usually air), enter 0 here and the composition of that gas in row G.

E.	PSIg	**1000**				
F.	PSIa (E+14.7)	**1014.7**				
G1.	FO_2	**.16**	G2. FHe	**.25**	G3. FN_2	**.59**
H1.	PPO_2 (FxG1)	**162.4**	H2. PPHe (FxG2)	**253.7**	H3. PPN_2 (FxG3)	**598.7**

GAS PRESSURES FOR MIXING

I1.	$dPPO_2$ (D1-H1)	**320**	I2. dPPHe (D2-H2)	**1253.6**	I3. $dPPN_2$ (D3-H3)	**426.3**
J1.	PSI O_2 to add B- (F+J2+J3)	**206.8**	J2. PSI He to add (I2)	**1253.6**	J3. PSI Air to add (I3/0.79)	**539.6**

Check: The partial pressure of oxygen (PPO_2) due to residual gas (H1) plus PPO_2 due to oxygen added (J1) plus PPO_2 due to air added (J3 x 0.21) should equal the final PPO_2 (D1).

H1. **162.4** + J1. **206.8** + J3x0.21 **113.3** = D1. **482.5**

Another way to mix Trimix is by combining NITROX and helium. For many NITROX pumping facilities, this method is very convenient. It involves adding helium to an empty cylinder, then filling the cylinder by pumping NITROX from storage banks. The following example illustrates the method for determining the helium and nitrogen percentages that will result from such a mixture, and the required pressures of helium and NITROX. The worksheet is used with one minor modification: At item J3, instead of dividing I3 by 0.79, divide by the FN_2 of the NITROX mixture.

EXAMPLE #4

A 19% oxygen Trimix at 3000 psi is to prepared by adding helium, then 32% oxygen NITROX to a cylinder. The cylinder should first be purged with helium or NITROX. In this example helium is used as the purge gas.

(1) First determine the final gas mixture.

The fraction of NITROX in the mix is 0.19/.32 = 0.594

The fraction of helium in the mix is 1 - 0.594 = 0.406

The fraction of nitrogen in the mix is 1 - (0.406+0.19) = 0.404

(2) Check the above calculations:

FO_2 + FHe + FN_2 should equal 1.00.   0.19 + 0.406 + 0.404 = 1.00

The percentage of nitrogen in the mix due to NITROX, should equal the final percentage of nitrogen in the mix. 0.594 x 0.64 = 0.404

(3) Calculate the required gas pressures.

Use the worksheet to determine the gas pressures, but when calculating Item J3, instead of dividing I3 by 0.79, divide by the fraction of nitrogen in the NITROX used for mixing (0.68 in this case). The amount of oxygen to add (Item J1) should be zero psi (within one or two psi to allow for rounding errors). This value serves as an additional calculation check.

It is necessary to purge the cylinder in this example to prevent residual air from interfering with the mix. In examples two and three, purging was not necessary because the mixing components could compensate for the residual gas. To illustrate this point, rework this example assuming that the residual gas is air at 0 psig. The worksheet will indicate that two psi of pure oxygen needs to be added. This amount is needed to compensate for the ambient pressure air that is in the cylinder. This amount is insignificant given the mixing and analysis equipment in use, but the point is made in order to provide a complete and correct discussion.

#4 GAS MIXING WORKSHEET CONCLUSION

Instructions: Enter final (desired) and residual (remaining in tank from previous mix) gauge pressures and fraction of oxygen (FO_2), helium (FHe), and nitrogen (FN_2) in the spaces indicated. Perform calculations and checks as indicated. If Item I1, I2, or I3 is less than zero, then some of the residual gas must be drained from the cylinder. Items J1, J2, and J3 are the respective increases in pressures for each gas added to the cylinder.

REQUIRED FINAL MIX

A. PSIG **3000**

B. PSI
   (A + 14.7) **3014.7**

C1. FO_2 **.19**	C2. FHe **.406**	C3. FN_2 **.404**
D1. PPO_2	D2. PPHe	D3. PPN_2
(BXC1) **572.8**	(BXC2) **1224.0**	(BXC3) **1217.9**

RESIDUAL GAS

Note: If an empty cylinder is to be purged (emptied of any residual gas by flushing with a pure gas), enter 0 for psig at E and the composition of the flush gas in row G. If the cylinder contains a residual gas at ambient pressure (usually air), enter 0 here and the composition of that gas in row G.

E. PSIg **0**

F. PSIa **14.7**
   (E+14.7)

G1. FO_2 **0**	G2. FHe **1.0**	G3. FN_2 **0**
H1. PPO_2 **0**	H2. PPHe **14.7**	H3. PPN_2 **0**
(FxG1)	(FxG2)	(FxG3)

GAS PRESSURES FOR MIXING

I1. $dPPO_2$	I2. dPPHe	I3. $dPPN_2$
(D1-H1) **572.8**	(D2-H2) **1209.3**	(D3-H3) **1217.9**
J1. PSI O_2 **0**	J2. PSI He **1209.3**	J3. PSI NTX32 **1791.0**
to add	to add	to add
B- (F+J2+J3)	(I2)	(I3/0.68)

Check: The partial pressure of oxygen (PPO_2) due to residual gas (H1) plus PPO_2 due to oxygen added (J1) plus PPO_2 due to air added (J3 x .32) should equal the final PPO_2 (D1).

H1. **0** + J1. **0** + J3x0.21 **573.1** = D1. **573.1**

REAL GAS EFFECTS

The preceding examples are valid only to the point where the component gases in the mixture either follow ideal gas laws or have real gas effects which tend to cancel those of the other components. The *U.S. Navy Diving Gas Manual* provides tables of pressure, density, temperature, molecular weight, and other factors for various pure gases and mixtures. The method of applying these values to compensate for the real gas effects are effective but somewhat cumbersome. Computer spreadsheets and programs have been developed and are the method of choice for these calculations.

Many gas mixers achieve excellent results by applying compensation factors based on experience or a subjective view of real gas theory. As an example, for mixtures where pure oxygen is added to an empty cylinder first, deduct 10% from the pressure calculated for the oxygen using ideal gas methods. Then compensate for the 10% reduction in total pressure by increasing the amount of other component gases. This method is based upon the Beattie-Bridgeman Equation of State, which indicates that oxygen is 10% more compressible than helium or nitrogen at pressures in the 2000 to 4000 psi range. This method is very accurate for mixing Heliox when oxygen is added to a purged cylinder first, then the fill is completed with helium. For cases where a cylinder contains a residual gas at 1000 psi or more, this method is not adequate and real gas techniques or known compensation methods must be used.

In most cases the difference in oxygen percentage between ideal and real gas mixing methods is less than one percent. If the mixer finds a greater difference, or otherwise considers the mixes obtained unacceptable, additional factors or true real gas techniques should be employed.

MAKING CORRECTIONS OR ADJUSTMENTS TO A MIXTURE

After a gas mixture is prepared and analyzed, the oxygen percentage may be different than expected due to some error in the mixing, or for reasons previously discussed. It is best to completely drain the cylinder and start over, removing any question as to the components of the gas mixture or the type of error that was made in the mixing. If the mixer is certain that the error was due to a misproportion of the components used in the mixing, such as too much helium when mixing Trimix or too much oxygen when mixing NITROX, an adjustment can be made, allowing most of the gas to be saved.

Attempting to correct a Trimix mixture that was prepared by mixing three components, such as oxygen, helium, and air is not recommended. It is not possible to be certain which component caused the oxygen percentage change, and while the oxygen percentage of the corrected mixture may be correct, the helium and nitrogen percentage may differ from requirements substantially. Of course, if the mixer has analysis equipment capable of measuring the helium and nitrogen percentages, this limit, faced by the typical technical diver equipped only with an oxygen analyzer, is removed.

The "Gas Adjustment Worksheet" is similar to the "Gas Mixing Worksheet" but has some limitations. It allows adjustment only of mixtures that were prepared with two components, such as helium and air for Trimix, or oxygen and air for NITROX. Also, the gas added to make the adjustment must be the same as one of the components used in the original mixture. Finally, the pressure after the adjustment must be the same as the pressure before the adjustment. That is, some of the original mix will be drained to "make room" for the adjustment gas. Some of these limits may be overcome by using the "Gas Mixing Worksheet" and a trial-and-error approach to determining the amount of gas that needs to be drained, but the adjustment worksheet is adequate for common corrections.

The "Gas Adjustment Worksheet" is used to determine the optimum amount of gas to be drained from the cylinder. After this amount is removed, the adjustment is made by adding only one component, for example, air to decrease the oxygen percentage of an incorrect NITROX mixture. The worksheet treats each of the component gases as a generic gas without regard to their composition. For example, if the component mixes are air and oxygen, air is considered as "Gas A", oxygen as "Gas B", although air contains oxygen. This technique allows the worksheet to be used for both helium-NITROX and oxygen-air mixtures.

INSTRUCTIONS AND EXAMPLES

Row A. Enter the required final gauge pressure (psi) of the mixture.

Row B. As indicated, add 14.7 to Item A.

Row C. Enter the fraction oxygen according to the analyzer.

Row D. Enter the required fraction of oxygen.

Row E. Enter the required fraction of nitrogen.

Row F. Enter the fraction of oxygen in Gas A. Gas A is either air or NITROX.

Row G. Enter the fraction of nitrogen in Gas A.

Row H. Calculate the actual fraction of nitrogen in the faulty mix. Note that the formula for determining this value depends upon whether Gas B is helium or oxygen.

Row I, J Calculate the actual and required fractions of Gas A and Gas B as indicated. Note that for NITROX, FGasB will not equal FO_2. Remember that FO_2 is equal to oxygen due to the air in the mix plus oxygen due to pure oxygen added.

Row K, L Calculate the actual and required partial pressures of Gas A and Gas B.

Row M. Subtract the actual (K) and required (L) partial pressures of the component gases to find the change in the pressures necessary to achieve the required mix. For one of the columns, this result will be a negative number, do not enter a negative number; only the positive number is considered.

Row N. Divide M by I for the column with the positive number to find the pressure to remove from the cylinder.

Check: This step verifies the above calculations and indicates which gas (A or B) is to be added after draining the amount specified in Item N. One of the entries in Row P should be zero (plus or minus one or two psi to account for rounding errors), the other entry should be equal to the entry at N and its column indicates which gas is to be added.

#5 SAMPLE GAS ADJUSTMENT WORKSHEET

Instructions: Enter the pressure at item A, the oxygen analyzer reading at item C, the required gas composition at D and E, and the composition of air or nitrox at F and G. Perform all calculations as indicated. Do not consider values less than zero for row M. Item N indicates the amount of gas to drain from the cylinder. The column in which the value found in item N appears in row P indicates which gas is to be added.

A. PSIg   _____

B. PSIa
   (A + 14.7)   _____

C. Actual FO_2 _____

D. Req'd FO_2 _____

E. Req'd FN_2 _____

F. FO_2 GasA   _____

G. FN_2 GasA   _____

H. FN_2 actual (If Gas B is helium, $(C \times G / F)$
               (If Gas B is oxygen $1 - C$)   _____

I1. Actual F Gas A	I2. Actual F Gas B
(H / G) _____	(1 - I1) _____
J1. Req' F Gas A	J2. Req'd F Gas B
(E / G) _____	(1 - J1) _____
K1. Actual PP Gas A	K2. Actual PP Gas B
(B x I1) _____	(B x I2) _____
L1. Req'd PP Gas A	L2. Req'd PP Gas B
(B x J1) _____	(B x J2) _____
M1. Change PP Gas A	M2. Change PP Gas B
(K1 - L1) _____	(K2 - L2) _____

N. PSI to drain from cylinder
  (M1/I1 or M2/I2, whichever is greater than zero)   _____

Check:

O1. Residual PP Gas A	O2. Residual PP Gas B
(B-N) x I1 _____	(B-N) x I2 _____
P1. dPP Gas A	P2. dPP Gas B
(L1 - O1) _____	(L2 - O2) _____

    One of the entries in row P should be zero, the other should be equal to N. The column with the non-zero value represents which gas to add and its pressure.

EXAMPLE # 5

A NITROX gas mixture was prepared by combining air and oxygen. The oxygen analyzer reads 40%, but the required value is 36%. The cylinder pressure is 3000 psig. Determine how much gas needs to be drained from the cylinder and which gas (oxygen or air) needs to be added.

Enter the known values in columns A and C through G, with air as Gas A and oxygen as Gas B. Perform the calculations and checks as indicated. Since Gas B is oxygen in this example, use 1.00 minus C to calculate Item H (1.00 - 0.40 = 0.60). Item N indicates that 638 psi should be drained from the cylinder. This same figure appears in Row P under the Gas A column, indicating that the cylinder should be refilled with 638 psi air to its original pressure of 3000 psi.

#5 GAS ADJUSTMENT WORKSHEET CONCLUSIONS

Instructions: Enter the pressure at item A, the oxygen analyzer reading at item C, the required gas composition at D and E, and the composition of air or nitrox at F and G. Perform all calculations as indicated. Do not consider values less than zero for row M. Item N indicates the amount of gas to drain from the cylinder. The column in which the value found in item N appears in row P indicates which gas is to be added.

A. PSIg ___3000___

B. PSIa
   (A + 14.7) ___3014.7___

C. Actual FO_2 ___.40___

D. Req'd FO_2 ___.36___

E. Req'd FN_2 ___.64___

F. FO_2 GasA ___.21___

G. FN_2 GasA ___.79___

H. FN_2 actual   (If Gas B is helium, (C x G / F)
                   (If Gas B is oxygen 1 - C)   ___.60___

I1. Actual F Gas A	I2. Actual F Gas B
(H / G) ___.759___	(1 - I1) ___.241___
J1. Req' F Gas A	J2. Req'd F Gas B
(E / G) ___.810___	(1 - J1) ___.190___
K1. Actual PP Gas A	K2. Actual PP Gas B
(B x I1) ___2288.2___	(B x I2) ___726.5___
L1. Req'd PP Gas A	L2. Req'd PP Gas B
(B x J1) ___2441.9___	(B x J2) ___572.8___
M1. Change PP Gas A	M2. Change PP Gas B
(K1 - L1) ___—___	(K2 - L2) ___153.7___

N. PSI to drain from cylinder
   (M1/I1 or M2/I2, whichever is greater than zero)   ___637.9___

Check:

O1. Residual PP Gas A	O2. Residual PP Gas B
(B-N) x I1 ___1804___	(B-N) x I2 ___572.8___
P1. dPP Gas A	P2. dPP Gas B
(L1 - O1) ___637.9___	(L2 - O2) ___0___

One of the entries in row P should be zero, the other should be equal to N. The column with the non-zero value represents which gas to add and its pressure.

EXAMPLE #6

A Trimix gas mixture was prepared by combining helium and NITROX 32. The oxygen analyzer reads 17%. The required composition is 19% oxygen, 41% nitrogen, 40% helium. The cylinder pressure is 3000 psig. Determine how much gas needs to be drained from the cylinder and which gas (helium or NITROX 32) needs to be added.

Enter the known values with NITROX as Gas A and helium as Gas B. Since Gas B is helium in this example, use the formula, C x G / F to calculate Item H (0.17 x 0.68 / 0.32 = 0.361). Item N indicates that 366 psi should be drained from the cylinder. This same figure (within one psi due to rounding) appears in Row P under the Gas A column, indicating that the cylinder should be refilled with 367 psi NITROX 32 to its original pressure of 3000 psi.

#6 GAS ADJUSTMENT WORKSHEET CONCLUSIONS

Instructions: Enter the pressure at item A, the oxygen analyzer reading at item C, the required gas composition at D and E, and the composition of air or nitrox at F and G. Perform all calculations as indicated. Do not consider values less than zero for row M. Item N indicates the amount of gas to drain from the cylinder. The column in which the value found in item N appears in row P indicates which gas is to be added.

A. PSIg   **3000**

B. PSIa
  (A + 14.7)   **3014.7**

C. Actual FO_2 **.17**

D. Req'd FO_2 **.19**

E. Req'd FN_2 **.40**

F. FO_2 GasA   **.32**

G. FN_2 GasA   **.68**

H. FN_2 actual   (If Gas B is helium, (C x G / F)
                (If Gas B is oxygen   1 - C)   **.361**

I1. Actual F Gas A	I2. Actual F Gas B
(H / G) **.531**	(1 - I1) **.469**
J1. Req' F Gas A	J2. Req'd F Gas B
(E / G) **.588**	(1 - J1) **.412**
K1. Actual PP Gas A	K2. Actual PP Gas B
(B x I1) **1601**	(B x I2) **1414**
L1. Req'd PP Gas A	L2. Req'd PP Gas B
(B x J1) **1773**	(B x J2) **1242**
M1. Change PP Gas A	M2. Change PP Gas B
(K1 - L1) **—**	(K2 - L2) **172**

N. PSI to drain from cylinder
  (M1/I1 or M2/I2, whichever is greater than zero)   **367**

Check:

O1. Residual PP Gas A	O2. Residual PP Gas B
(B-N) x I1 **1406**	(B-N) x I2 **1242**
P1. dPP Gas A	P2. dPP Gas B
(L1 - O1) **367**	(L2 - O2) **0**

    One of the entries in row P should be zero, the other should be equal to N. The column with the non-zero value represents which gas to add and its pressure.

ABBREVIATED MIXING WORKSHEET

Tom Mount Method • #1: Partial NITROX Fills

1. Determine total oxygen needed in a mix with a given FO_2.
2. Determine oxygen in present in mix before topping off.
3. Subtract 1 and 2: 1-2 = Balance oxygen needed
4. Adjusted FO_2 = $\dfrac{\text{Balance O}_2 \text{ needed (from 3)}}{\text{psig to add}}$
5. $\dfrac{\text{Adj. FO}_2 - .21}{.79}$ x psig to add = O_2 to add

Example:

A mix contains 32% O_2. It has 1400 psig remaining in the cylinder. This cylinder is to be filled to 3000 psig. The new mix is planned for 36% O_2. How much O_2 must be added before topping off with air?

1. Total O_2 = .36 x 3000 = 1080 psig
2. Present O_2 is 32%, therefore, .32 x 1400 = 448 psig
3. 1080 - 448 = 632 psig
4. New adj. FO_2 = $\dfrac{632}{1600 \text{ psig}}$ = .40
5. $\dfrac{.40 - .21}{.79}$ x 1600 = 384 psig

Add 384 psig of oxygen to the cylinder and then fill with air to 3000 psi.

ABBREVIATED MIXING WORKSHEET

TOM MOUNT METHOD • # 2: Mixing NITROX from Air

$$\frac{FO_2 - .21}{.79} \times psig$$

FO_2 = Fraction of oxygen to be in final mix
.21 = Constant percentage of oxygen in air
.79 = Constant percentage of nitrogen in air
psig = Total working pressure of cylinder in final mix

Example:

A mix of 25% O_2 is planned. The final tank pressure is 3000 psig. How much O_2 will be added to produce this mix?

$$\frac{.25 - .21}{.79} \times 3000 \, psig$$

Answer:

150 psig
Add 150 psig of oxygen to the cylinder before topping off with air

Example:

A NITROX mix of 32% O_2 has 1400 psig remaining in the cylinder. It is to be to 3000 psig and needs to maintain the 32% O_2 mixture. How much O_2 will need to be added?

$$\frac{.32 - .21}{.79} \times 1600$$

Answer:

224 psig
Add 224 psig of oxygen to the cylinder before topping off with air.

ABBREVIATED MIXING WORKSHEET

Tom Mount Method • #3: Trimix

1. Determine helium to be added to mix: FHe x Pt
    (fraction of helium x total pressure)
2. Determine oxygen needed in mix: FO_2 x Pt
    (fraction of oxygen x total pressure)
3. Determine total gas to be added on top of helium: Pt - PHe

4. Determine adjusted FO_2: $$\frac{\text{total } O_2 \text{ from step 2}}{\text{total gas to add from step 3}}$$

5. Determine O_2 to add to mix: $$\frac{\text{adjusted } FO_2 - .21}{.79} \text{ x psig to add}$$

Example:

     In a 3000 psig tank, a mix is made up of 16% O_2, 40% He, and 44% N_2. How much He will be added? How much O_2?

1. He = .40 x 3000 psig = 1200 psig
2. O_2 = .16 x 3000 psig = 480 psig
3. Gas to add: 3000 - 1200 = 1800 psig
4. Adjusted FO_2: $\frac{480}{1800}$ = .27
5. Add O_2: $\frac{.27 - .21}{.79}$ x 1800 = 144 psig

     Fill initially with 144 psig of O_2, then add 1200 psig of He. The balance of the fill is obtained by topping off with air.

ABBREVIATED MIXING WORKSHEET
Tom Mount Method • #4: Trimix Topping Off a Partial Fill with Air

1. Determine present amount of He in mix: FHe x remaining psig in tank
2. Determine adjusted FHe: $\dfrac{\text{He in psig in current mix}}{\text{total psig to be in mix}}$
3. Determine present amount of O_2 in mix: FO_2 x remaining psig in tank
4. Determine amount of air to add to mix: total psig - psig remaining
5. Determine oxygen in air to be added to mix: .21 x psig to be added
6. Determine adjusted FO_2:
    A. total O_2 psig + O_2 psig in present mix
    B. $\dfrac{\text{balance } O_2 \text{ mix from A}}{\text{total psig}}$

Example:
   A mix of 16% O_2 and 40% He has 1300 psig remaining in the cylinder. What will be the new mix if the tanks are topped off to 3000 psig with air?

1. .40 x 1300 = 520 psig He in current mix
2. 520 divided by 3000 = .17 or 17% He in final mix
3. .16 x 1300 = 1700 psig of air to add
4.   3000 - 1300 = 1700 psig of air to add
5. .21 x 1700 = 357 psig O_2 in air to be added
6. 208 + 357 = 565 total psig O_2 in mix divided by 3000 = 19% O_2

ABBREVIATED MIXING WORKSHEET

Tom Mount Method • #5: Trimix Adjusting Mix From a Balance Gas

1. Determine psig of He in present mix: FHe x psig
2. Determine target He psig for new FHe: target FHe x full psig
3. Determine amount of He to adjust:
   - A. Target He psig - He psig in present mix
   - B. Add He from step A
4. Determine amount of O_2 to be in final mix: FO_2 x total psig
5. Determine amount of oxygen in present mix:
   present FO_2 x existing psig
6. Detemine amount of gas to add to mix:
   full psig - He psig to add + existing psig
7. Determine adjusted FO_2
   - A. value from step 4 - O_2 psig from step 5
   - B. $\dfrac{\text{value from step A}}{\text{value from step 6}}$
8. Determine O_2 to add: $\dfrac{\text{adjusted } FO_2 - .21}{.79}$ x psig to add from step 6

Example:

   A mix has 18% O_2 and 32% He with 1200 psig remaining. It is decided to top the mix off with a final mixture of 21% O_2 and 40% He.

1. .32 x 1200 = 384 psig He in current mix
2. .40 x 3000 = 1200 psig He for final mix
3. 1200 - 384   = 816 psig of He is to be added to the mix
4. .21 x 3000 = 630 psig O_2 in final mix
5. .18 x 1200 = 216 psig in present mix
6. 3000 - (1200+816) = 984 psig to add (air of O_2)
7. 630 - 216 = $\dfrac{414 \text{ psig additional } O_2}{984}$ = .42
8. $\dfrac{.42 - .21 \text{ x } 984}{.79}$ = 262 psig of O_2 to add

CHAPTER 16

Production of Oxygen Enriched Air Mixtures
(EANx or NITROX)

This information is offered as an overview to the gas blending procedures currently in use to produce oxygen enriched air. SafeAir, NITROX and EANx are all terms in wide use to describe these custom breathing mixtures of oxygen and nitrogen; in essence, they mean the same thing. Precise terminology should be dealt with, but not in the scope of this brief chapter. The primary concern is pure, contaminant-free breathing gas as the final end-product. How that is achieved at the cylinder refill station is varied.

PRE-MIX

The simplest way to dispense a gas mixture other than air is to purchase professionally pre-blended gas from a gas supplier. For NITROX blends used in recompression chamber facilities as a therapy gas, standard procedure is to order NITROX pre-blended in this manner to typically yield a 50/50 or 60/40 Nitrogen/oxygen mixture. These cylinders may then be plumbed into the therapy gas manifold just as medical oxygen cylinders are. A NITROX refill station for use in open circuit scuba equipment could use this same system. It is still suggested that the end-user analyze the gas in each cylinder prior to hooking the storage cylinders into the cascade/bank connection. Connect the cylinders and dispense by using an oxygen clean, oxygen service booster pump. The gas quality of gas mixtures dispensed in this manner is high as no impurities or contaminates are likely to be present.

DYNAMIC GAS MIXING

This method is generally employed by commercial diving operations or facilities that will have need for high volumes of mixed gas. In most situations, this is beyond the budget or needs of most sport or scientific programs. In this system, the high pressure gases are supplied to a mixer, then analyzed and discharged to a special compressor for pumping to storage, or directly to the diver in surface supplied operations. (Butler, G. 1991)

PARTIAL PRESSURE BLENDING

Partial pressure, or "cascade" mixing is probably the best known and most common method of gas mixing. These systems can be as simple as a fill hose, adapter and oil free compressor used to fill a single scuba tank at a time, or designed for the production of thousands of cubic feet per day of NITROX, Heliox or Trimix. Based on Dalton's Law of Partial Pressures, this method employs several high pressure gas sources to produce a mixture based on the partial pressure of each component gas. (Butler, Glenn 1991)

One method that is employed by some is to use the aforementioned method, but purchase U.S.P. grade air and U.S.P. grade oxygen. By having two "unmixed" gases, (of course, air is a mixture of gases) the operator may achieve any desired mixture of oxygen enriched air. By storing different mixtures in different banks, the refill station may immediately

NITROX high pressure storage bank clearly labled "NITROX Only". Thousands of cubic feet of NOAA NITROX I (32% O2/68% N₂) are blended and stored for use at this facility. Photo by Bret Gilliam

dispense several NITROX mixtures. Air is a NITROX mixture with "impurities" from other trace gases present in the natural atmosphere.

Some operators use their oil-lubricated compressors to produce high pressure air and then filter it again to remove even more hydrocarbon contaminants. They then refill banks after adding pure oxygen to enrich the mixtures to the desired levels. This is the cheapest way to offer this service as only a separate bank and filter is required. There are numerous safeguards that could and should be added to this type of system. While this system can work with the proper safeguards in place, it does require vigilance and dedi-

View of Dick Rutkowski's NITROX blending station showing double filtration canisters to remove hydrocarbons from compressed air, in-line oxygen analyzer, Haskell booster pump, and NITROX storage cylinders in background. Photo by Bret Gilliam

cation to proper filtration to insure hydrocarbon free air. Using this method, there is a progression of lube oil and contamination aggregate. This amount is a function of relative volume/use to compressor wear, maintenance and filter quality. This system has been used with complete success and no sacrifice in air quality by facilities such as Dick Rutkowski's IAND for over five years.

The most hazardous procedure is partial pressure blending in individual scuba cylinders (commonly known as "home brew"). This is particularly dangerous when divers conspire to "sucker" an unknowing refill operator into completing the fill process for them. A small amount of oxygen is transferred from an oxygen storage cylinder to an empty scuba cylinder and then it is taken to an unsuspecting dive store to be topped off with air. This practice has been most prevalent in Florida. Even the casual observer can see the obvious serious potential for improper blends, fire/explosion risk etc. when an unwitting fill operator is duped in such a manner. Although this method has been practiced successfully and with reasonable safety in the field for years by many highly experienced, trained professionals, it is strongly discouraged for *all others* for several reasons:

1. The equipment is seldom properly oxygen cleaned.
2. This process requires handling of high pressure oxygen. This is dramatically different and potentially more hazardous than high pressure air.
3. The air used in the top-off fill generally comes from an oil lubricated compressor and may have too many hydrocarbon contaminants.
4. Even if the equipment starts out oxygen cleaned, after several refill cycles from an oil lubricated compressor, the equipment is usually contaminated with hydrocarbons increasing the risk of explosion or carbon monoxide transfer. The manufacturer of the oil-lube compressor would deplore and condemn the use of their discharge gas for this purpose.
5. Pure oxygen should not be added to scuba cylinders that are not compatible with 100% oxygen.
6. Gas analysis with accurate analyzers is not always done. Remember, this is largely regarded as the cheap way out.
7. Unless the cylinder is totally empty and O_2 purged, this procedure yields even more inaccuracy.
8. Gas transferred must stand for considerable time to permit thorough mixing through molecular migration.
9. Gauges used to measure pressure are seldom accurate enough for this purpose. A gauge selected for this purpose should have an accuracy of +/- .25%. That's 1/4 of 1%!
10. Gas must be again analyzed prior to use. This rule should be applied to any gas mixtures.

ATMOSPHERIC ENTRAINMENT MIXING
(CONTINUOUS BLEND)

The development of the NOAA Continuous Mixing System in 1987 by Dr. J. Morgan Wells, has revolutionized and greatly simplified enriched air techniques. This method incorporates an oil-free or oil-less lubricated compressor as the main component. By injecting low temperature/low pressure oxygen into the gas stream, the percentage of oxygen may be carefully controlled. This allows storage banks or individual cylinders to be effectively and safely refilled. By utilizing this system, low pressure or liquid oxygen (LOX) can be used. This is the preferred

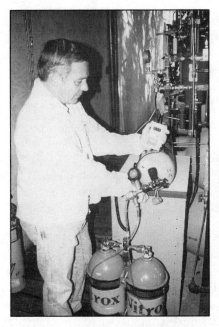

IAND founder, Dick Rutkowski, analyzes NITROX mixture to ensure its proper oxygen content. Blended gases are analyzed at the time of mixing and again after the fill into individual NITROX cylinders. Photo by Bret Gilliam

Close-up view of Mini-ox I digital analyzer showing 31.9% oxygen content. Target mixture was 32% so this is as close as a blender can reasonably expect to get with field instrumentation. Photo by Bret Gilliam

procedure and is approved by virtually all engineering experts as the currently accepted standard method. This eliminates many of the attendant hazards involving the transferring of high pressure oxygen.

UNDERSTANDING THE LIMITS OF A MIXTURE FOR DIVING

A variety of factors influence our decisions as divers: how deep, how long, what thermal protection to wear, how many dives to make in one day, and what type of table or decompression computer to use. One of the most important controlling elements of diving is our exposure to oxygen. Oxygen is present in any diving gas from regular compressed air to nitrox or exotic mixed gases such as heliox or Trimix. Without oxygen we cannot survive, but too much of a good thing can be dangerous. Exposures to high partial pressures of oxygen can result in what it is known as acute or central nervous system (CNS) oxygen toxicity.

An assortment of NITROX cylinders showing proper tagging. In addition, each cylinder will be labled or marked with the NITROX oxygen content and maximum depth that this mixture can be used safely. Photo by Bret Gilliam

A quick review of physics is probably helpful at this point. It's important to understand that the *percentage* of oxygen in a breathing gas is not the critical element. Instead, the *partial pressure* of oxygen is what controls our operational physiology with respect to its dose (time and depth). Blowing the dust of Dalton's Law, we will remember that each gas in a mixture has its own partial pressure determined by its percentage in the mixture multiplied by the number of atmospheres absolute (ATA).

The diver's most common breathing gas is natural air comprised of approximately 21% Oxygen (O_2) and 79% Nitrogen (N_2). To find the partial pressure of O_2 we express the percentage in decimal format (.21) and multiply by the number of ATA's. At the surface, we are at one ATA of pressure, therefore the partial pressure of oxygen can correctly be expressed as .21 ATA. For each 33 feet of seawater (fsw) that we descend we add another ATA. How much would the partial pressure of O_2 be at 66 fsw? *The math looks like this:*

.21 (the percentage of O_2) multiplied by the number of ATA's

At 66 fsw we are subjected to two atmospheres of seawater plus the surface weight of the atmosphere of air surrounding the earth. That equals three ATA's. To solve then it's really as simple as: .21 x 3 = .63 ATA of O_2

We commonly express partial pressure of a gas as Pg. In the above example, the PO_2 would be .63 ATA.

If you have been diving for a while, you may remember that in the early 1970's we used a maximum working (swimming) diver exposure of 2.0 ATA's of O_2. That was attained at approximately 300 feet. However, over the last two decades that has been modified to 1.6 ATA for up to 45 minutes. In virtually all discussions of NITROX, mixed gas or air scuba use, adherence to the 1.6 PO_2 guideline is observed. It would be helpful if the equation used in determining such exposures is illustrated:

$$MOD = \left(\frac{1.6}{FO_2} - 1\right) 33$$

MOD is the maximum operating depth in fsw
FO_2 is the fraction (percentage) of oxygen in the mixture 1.6 represents the O_2 ATA limit

To solve for MOD with compressed air (21% O_2):

$$\left(\frac{1.6}{.21} - 1\right) 33 = 218.4 \, fsw$$

To solve for MOD with NOAA NITROX I (32% O_2):

$$\left(\frac{1.6}{.32} - 1\right) 33 = 132 \, fsw$$

To solve for MOD with NOAA Nitrox II (36% O_2):

$$\left(\frac{1.6}{.36} - 1\right) 33 = 113.6 \, fsw$$

To solve for MOD with pure oxygen (100% O_2):

$$\left(\frac{1.6}{1.0} - 1\right) 33 = 19.8 \, fsw \quad \text{(commonly used as a decompression gas)}$$

Another important thing to remember is that we round off depths to the *most conservative* exposure, not the *next greater* depth. Therefore, the recommended limit for oxygen exposure would be 210 fsw for compressed air, 130 fsw for NITROX I, and 110 fsw for NITROX II. Only in the computation of inert gas exposures such as nitrogen, helium etc. do we round off to the next greater depth. By this method, we apply the greatest factor of conservatism. You can apply this simple formula to any breathing gas and it will yield the safe diving depth within the guidelines for O_2 exposures. (Other factors may influence dive planning such as narcosis, water temperature, current etc.)

CONCLUSION

Do not attempt to blend or mix gases on your own without formal training from a credentialed professional. Blending is a precise science that requires specialized training and equipment. The use of enriched air breathing mixtures have many safety and physiological advantages if used correctly. Production of the suitable blend is only one step in the process and most divers will obviously prefer to leave such procedures to professional operators.

REFERENCES

Betts, Ed (ANDI) personal communication 12-91

Butler, Glenn; *Getting Your Fill*, Technical Diver, Vol. 2-2 1991

Gilliam, Bret; *DEEP DIVING: An Advanced Guide to Physiology, Procedures and Systems*, Watersport Publishing 1991

Mastro, Stephen and Butler, Glenn *Air Quality Requirements For the On-site Production of Oxygen Enriched Breathing Mixtures,* NOAA

Menduno, Michael, editor *Technical Diver:* NITROX Issue, AquaCorps Publications 1991

Mount, Tom personal communication 12-91

Rutkowski, Dick *NITROX Manual,* International Association of Nitrox Divers

Rutkowski, Dick (IAND) personal communication 11-91

Wells, J. Morgan, *The Use of Nitrogen Oxygen Mixtures as Divers' Breathing Gas,* Proceedings: Oceans '88

C. Randy Bohrer

CHAPTER 17

PRODUCTION OF MIXED GAS

Oxygen Cleaning and Handling Procedures

Throughout this book references are made regarding equipment which must be "cleaned for oxygen service". General descriptions or definitions of this "oxygen clean" standard are made, but specific procedures with associated background information are not described. This information is necessary to assist the technical diver or gas mixer in developing techniques for cleaning gas systems. This section includes information regarding oxygen cleaning standards, procedures, equipment, and materials. While commercial, government, and diver training agency standards are discussed, this section should not be interpreted to advocate a particular standard. The information presented should be used a guide, and as standards are changed or developed, adjusted accordingly.

INTRODUCTION TO OXYGEN CLEANING AND HANDLING

Explosions are known or suspected to have occurred in various high pressure gas systems which were not properly cleaned and maintained. Safe operation of these systems, including the prevention of explosions and maintenance of gas purity can be ensured by eliminating all incompatible materials, especially hydrocarbons, before the system is placed in service, and by avoiding the accumulation of such materials during use. Therefore, the system must use only oxygen compatible components and must be cleaned for oxygen service. Furthermore, recontamination must be prevented by avoiding contact between system components and incompatible materials.

Different levels of cleanliness are required for various equipment defending on the type of equipment, its intended use, and the concentration of oxygen to which it is exposed. For example, an compressor pumping pure oxygen requires a higher level of cleanliness than a second stage breathing regulator delivering NITROX to a diver. Achieving the most stringent level of cleanliness is obviously the safest, but is sometimes neither necessary nor practical.

In general terms, oxygen cleaning involves two distinct elements. First, the evaluation and replacement as necessary of the materials used in the system, such as o-ring seals, and second, the removal of all particles, grease, oil, wax, and residue by cleaning with solvents and detergents. After completing these procedures, the system is then safe for oxygen service within the limits of the cleaning and materials standards employed.

FUNDAMENTALS OF COMBUSTION

Combustion is a chemical process where a fuel, such as wood, and an oxidizer, such as oxygen combine to form a new compound, generating heat in the process. The oxidizer itself is not flammable, but supports the combustion of the fuel. In order for this process to take place, fuel, an oxidizer, and an ignition source are required. These three components form what is sometimes referred to as the "fire triangle". Combustion cannot take place if any one of these three components is missing. Removing the fuel and ignition source in compressed gas systems to varying degrees is the goal of preparing these systems for use with oxygen.

In the compressed gas application the fuel includes any of the materials to which oxygen is exposed. These materials include metals and nonmetals used in cylinders, valves, regulators, and piping. Materials which would not normally be considered flammable such as steel and brass are included because all materials will oxidize to some extent if the oxygen concentration and temperature are high enough.

The oxidizer in the technical diving application is oxygen. This oxygen can be a component of a mixture, such as air or NITROX, or can be in the form of a pure gas. The concentration and pressure of oxygen to which system components are exposed are a consideration in evaluating oxygen compatibility.

Ignition sources include heat from friction or rapid compression, and sparks from particle impact or electrostatic discharge. Another ignition source which is a special case of rapid compression, known as adiabatic compression is a hazard often encountered in gas pumping and delivery systems. This phenomenon can occur if gas flow paths are such that localized pressurization occurs rapidly. Under these conditions, momentary gas temperatures well in excess of that required to ignite many materials can occur. Adiabatic compression can be controlled by valve and regulator design and by controlling the rate at which systems are pressurized. Experience has shown that an operator can open a one quarter turn ball valve quickly enough to cause a catastrophic adiabatic compression reaction in high pressure oxygen systems.

It is not possible to remove all of the fuel from the "fire triangle", since virtually any material will burn under the right conditions. It is also not possible to remove all ignition sources. By removing or replacing the materials which have a propensity to burn, and by minimizing ignition sources, it is possible to reduce the risk associated with high pressure oxygen handling.

OXYGEN CLEAN, OXYGEN COMPATIBLE, AND OXYGEN SERVICE

It is important to provide proper definitions of the terms oxygen clean, oxygen compatible, and oxygen service. These terms are related bit have different implications which cause confusion if they are used interchangeably.

Oxygen clean refers to the cleanliness of the system or component, or more specifically, the absence of contaminates. Contaminates vary but the most serious are those which act as fuel or ignition sources such as oil, grease, paint, fingerprints, soot, lint, dust, metal particles, rust, cleaning solvents, and cleaning detergents. A high pressure fitting may not be oxygen clean because rust particles or other materials which are not "compatible" with oxygen are present.

Scuba equipment shipped from the factory is never rated oxygen clean; however, equipment may be rendered so by means of a variety of cleaning processes. Such service can be obtained through a professional scuba facility such as those listed in the Reference section or through an ANDI or IAND affiliate. The diver has the option of having the original equipment cleaned or purchasing pre-cleaned and labeled NITROX or oxygen valves, regulators, and cylinders.

Oxygen compatibility usually refers to materials which will be exposed to oxygen and their combustibility. Some items, such as petroleum oils may be incompatible with oxygen because of the fire hazard. Other items may be incompatible because their decomposition rates increase to unacceptable levels in an oxygen environment. Briefly stated, compatibility means that all of the materials that are in contact with the gas are compatible with the gas at the working pressure of the system.

Oxygen service refers to the suitability of a system or component for use in an oxygen environment. Oxygen service requires BOTH oxygen clean AND oxygen compatible components. Therefore, the oxygen service requirement not met if an oxygen compatible component is contaminated (not oxygen clean). Likewise, a flammable rubber or plastic can be oxygen clean, but not oxygen compatible. This distinction is important since "oxygen compatible" components may be purchased from a supplier, but may require "cleaning" for "oxygen service" before installation.

Oxygen clean, compatible, and service are also relative terms. Some components and systems may be acceptable for use in an oxygen environment under some conditions, but unacceptable under others. Different levels of cleanliness are also specified according to the application and oxygen concentration.

EVALUATING MATERIALS FOR OXYGEN COMPATIBILITY

A variety of tests have been performed by engineers and scientists in both the commercial and government sectors to determine parameters used in evaluating the oxygen compatibility of various materials. The results of these tests are published in journals and workshop proceedings of organizations such as the American Society for Testing and Materials (ASTM).

Parameters of interest determined by these tests are the oxygen index (OI) and the Spontaneous Ignition Temperature (SIT), also referred to as the auto ignition temperature. The OI indicates the oxygen volume percentage required for a material to burn at atmospheric pressure. The higher the oxygen index, the less likely the material is to burn under the test conditions. The SIT indicates the temperature at which the material will ignite in a pressurized pure oxygen environment. Since the SIT and OI do not always correspond with each other, the SIT is more appropriate for the diving gas mixing application, since pressurized oxygen and oxygen mixtures are used.

For general use, where there is no risk of adiabatic compression or other severe ignition sources, non-metal should have a SIT higher than 400 degrees centigrade. Following ignition, the temperature rise should be no more than 10 degrees C and the pressure rise no more than 15 bar (220 psi). Materials with a SIT between 200 and 400 degrees can be used under certain conditions. For elastomer seals, SIT as low as 300 degrees are accept-

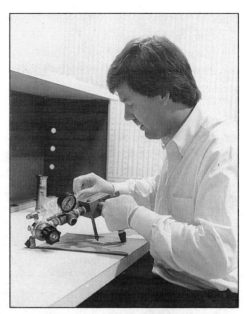

Randy Bohrer at work in his Underwater Applications lab. Photo by Norma Bohrer.

able; for valve and regulator seats, nylon with an SIT higher than 200 degrees is acceptable. Materials with SIT less than 200 degrees are acceptable in low pressure systems (less than 350 psi).

Considering the previous discussions, it is not clear which materials are oxygen compatible, since some meet the SIT criteria, but not the temperature or pressure rise criteria. Oxygen compatibility is therefore relative and is also often a trade-off. The system design and application must be considered. In general, PFTE seats are acceptable in many valves and regulators. Viton and silicone seals are commonly used in oxygen valves, regulators, and compressors. Krytox and Halocarbon greases are acceptable, but silicone should only be used in low pressure applications. For more information and assistance in evaluating these materials, the manufacturer of the gas system, or of the seals, seats, or other components should be consulted.

CLEANING SYSTEMS AND COMPONENTS FOR OXYGEN SERVICE

After the oxygen compatibility question is addressed and resolved, the issue of cleaning can be considered. The particular items which need to be cleaned are clearly all items which are directly exposed to oxygen. Often overlooked are those items which are not directly exposed to oxygen, but which could become so due to some equipment failure or operator error. An example is a storage bank system where oxygen and air cylinders are piped to the same gas delivery panel. The air cylinders and piping must be "oxygen clean" because an operator error or check valve failure could result in oxygen entering the air cylinders.

New items from a supplier must also be cleaned, unless they are sealed and labeled indicating that they are already oxygen clean. Components such as fittings and hoses may have machining fluids, residue, particles, or lubricants remaining which could create a hazardous condition in an oxygen environment. Since the conditions under which the components were manufactured or packaged are unknown, an assumption that oxygen cleaning is required must be made.

CLEANING AGENTS FOR OXYGEN SYSTEMS

Cleaning agents include solvents, detergents, acids, alkalies, and abrasives. Acids and alkalies are commonly used in the dive shop for removing scale, rust, and organic matter. These agents are used in the same manner for pre-cleaning and intermediate cleaning of oxygen systems. Abrasives such as wire brushes, sand-blasters, and grinding wheels are used for removing difficult rust, scale, and other surface contaminates. Acids, alkalies, and abrasives are not unique to oxygen cleaning and are familiar to most dive shop personnel. The use of solvents and detergents for intermediate and final cleaning is probably less familiar and therefore of particular interest.

SOLVENTS

The solvent of choice for cleaning of military components for oxygen service is trichlorotrifluoroethane, also known as R-113 or Freon 113. It is sold in spray cans in electronic supply companies under trademark names such as Dry-Klean and Freon TF. It is also available through chemical suppliers in liquid containers of various sizes. R-113 is a very effective degreaser, is less toxic than the other solvents discussed in this chapter, but has several disadvantages. Although its toxicity is not excessive, it evaporates quickly and displaces oxygen. A large spill in a confined area could be hazardous. R-113 is also a Chlorinated Fluorocarbon (CFC) that is damaging to the atmosphere. It is expected that increased government regulations will make it unavailable within the next three years. A final and important characteristic about R-113 is that if it is exposed to flame or excessive heat, it decomposes into the highly toxic gas, phosgene. Special care should be used when using R-113 because of these particular hazards.

Another effective solvent is 111 trichloroethane. It is available in hardware and paint stores under trademark names such as "Parks Carbotrichor" and "Cleaning Solvent". This solvent is more toxic than Freon 113, but is not damaging to ozone and is less expensive. Components cleaned with this solvent require agitation through ultrasonic cleaning, swabbing, or wiping.

Other solvents such as trichloroethylene and methylene chloride are much more toxic than R-113 or trichloroethane and are probably a less desirable choice. Carbon tetrachloride should not be used because of its high toxicity. Petroleum based solvents, paint thinners, and similar materials are also unacceptable due to their toxicity, flammability, and tendency to leave a residue after cleaning.

The cleaning solvents discussed have some additional hazards. Most have an anesthetic effect when breathed, therefore adequate ventilation is required during their use, and all remaining solvent must be removed from system components by rinsing or thorough drying before final assembly or use. Since these chemicals are capable of dissolving the natural oils in the skin, gloves should be worn or contact with the solvent avoided. When handling these or any other chemicals which are damaging to the eyes, proper eye protection is required.

Finally, some solvents may extract chemicals from certain plastics such as PVC. In addition to changing the properties of the plastic, the extracted chemicals may be deposited on other system components, resulting in contamination. The commonly used solvents are considered acceptable for use with Teflon (PFTE), polyethylene, and polypropylene. If PVC or other incompatible plastics require cleaning, or there is a question regarding compatibility, detergents can be used as the cleaning agent.

DETERGENTS

Detergents and water are often used for cleaning and degreasing system components, including non-metals. A particular detergent solution described and recommended in MIL-STD-1330C is Tribasic Sodium Phosphate or TSP. This compound is chemically similar to household laundry detergent. The mil-standard specifies that the cleaning solution is to be prepared by dissolving two pounds of type I, or 4.5 pounds of type II TSP in five gallons of water. The solution must be heated and maintained at a temperature between 160 and 190 degrees Fahrenheit during cleaning. TSP is available from chemical supply companies or some hardware stores. Often, the ingredients list indicates that both TSP and a non-ionic detergent make up the particular detergent. This combination forms an acceptable and effective cleaner and is referenced in other military procedures.

Practical detergent cleaners for the technical diver include household laundry detergent, dishwashing liquid, and cleaners such as 409 and Fantastik. These cleaners may be used in place of or in addition to various solvents for intermediate and final cleaning. In all cases, the parts must be thoroughly rinsed of the cleaning agent. Samples of rinse water can be shaken vigorously and observed for foaming or bubbling indicating the presence of detergent.

CLEANING TECHNIQUES
Pre-Cleaning

Techniques for pre-cleaning of components are similar to the standard techniques employed in servicing standard scuba equipment. The equipment is disassembled, placed in various acid, alkaline, or detergent baths to remove all surface fouling. Large components such as parts from compressors or boosters can be pre-cleaned by running them through one or more cycles of a standard household dishwasher. Successful removal of contaminates is more important than the particular pre-cleaning method.

Intermediate Cleaning

The next cleaning stage is sometimes omitted or combined with the final cleaning and assembly stages, depending upon the degree of cleaning required, and the effectiveness of pre-cleaning. While the acid and alkaline baths which are commonly used in dive store service departments remove many contaminates, including some grease and oil, this next stage is the primary means of degreasing components.

Procedures used include soaking, swabbing, and wiping using a solvent or detergent bath, Q-tips, and paper towels. An ultrasonic cleaner is excellent for this purpose. Throughout the cleaning process, the cleaning agent should be inspected and compared against a clean reference sample for discoloration or particle content indicating contamination and the need for replacement with fresh cleaner. Parts must be rinsed of all cleaning fluid and dried thoroughly. Some solvents evaporate without leaving a residue. Components cleaned with these solvents do not necessarily require a water rinse, but thorough drying is necessary to remove all traces of solvent.

Final Cleaning, Inspection, and Assembly

The goal of oxygen cleaning is to reduce to the extent possible those two elements of the "fire triangle" that can be controlled — the fuel and the ignition source. The final cleaning, inspection, and assembly stage is used to remove any remaining oil, grease, lint, rust particles, dust, and other contaminates. The components must also be inspected for cleanliness and protected from recontamination before and during assembly.

Inspection techniques primarily involve observing the components under strong white light. Particles not visible to the unaided eye are generally acceptable. Specific particle sizes and their quantity for a given surface area are specified in government and commercial standards. At this stage, the technical gas mixer or diver should strive for no visible particles. This is not an unreasonable level of cleanliness given that the components are usually small and accessible. Components can also be wiped with a white, lint-free towel, which can then be observed for contaminates. This technique is especially useful for inspecting areas which are not visible. A more complete inspection can be accomplished by also viewing the components or "test wipe" under an ultraviolet (UV) or "black" light. Greases and oils and many particles such as lint, fluoresce when exposed to UV light and can be quickly detected.

Protecting components against recontamination is important to prevent the time and effort of cleaning from becoming futile. Components which are not to be immediately placed in an assembly can be sealed in plastic bags. Hoses and fittings with openings can be capped or plastic bags can be tied or taped over the openings. Final cleaning and assembly is best accomplished in a "clean room". Establishing a proper clean room is not usually practical, but an area of reasonable cleanliness, with low levels of dust and other airborne contaminates should be used.

PROCEDURES FOR CLEANING SPECIFIC EQUIPMENT

Preparing cylinders, valves, regulators, hoses, tubing, and various gas fittings and hardware for oxygen service is within the capabilities of most dive facilities and individuals proficient in servicing scuba and high pressure gas equipment. Procedures and recommendations outlined in this book and established by ASTM, CGA, and equipment manufacturers must be observed. This section outlines methods for cleaning scuba equipment. Procedures for cleaning compressors and gas booster pumps are not included because this equipment requires a high level of cleanliness that most dive facilities and individuals can probably not attain. Pumping oxygen carries additional hazards and increased risks; preparing this equipment for oxygen service should not be attempted without special training.

Cylinders

Scuba and storage cylinders can often be cleaned for oxygen service by large gas suppliers which offer hydrostatic testing. Utilizing these services is preferable both economically and practically. If this alternative is not acceptable, the cylinders can be cleaned in the dive facility using the procedures described in this chapter.

The cylinder is first inspected internally for particles, rust, and other contaminates. If surface corrosion is present, it must be removed by tumbling or the use of an abrasive "whisk" or similar cleaning techniques. The tank is then washed internally with a detergent or solvent. One pint or more of the cleaning agent is usually required. The solution drained from the cylinder is inspected for discoloration or particles using clean solution as a reference. This procedure is repeated with fresh cleaning solution until no discoloration or particles are observed. The cylinder is then thoroughly rinsed, then dried with oil free air or nitrogen. A final internal inspection is performed to verify the cleaning procedure.

It is important to ensure that all solvent is cleaned from the inside of the cylinder. Trichloroethane has a tendency to penetrate the cylinder walls, then become liberated upon the application of pressure. The gas from this cylinder which had no detectable odor before filling may then have an overwhelming odor of solvent. In 1990, a great deal of concern was raised within various levels of the Army Troop Support Command regarding trichloroethane contamination of their diving equipment. A decompression chamber which had been cleaned with this solvent and appeared to be properly purged, exhibited a strong solvent odor when it was pressurized. Thorough rinsing with hot water is effective in removing the solvent. Alternatively, the cylinder can be purged by pressurization with oil free air or nitrogen to 100 psi or more, then draining the cylinder and repeating this process until the odor of solvent is no longer present.

Valves

Valves are disassembled and cleaned of scale and corrosion in an acid bath such as white vinegar, or commercially available solutions. Valve components are then cleaned in a solvent or detergent degreasing solution by soaking, swabbing with Q-tips, and wiping with paper towels. The components are then rinsed to remove all traces of the solvent or detergent.

Soft goods, such as o-rings, seats, and backup rings can be cleaned in a similar manner. It is important to limit the exposure of these soft goods to solvents due to solvent and materials compatibility issues discussed previously. If the soft goods are not appropriate for use with oxygen, they must be replaced. Most o-rings are available in Viton material, and complete kits for various valves are available from many technical diving suppliers.

O-rings which require lubricant are lubricated with oxygen compatible grease, such as Krytox (Dupont), Fomblin (Montedison), Halocarbon (Halocarbon Products), Fluorolube (Hooker), Tribolube (Aerospace Lubricants), or Chrisolube (Lubrication Technology). It is also advisable to lubricate the threads of the valve before installation. Often, friction from the installation of the valve loosens metal particles which can become a hazard. Extra grease in this area helps to contain these particles and also controls corrosion at the cylinder to valve interface.

Regulators

Cleaning procedures for regulators are the same as for those of valves, but there are special considerations regarding soft goods. Some regulators use Nitrile (buna-N) and other materials which are not advised for use in oxygen systems. If oxygen compatible components are not available as replacements for these parts, a different regulator must be selected. Whether the parts are exposed to cylinder pressure or intermediate pressure is also a consideration. Although the second stage and low pressure section of the first stage needs to be clean, materials such as buna are acceptable although not preferred.

MAINTENANCE

In order for an oxygen system to remain safe for use with oxygen, it must be maintained such that contamination does not occur. Special precautions include protecting the system from dust and other contaminates when not in use, avoiding contamination with incompatible gases, and periodic inspection and re-cleaning.

Cylinders, valves, regulators, and pumping equipment must be sufficiently protected from dust and moisture when not in use. Gas inlets and outlets must be protected with suitable caps, dust covers, or plastic bags. Before filling a cylinder, a small amount of residual gas should be released to dislodge any dust or moisture at the valve orifice. The area in which the equipment is used or stored should be reasonably clean and free of materials that are hazardous when exposed to oxygen such as petroleum greases and fuels. These precautions decrease both the risk of contaminating the systems and the frequency and difficulty of re-cleaning.

Dedicating systems for use with oxygen and oxygen compatible mixtures is also required. If an oxygen regulator or cylinder is used with standard high-pressure breathing air, minute quantities of compressor oil can accumulate over time, rendering the equipment no longer clean for oxygen service. Switching systems between oxygen, air, and other gases, must be avoided.

Periodic disassembly, inspection, and re-cleaning of equipment is also required. The annual servicing of cylinders and regulators which is standard in the diving industry provides an opportunity to inspect and re-clean cylinders and regulators if necessary. This frequency is probably sufficient if the preventative measures in the previous paragraphs are observed. However, many technical divers inspect and re-clean their equipment every six months or even every three months if the equipment is used heavily. The equipment must also be inspected and cleaned if there is reason to believe that contamination has occurred.

Necessary maintenance procedures are easy to follow. Prevention of contamination is probably the most important maintenance activity because it decreases the risk associated with using oxygen and decreases the difficulty of re-cleaning when it is required. Periodic inspections and servicing of diving equipment is already a standard practice, and provides and excellent opportunity to asses the cleanliness of the system components. These maintenance procedures are required and ensure the continued safe operation of the systems.

OXYGEN MIXTURES

In addition to items exposed to pure oxygen, items exposed to oxygen mixtures may also need to be cleaned. The question of the level of cleanliness required for mixtures with higher than normal percentages of oxygen is currently surrounded by controversy. The National Oceanic and Atmospheric Administration's (NOAA) experience with NITROX has shown that mixtures containing up to 40% oxygen at pressures of several thousand psi are safe in scuba cylinders, valves, and regulators without special cleaning. Some gas mixers and divers are comfortable using NITROX mixtures containing up to 50% oxygen without special cleaning.

American Nitrox Divers, Inc. (ANDI) recommends oxygen cleaning of any systems exposed to higher than normal concentrations of oxygen. The position of the International Association of NITROX Divers (IAND) is that mixtures of up to 40% oxygen can be treated the same as air for use in scuba equipment. However, both organizations agree that if NITROX is mixed in the scuba cylinder, the cylinder and valve must be for oxygen service clean since pure oxygen is used in the mixing process. Most organizations and gas prepares agree that pumping equipment such as compressors and booster pumps need to be oxygen clean when used with mixtures containing more than 23% oxygen. Haskel, Inc. indicates that their boosters are already sufficiently clean; the difference between their air and oxygen boosters is seal material and testing procedures.

As specific training agency standards are developed and revised, the technical diver should observe current standards regarding the handling of enriched oxygen mixtures. If there is any question regarding the required level of cleanliness, the oxygen clean standard should be observed.

CONCLUSIONS

High pressure gas, especially oxygen, can be very hazardous if proper procedures are not followed. If the elements of the "fire triangle" can be minimized sufficiently, a relatively safe condition can be attained. Removing the fuel and ignition sources by thorough cleaning and replacement of incompatible materials is required to achieve this safe condition.

The best advice regarding the preparation of systems for oxygen is to "Do it right". There are many individuals using oxygen with equipment that has been cleaned improperly or not at all. These individuals are literally "playing with fire". "Doing it right" is not difficult. Oxygen compatible parts for regulators and valves are now available at dive shops, technical diving suppliers, and some manufacturers. Cleaning solvents are available from paint and hardware stores and some dive shops. All that is required to select the appropriate solvent is reading the ingredients list. If purchasing the solvent is a problem, household detergents such as dishwashing liquid or 409 with lots of hot water form an effective degreaser. White vinegar from the grocery store is excellent and safe for removing scale and other surface contaminates from components.

This chapter forms the basis for developing cleaning procedures for specific equipment. For more information, publications are available from ASTM, CGA, and the US Government to assist in designing, modifying, or otherwise preparing systems for oxygen use. Issues discussed include the level of cleanliness required, evaluating materials, cleaning and inspection procedures, cleaning agents, and maintenance.

Both the information, materials, and services are available to make oxygen use easy and safe. If it is not practical for a user to acquire the necessary supplies and skill, many dive shops and gas suppliers offer oxygen cleaning services. The hazards associated with high pressure oxygen can be minimized with a small amount of forethought and effort. Decreasing the risk is important not only for safety, but to attain the confidence level required to comfortably achieve the impressive objectives that technical diving has recently seen and the future promises.

REFERENCES

American Society for Testing and Materials (ASTM), Standard G93-88, *Cleaning Methods for Material and Equipment Used in Oxygen-Enriched Environments,* April, 1988, ASTM, 1916 Race St., Philadelphia, PA 19103

American Society for Testing and Materials (ASTM), STP 1111, *Flammability and Sensitivity of Materials in Oxygen-Enriched Atmospheres,* June, 1991, ASTM, 1916 Race St., Philadelphia, PA 19103

Butler, Glen J., *Technical Diver,* Issue No. 1, Winter 1991, Aqua Corps, Key West, FL

Compressed Gas Association, Inc. (CGA), CGA Pamphlet G-4.1, *Cleaning Equipment for Oxygen Service,* 1985, CGA, 1235 Jefferson Davis Highway, Arlington, VA 22202

Compressed Gas Association, Inc. (CGA), CGA Pamphlet G-4.4, *Industrial Practices for Gaseous Oxygen Transmission and Distribution Piping Systems,* 1980, CGA, 1235 Jefferson Davis Highway, Arlington, VA 22202

Department of the Navy, Naval Sea Systems Command (NAVSEA), Military Standard MIL-STD-1330C, *Cleaning and Testing of Shipboard Oxygen, Nitrogen, and Hydrogen Gas Piping Systems,* Feb 1, 1985, NAVSEA, Washington, DC 20362

Department of the Navy, Naval Ships Systems Command (NAVSHIPS), Military Standard MIL-STD-1622, *Cleaning of Shipboard Compressed Air Systems,* Sept. 20, 1973, NAVSEA, Washington, DC 20362

Parker Hannifin Corporation, *Parker O-ring Handbook,* Parker Hannifin Corp, Cleveland, OH

CHAPTER 18

Lee H. Somers, Ph.D.

Mixed Gas in Scientific Diving

The use of gas mixtures other than air in scientific diving [1] began in the 1960's in conjunction with various saturation diving programs. Although, the primary emphasis of these early sea floor living experiments was to prove the feasibility saturation diving and underwater habitats, some marine science research was accomplished. These early aquanauts lived in a helium/oxygen and helium/nitrogen/oxygen atmosphere for days to weeks at a time and breathed mixed gases during excursions from their habitats. Today, to my knowledge, only one undersea laboratory program remains active in the United States: The Aquarius Habitat Program under the direction of the National Oceanic and Atmospheric Administration (NOAA) [2].

Dr. Walter Stark used a unique closed-circuit mixed-gas scuba for scientific observation and collection at a depth of 300 feet in the late 1960's. [3] Paul Tzimoulis, the publisher-editor of Skin Diver, dived to 300 feet with Dr. Stark and published an excellent article in his magazine. The same magazine included an advertisement offering the Electrolung II to the diving public at a cost of $2975 (plus training). Unfortunately, the Electrolung never achieve popularity with in the scientific or recreational community and it was soon removed from the market. There were allegedly some operational and financial problems. The unit was, in my opinion, simply a decade or so ahead of it's time. However, the fact remains that mixed gas (Trimix) and closed-circuit mixed-gas scuba was successfully used by scientists 25 years ago.

In 1978 the NOAA introduced diving procedures and tables for the use of a mixture of nitrogen and oxygen and formally presented this informa-

The 1970 model "Electrolung" rebreather enjoyed a brief popularity before fading into obscurity, a victim of technology ahead of its time. Note breathing bag on chest of diver. Photos by Bret Gilliam.

tion to the scientific community in the NOAA Diving Manual in 1979. [4] The first mixture used was 68% nitrogen/32% nitrogen (NOAA I). More recently NOAA authorized the use of 64% oxygen/36% nitrogen (NOAA II).[5] Although, mixed gases had seen limited use in some scientific diving activities previously, I feel NOAA can be credited for the formalization of mixed gases in scientific diving.

CURRENT STATUS

A report on governmental scientific diving during the year 1990 published in the newsletter of the American Academy of Underwater Science (AAUS) revealed that only 110 of 13,575 dives (or .8%) reported were to depths in excess of 130 feet and more than 96% of all dives were within no-decompression time limits.[6] In fact, approximately 81% of these dives were to depths of 60 feet or less (51% were to less than 30 feet). Furthermore, only about 0.7% of these dives were made using mixed gases (i.e.,). Statistics compiled by the AAUS for 30,638 dives made by nongovernmental scientist (primarily academic personnel) during the years of 1987 and 1988 indicate that 1.6% of these dives were in the range of 100 to 130 feet and only 0.115% exceeded a depth of 130 feet. Based on these statistics, it appears that the vast majority of underwater studies are conducted in shallow water breathing compressed air.

Unfortunately, statistical data for nearly four decades of organized scientific diving is scattered in the files of individual institutions. A formal national data collection system has only been in existence for less than 10 years and this system only compiles dive statistics from less than forty member organizations of the American Academy of Underwater Sciences. Although these figures and trends appear to be representative of the entire scientific diving community, this data is still far from complete.

Historically, modern day scientific diving in the United States emerged in about 1950 at the Scripps Institution of Oceanography with the establishment of the first scientific diving program and training course by Conrad Limbaugh. In the early years, depth certifications for the use of compressed air and scuba to 200 feet or greater were issued to scientists who met stringent training and experience progression standards.[7] For example, between 1953 and 1964 Robert F. Dill, then a graduate student at Scripps, made more that 500 scuba dives in the head of Scripps Submarine Canyon. Although most of these dives were in the depth range of 45 to 160 feet, some were to a depth of 225 feet.[8] Through subsequent years up to the present, a select group of close-lipped scientists have conducted underwater studies in depths of 130 to 300 feet breathing compressed air and, often, using in-water oxygen decompression procedures. It is interesting to note that working depths are conspicuously absent in some research reports and scientific papers.

Modern recreational scuba diving evolved from early scientific scuba diving. However, over the past few decades the evolution of recreational scuba diving has been somewhat guided by marketing philosophies. In order to market scuba diving instruction, equipment, and travel to a large consumer population, trainee selection criteria, training standards, and scuba diving limitations have be modified to appeal to the largest possible consumer group. The more restrictive (and therefore supposedly safer) the operational parameters are for recreational scuba diving, the larger the potential consumer population. This philosophy has attracted a large number of individual into scuba diving and diver training has been modified to accommodate individuals of limited water skill ability and physical fitness. Many divers meeting current standards for certification lack the knowledge, skill, and self-discipline compulsory for safe diving.

Unfortunately, the evolution of scientific diving has, in my opinion, been somewhat stifled by recreational diving concepts and philosophies.

Today, most persons entering scientific diving programs have previous recreational diver training. Furthermore, most scientific divers are trained by instructors holding recreational diver instructor certifications. Although many instructors themselves exceed the depth, gas, and equipment parameters of recreational diving, they are reluctant to offer instruction in deep and decompression diving or encourage scientists to work outside of the recreational diver envelope. Insurance restrictions, perception of liability problems, and standard of the recreational diving community are often given as reasons for imposing stringent depth and gas limits on scientific scuba divers. It is unfortunate that regardless of the distinctly higher level of training and supervision available to the scientific diver, they are still measured and, to some degree, controlled by recreational diver standards.

The issue is further complicated by the conditions of exemption for scientific divers from control under federal Occupational Safety and Health Administration (OSHA) regulations for commercial diving. Many scientific divers are of the opinion that the OSHA exemption mandates that scientific divers be restricted to compressed air scuba diving. This is not the case.

Fortunately, a small number of scientific divers have rejected the plunge into mediocrity. Dr. Robert Dill, Dr. Judy Lang, Dr. David Liddel, Dr. Mendel Petersen, Dr. Allan Albright, Dr. George Bass, and Daniel J. Lenihan are among a small number of scientist who have insulated themselves from the conservatism of today's scientific and recreational diving communities. It should also be noted that some scientific divers do conform to the training standards and operational guidelines of the cave diving community. Fortunately, this small group of dedicated scientist-adventurers have "held their ground" during the mediocrity plunge. Individuals who have traditionally worked outside of conventional scientific and recreational diving conservatism are the ones who will, if given an opportunity, mold a new generation of underwater researchers.

Today, Ichthyologist Richard Pyle, working under the direction of Dr. John E. Randall of the Bishop Museum in Honolulu, is leading the scientific community to depths of 200 to 350 feet using Trimix and in open-circuit scuba. [9] He has already discovered many new species of fish. Unfortunately, he has had to personally fund his deep research. It appears that most scientific institutions and granting agencies still adhere to conventional scientific and recreational diving conservatism. [10]

Unfortunately, the recreational influence on scientific diving is strong. In spite of the fact that the National Oceanic and Atmospheric Administration (NOAA) introduced scientists to enriched air diving some 15 years ago, only

Richard Pyle in deep diving rig for 380 ft. dive. Pyle's research diving in the 200 to 400 foot levels led to the discovery of several new fish species and marks some of the deepest depth obtained in scientific diving. Photo by Bret Gilliam

a few scientific groups use it today. I feel that this fact is directly related to the reluctance of the recreational diving community to accept the use of alternative gas mixtures. Ironically, it is the controversial fringe element of the recreational diving community (American Divers, Incorporated and the International Association of Divers) that is currently fostering interest in alternative gas mixture diving within our colleges and universities. In the past two years, in my opinion, these organizations have advanced the acceptance and use of for scientific diving by non-NOAA scientist more than the NOAA program did in 15 years.

The advantages of alternative gas mixtures for scientific diving are obvious. Proper and prudent use of alternative gas mixture can lead to vast savings in both money and logistical support. For example, breathing an EANx 45% mixture[11] the scientist can complete 150 minutes of sampling and observations a depths not exceeding 70 feet without incurring a decompression obligation or exceeding oxygen dose limits. This is a greater amount of time than I have observed some scientists working in the water at depths of 50 to 70 feet in a given day when diving from a saturation habitat. The cost of scientific saturation diving will far exceed $2,000 per day. The cost of EANx for a dive team is only a few 10's of dollars per day.

Today, adventurous technical divers[12] equipped with open circuit scuba are currently using alternative gas mixtures to increase bottom time, dive more conservatively to deeper depths with reduce narcosis impairment or risk of oxygen toxicity, and shorten decompression times. Some scientists

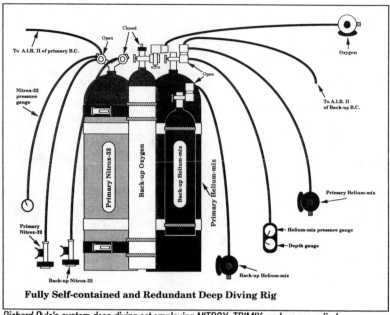

Fully Self-contained and Redundant Deep Diving Rig

Richard Pyle's custom deep diving set employing NITROX, TRIMIX, and oxygen cylinders.

are already recognizing the same advantages. No doubt many scientists breathing compressed air have avoided extending their research into deeper depths for fear of seriously compromising the accuracy of their scientific observations and data collection as well as their safety. Now, using the proper mixture of helium, nitrogen, and oxygen (Trimix), the scientist can reduce the narcotic effect to an equivalent of about 100 feet when working at a depth of 300 feet.

THE FUTURE

Within the next few years, I feel that the use of enriched air will become common place in many scientific diving programs. An increasing number of scientific diving instructors are also qualifying as enriched air instructors and several major universities already have gas mixing facilities and trained mixing technicians. Initial acceptance will no doubt be influenced by the fact that by increasing the percentage of oxygen [and subsequently decreasing the percentage of nitrogen] in a mixture, air based dive tables and computers can be used in a much more conservative fashion within the acceptable depth range of the gas mixture. Furthermore, basically any scientist who has been trained to use open-circuit scuba can easily be trained to use enriched air within a few hours. Some researchers will take advantage of the extended no-decompression [no-stop] dive time afforded by the use of enriched air. As the scientific community becomes more familiar with the advantages of enriched air and comfortable with its use, enriched air will be the gas of choice for many diving operations and customized optimal blends will see increased usage.

Rob Parker with heliox rebreather preparing for dive in "Stargate" cave system in Andros Blue Hole. Photo by Rob Palmer

The time frame for acceptance of deep diving Trimixes will depend on the development of instructional programs and availability of gas blending facilities. Although very few universities and research organizations currently have Trimix training and diving programs, they are the logical place for the aspect of diving to develop. Scientific diving programs have the advantage of diving control boards, technical support personnel, and institutional insurance programs. In addition, prospective Trimix diver trainees in scientific diving programs will generally have the necessary academic background for more easily learning and understanding the concepts associated with mixed gas physics and physiology. However, based on years of experience within the scientific diving community, I fear that most scientists will not wish to commit the personal time that is necessary to achieve and maintain a mixed gas diving certification.

Yet, there will be dedicated scientists such as Richard Pyle who will immediately seek that advantages of Trimix diving to further their scholarly work. Open-circuit Trimix diving will, in my opinion, be limited to only the most dedicated and adventurous young diver-scientist. However, technological advancement in scuba design may greatly increased the attractiveness of alternative gas mixture diving.

Closed-circuit mixed gas scuba has been used by scientific, commercial, and military divers since the 1960's Today, one company has developed a very sophisticated closed-circuit scuba for technical cave explorers and at least two others are developing similar equipment. In the relatively near future, a new generation of closed-circuit mixed gas scuba will make its debut in recreational and scientific diving. The scientific community should be among the first to reap the benefits of this new scuba. Several models of closed-circuit scuba will be introduced before the end of this decade. As we near the end of the decade, advancement in computer technology, system design, and equipment reliability complemented by diver acceptance and moderate cost will stimulate the development of a scuba that far exceeds the imagination of today's diver.

The future of mixed gases and closed-circuit scuba in scientific diving depends on many factors. The ultraconservative barriers will have to be bridged and diver education will have to be redefined. The current technical diving community will have to demonstrate to scientists and the diving community at large that the equipment, techniques, and decompression protocols are safe and reliable. And, of course, the economic feasibility of deep, mixed has diving will have to be shown. Finally, the scientist will have to envision significant benefits associated with ambient pressure diving.

In my opinion, mixed gases and closed circuit scuba have a distinct place in scientific diving. The time frame is unclear at this time. However, I do envision exciting technological and operational advancement in the future. With the advancement and acceptance of closed-circuit scuba, use of compressed air scuba diving for scientific research, as we know it today, will fade into obsolescence. Scientists working in shallow water will breathe optimal mixtures of nitrogen and oxygen that will be contained and mixed in a scuba that is smaller and weighs far less than the single cylinder open-circuit scuba used today. The gases will be contained in miniature ultra-high pressure cylinders. A cylinder of oxygen and a cylinder of (possibly compressed air) will be fitted to connectors in the scuba. Under normal diving conditions these cylinders will supply sufficient breathing gas for 10 to 12 hours of diving.

An optimal gas mixture will be selected by the scuba's computer based on depth, oxygen partial pressure, daily repetitive dive requirements, cumulative oxygen dose, diver decompression or no-decompression preference, safety factors, and other parameters entered by the diver. The diver will play an integral role in planning an optimal dive, however, the computer will, based on prior programming, restrict the diver to operate within acceptable gas physiology parameters. Oxygen partial pressure will be adjusted throughout to dive in order to minimize inert gas absorption and prevent oxygen toxicity. Cumulative oxygen dose permitting, shallow decompression will be completed breathing high oxygen or 100% oxygen. Naturally, the diver's inert gas status will be computer monitored and continuously updated based on depth, oxygen partial pressure, and time.

During normal operation at depth, all gas is recirculated. The only gas

The "Michigan Mafia": Dr. Lee Somers, Karl Huggins, and Dr. Harris Taylor at surface supply diving seminar. Photo by Bret Gilliam

consumed will be the oxygen required to meet the diver's metabolic needs. The diver's exhaled breath will pass through a highly-efficient carbon dioxide absorbent chemical into a breathing bag or canister where the oxygen content will be measured and replenished as needed. The recirculating gas will continuously be monitored by multiple oxygen, carbon dioxide, and moisture sensors. These sensors will be linked to redundant miniature computers (probably no larger that today's smaller dive computers) where the data will be continuously analyzed and displayed to the diver either on a wrist-mounted display console or, more likely, a heads-up display on the mask lens.

Air compressors will no longer be required in the field. Crates of miniature cylinders of oxygen, Trimix, and will be transported to the dive location. The same will be true for carbon dioxide absorbent canisters. Theoretically, a supply of gas cylinders and carbon dioxide absorbent canisters sufficient for 200 to 300 hours of dive time will weigh less that today's portable air compressor. Keep in mind that gas volume requirements are more or less independent of depth when using closed-circuit scuba. In theory, this gas supply volume, depending on mixture, could support routine diving to depths of 500 feet or more. The diver's fatigue, thermal stress, and decompression time parameters now become the limiting factors. Expended gas cylinders and absorbent canisters will be returned to service centers for refilling to user specifications. All gas mixtures will be analyzed and certified by service center gas technicians.

Gas requirements for buoyancy control will be minimized as diving suits are refined. In warmer waters, new neutral buoyant wet-type diving suits that are unaffected by pressure will provide ample thermal protection. The suit will not compress at depth and, thus, no gas will be required for buoyancy compensation. Dry suit gas requirements will be handled with a separate small cylinder of argon or other gas with minimal heat transfer capacity. The buoyancy of the scuba will change only slightly during a dive since only a small amount of oxygen is actually used in metabolism. Incidental gas loss will be minimal.

Within only a year or two, the first models of this new generation of closed-circuit mixed gas scuba will be available to scientific and recreational divers. Initially, cave explorers and adventurers will probably be the primary user group. These divers will push to dive depths and durations previously limited to commercial saturation divers. Although a select group of scientific divers will immediately embrace the depth capability of these scuba, the majority of new users will probably take advantage of the latitudes afforded by optimized applications.

As closed-circuit scuba and mixed gas diving gains increasing acceptance in the so-called technical [recreational] diving community, an increasing number of young and more adventurous scientist will follow the lead of Pyle into the twilight zone. Unfortunately, many conservative barriers will have to be circumvented.

Today, thermal stress stands as the last major barrier to deep, long duration scientific ambient pressure scuba diving. Passive thermal protection afforded by present day dry suits has its limitations. Ultimately, scientific divers [all divers] must have a self-contained active diver heating system. Whether heat will be produced by electricity using highly efficient batteries or by controlled chemical reaction is unclear at this time. Ultimately, future success in deep mixed gas scuba diving will depend on the development of effective self-contained heating units for diving suits. For this reason, I suggest that most research applications of mixed gases will be first proven in tropical waters.

At present, hot water supplied to a suit via a hose from a surface-based hot water heater is still the best alternative for active thermal protection. Although most of today's technical divers favor free swimming without connection to the surface, the surface connection may be necessary as an interim means of dealing with the problems of thermal stress. When the use of umbilical supplied diver support is mentioned, most divers envision the requirement of large support vessels and tons of equipment. They immediately reject the thought of being encumbered by an umbilical to the surface.

In reality, a self-contained mixed-gas scuba diver could operate with a reasonable degree of freedom at intermediate depths [exclusive of cave and wreck penetrations] using a water hose connected to the surface. However, because of the long in-water decompression requirements commonly associated with mixed gas diving, hot water system reliability would have to be assured. Use of a non-return hot water suit which will maintain satisfactory thermal protection for at least 30 minutes in the event of heating system shutdown is highly recommended.[13] Failure of an open-circuit hot water suit would almost immediately cause rapid cooling of the diver and life-threatening hypothermia.

Another possible, but untested, method of reducing thermal stress on a diver involves the use of a water filled flexible plastic open diving bell suspended below a vessel at decompression depths.[14] Hot water would be continuously pumped to the bell at very high temperatures via a hose from a hot wa-

Dr. Harris Taylor of the University of Michigan assists diver during training with lightweight commercial helmet and full surface supply systems including gas mixtures, hot water suit supply, and communications. Photo by Bret Gilliam

ter heater on the surface. The plastic bell would only serve to concentrate the hot water in a small space. Hot water entering near the lower potion of the bell would rise to the top [lower density] and displace colder water out of the open bottom. Naturally, considerable heat would be lost to the surrounding water through conduction. However, in theory, a parcel of warm water could be maintained in the bell with sufficient hot water input. The diver, dressed in a conventional dry thermal protection garment, would simply ascend into the confined parcel of hot water to complete in-water decompression in a standard manner. Exhaled gas would escape through holes in the top of the bell. The bell could be fitted with a movement system [possibly using controlled entrapment of the diver's exhaled gas] so that a diver could easily move it up the ascent line during decompression [the descent line passes directly through the center of the bell]. Many of the problems associated with dry bells or in-water decompression units would be avoided. For instance, very little weight would be needed to stabilize the unit in the water column since the only buoyancy that must be dealt with is that of the plastic material. As previously stated, this is only one possible interim solution to a major problem.

During this decade, the scientific community will fragment into several operational diving segments. No doubt, a large number, possibly a majority, of scientific divers will cling to current recreational diving philosophies and operational parameters. Another segment will seek the advantages of Atmospheric Diving Systems (ADS). A new generation of ADS suits will enable a diver to walk or swim about the sea floor at depths of several hundred feet in the comfort of an one-atmosphere environmental suit. An improved fluid suspended joint will facilitate unprecedented freedom of movement. After an hour or two at 300 feet, the diver will ascend directly to the surface with no decompression required. Some scientists will prefer to fly compact remotely operated vehicles (ROV) for the comfort of a shirt-sleeve environment of a control room onboard ship. A future generation of ROVs will probably be free-swimming and unencumbered by need for a cable to the surface. However, many scientists are also adventurers. They relish the challenge of the physical environment as well as science. These scientists will venture deeper and deeper into the twilight zone wearing scuba and breathing mixed gases. There is no substitute for viewing a new discovery with your own eyes and touching it with your own fingers.

FOOTNOTE REFERENCES

1. For purposes of this discussion scientific diving refer primary to marine research and the aquatic sciences. Scientific experimentation with mixed gases was conducted previous for physiological, medical, and human performance research.
2. Miller, J. and Koblick, I, *Living and Working in the Sea* (New York: Van Nostrand Reinhold Company, Inc., 1984).
3. Tzimoulis, P., *300 Feet on Computerized Scuba, Skin Diver* 19(9):28-33 (1970).
4. Miller, J. (Ed.), *NOAA Diving Manual* (Washington, D.C.: National Oceanic and Atmospheric Administration, 1979).
5. Anonymous, *NOAA Diving Manual* (Washington: National Oceanic and Atmospheric Administration, 1991).
6. Lang, M., *"Governmental Scientific Diving Program Conference Minutes,"* The Slate, February 1992.
7. Gilliam, B. and von Maier, R., *Deep Diving* (San Diego: Watersport Publishing, Inc., 1992).
8. Dill, R., *Contemporary Submarine Erosion in Scripps Submarine Canyon,* Ph.D Thesis (San Diego: University of California, 1964).
9. Pyle, R., *Deep Reef Set,* AquaCorps Journal, 3(2):17-21 (1992)
10. Gilliam, B. and von Maier, R., *Deep Diving* (San Diego: Watersport Publishing, Inc., 1992).
11. Referring to an Enriched Air mixture containing 45% oxygen and 55% nitrogen.
12. A growing component of recreational divers who operate far out side

of the depth and gas parameters of conventional recreational diving.
13. This is essentially a dry-style neoprene suit that is continuously filled with hot water; discharge water escapes through non-return valves. The suit is manufactured by Diving Unlimited International, Inc. of San Diego.
14. This is, to my knowledge, the first place that this concept has been presented. I have recommended this idea to several divers.

CHAPTER 19

NITROX?
Ready for Primetime

One of the hottest issues in recent years within the diving industry has been debate on the proper role that Oxygen Enriched Air, commonly known as NITROX, will play in the recreational diving community. Some diving veterans view this gas as a logical next step to increased diver safety and reduction of the incident rate of decompression sickness (DCS). Other experts have raised questions as to its appropriateness for inexperienced sport divers and whether or not dangers exist due to misuse or equipment incompatibility. Some historical perspectives are in order to see the arguments from both sides more clearly.

Dr. Morgan Wells, Chief Diving Officer for NOAA, has been largely credited as the "godfather" of NITROX and was responsible for standardizing two generic mixtures and implementing the first training and operational guidelines for usage. He remembers, "NITROX goes back quite a long way. In fact, my own initial interest in it was back in the mid-sixties during Mark 6 (a rebreather, ed.) training with the navy. In 1977 when I was writing up the justification and the data base for what we now know as NOAA NITROX I, I researched it a little bit more and found a reference to Dr. Chris Lambertsen back in 1943. He was quoted then as suggesting mixtures of nitrogen and oxygen be used to reduce decompression."

The use of NITROX by the sport diving community is relatively new. However, commercial divers and the U.S. Navy have been using it successfully for decades. Dr. Wells included tables and procedures for its use in the 1977 edition of the NOAA Diving Manual and from that source grew the initial interest in other applications of the technology.

Organizers of the 1992 Enriched Air Workshop in Houston: Mike Menduno (AquaCorps), Glenn Butler (Reimers Engineering), Dick Long (DUI), and Dr. Bill Hamilton (Hamilton Research). The two day conference addressed the pros and cons of nitrox usage and produced a proceedings summary that focused the industry concensus opinion. Photo by Joel Silverstein

Part of the problem for many divers with understanding NITROX is that it seems impossible for even the experts to agree on what to call these mixtures. Technically, the term NITROX can be used to describe any combination of nitrogen and oxygen (N_2/O_2). The air around us is NITROX. Your first dive on compressed air was a NITROX dive. Standard compressed air is a 79/21 NITROX mixture (79% N_2/21% O_2). This is referred to as a normoxic NITROX mixture; that is, the oxygen percentage is normal as it occurs freely in air.

A NITROX mixture with less than 79% nitrogen and more than 21% oxygen is generally called Oxygen Enriched Air or simply Enriched Air NITROX (EANx). Due to the decreased amount of nitrogen, an inert gas that is responsible for decompression sickness, significant safety and operational advantages may be gained.

Dr. Wells makes this observation, "Air has been used as a breathing gas by divers since the beginning of diving. Its principal advantage is that it is readily available and inexpensive to compress into cylinders or use directly from compressors with surface supplied equipment. It is not the 'ideal' breathing mixture because of the decompression liability it imposes. Since decompression obligation is dependent on *inspired nitrogen partial pressure* and time, not *depth* and time, this obligation can be reduced by reducing the nitrogen content of divers' breathing gas."

NOAA currently recognizes two standard NITROX mixes: NOAA NITROX I (68% N_2/32% O_2) and NOAA NITROX II (64% N_2/36% O_2). Due to operational oxygen toxicity limits, NOAA NITROX I has a depth limit of 130 feet and is the most commonly used mixture, whereas NOAA NITROX II, which is currently being evaluated, has a depth limit of approximately 100 feet.

NITROX/EANx allows the diver a whole new approach to managing his dive plan through increased bottom times, shorter surface intervals and reduced nitrogen narcosis. The decompression liability of compressed air is a distinct limiting factor. A review of the U.S. Navy No-Decompression Tables will show that at a depth of 60 fsw the no-stop time is 60 minutes. On the other hand, the no-stop limit for 60 fsw with NOAA NITROX I is 100 minutes. According to the Navy Tables, a dive to 60 fsw for 100 minutes would result in the diver being required to make an obligatory decompression stop at 10 fsw for 14 minutes. The benefit in this particular example is obvious: more bottom time, less decompression obligation.

Many divers have mistakenly thought of NITROX as a deep diving gas perhaps due to its technical sounding name similar to Heliox or Trimix. This blurring of distinction has led noted diving physiologist Dr. R.W. "Bill" Hamilton to urge, "call it Enriched Air. That sounds a lot less threatening to the uninitiated and more accurately describes the gas. Don't let this relatively benign breathing gas be forever branded as a 'high-tech' science. On the user level, it really is quite simple."

Several areas of interest for EANx have appeared in the traditional recreational diving community. If we were to accept the national training agencies' recommendations for less experienced divers to be 130 fsw, then EANx would really be the obvious choice.

Two agencies dedicated to training both users and instructors for EANx have developed in the last four years. American NITROX Divers Inc. (ANDI) and the International Association for NITROX Diving (IAND) have both published standards, manuals, certification cards, and support materials to effectively teach the safe use of EANx to recreational divers. Additionally, both agencies have more technical courses of training to educate and credential professional blenders, mixers and dispensers of the gas.

Dick Rutkowski, well known hyperbaric expert and ex-deputy Diving Director for NOAA, is the founder of IAND. Rutkowski has probably done more to promote NITROX diving outside of traditional scientific and commercial use than any other individual. He has published the *NITROX MANUAL* and set up the first large scale dispensing facility in Florida.

In the north Atlantic area, Ed Betts, founder of ANDI, has made equal inroads into the recreational diving community from his Long Island, New York headquarters. Betts is a graduate engineer with a commercial diving background and has owned several dive stores on Long Island for over two decades. Both men have devoted themselves to widening the industry's understanding of NITROX.

To avoid the stigma of mixed gas jargon and any tinge of "high tech" confusion, ANDI is promoting NITROX in this market as SafeAir (equivalent to NOAA NITROX I). They have aimed the program squarely at entry level divers and encourage the use of the gas in conjunction with standard air tables or air diving computers. With the elevated oxygen percentage and subsequent reduced nitrogen percentage, the mathematical probability of decompression sickness has been significantly reduced.

IAND provides a second level of more advanced training that explains the use of the special NITROX/EANx tables and use of other special mixtures containing higher oxygen percentages. Both ANDI and IAND offer training in the computation of Equivalent Air Depth (EAD) theory, an equation that allows the diver to calculate his "equivalent depth" for any conventional air table based on the nitrogen percentage of his mix. This is more complicated than using pre-calculated EANx tables and has led some critics to question if divers can be trusted to retain this knowledge and accurately handle the required math functions.

The standard entry level course by both agencies consists of approximately four hours of lecture followed by practical diving. There is new material to be assimilated by divers, but most will find the transition fairly easy and well within their reach. Phil Sharkey, Diving Officer for the University of Rhode Island, sums it up, "Boiled down to its simplest form, the NITROX diver needs to know three things: breathe in, breathe out, don't go below 130 feet."

One thing is for certain, the use of NITROX/EANx is growing at a remarkable pace. ANDI and IAND have over 300 active instructors and over 32,000 dives have been logged with a safety record that exceeds that of conventional air dives.

So where then lies the controversy? Dr. Peter Bennett, executive director of the Divers Alert Network (DAN), has raised several questions. "Breathing 32% oxygen/68% nitrogen in NOAA NITROX I, for example, will give you more bottom time than with air because the extra oxygen does not contribute to DCS. It sounds great, but as often occurs, when you reduce one problem, another shows up, in this case, oxygen toxicity of the brain. The danger of brain oxygen toxicity is epileptic-like convulsions. Oxygen convulsions are insidious, often occurring with little warning... convulsions underwater make death by drowning almost inevitable. According to the U.S. Navy guidelines, the depth during short duration air dives at which convulsions become a hazard is 218 feet. Yet with NOAA NITROX I, the convulsion hazard begins at 132 feet...thus, careful depth control is absolutely essential."

Tom Mount, President and training director for IAND, notes in rebuttal, "Dr. Bennett's warning is valid but the depth limit for NITROX is a primary thrust in our training programs. Realistically, divers have been conditioned to 130 feet as a limit on air for years. Our course and that of ANDI was designed to educate divers specifically to the special considerations of NITROX use. There has yet to be a case of oxygen toxicity or bends in any of our divers."

Gregg Stanton (Florida State) looks on as Bret Gilliam (Ocean Tech) makes a point during the Enriched Air Workshop. The program featured the industry's leading experts from the scientific, military, high-tech, recreational, and manufacturing communities. Photo by Joel Silverstein

A second consideration of NITROX use that Bennett has identified concerns post dive treatment in a DCS accident. "Potential for further complication due to oxygen toxicity of the lungs exists if a NITROX diver develops decompression illness. Oxygen toxicity of the lungs occurs when oxygen is breathed for extended periods at partial pressures above half an atmosphere. Its symptoms are similar to those of pneumonia, and the only treatment is to breathe less oxygen. Since the best therapy for decompression illness is 100% oxygen during transport to a chamber followed by recompression with 100% oxygen on the U.S. Navy treatment tables, prior NITROX diving gives a physician less freedom in using oxygen during therapy when it is needed most. This could make a difference in achieving full recovery."

This argument requires a more thorough understanding of the physiological relationship of oxygen tolerances. There is a computational method of tracking "oxygen dose" commonly referred to as Oxygen Tolerance Unit or OTU. At a recent conference on Enriched Air Technology held in Houston, Dr. Bennett's concern was specifically addressed by NASA hyperbaric medical expert, Dr. William Norfleet. A "worst case" scenario for NITROX diving in repeated repetitive exposures for a single day of diving was detailed and the accumulated OTU count noted. In Dr. Norfleet's opinion, "I am unable to agree with Dr. Bennett's conclusion. It would take an unrealistic and probably unattainable dive profile to have a consequential effect on post-dive treatment."

Not all of Dr. Bennett's comments on NITROX are so negative. He is most concerned with improper use by untrained individuals. "While NITROX and oxygen can be used with reasonable safety in diving, extra equipment and training are required as well as the recognition of the additional risks. What are your goals in diving? Are they worth the added training and equipment? If so, then fine, proceed. But do so with a fair recognition and acceptance of the added risks," he concludes.

The consensus opinion from leading experts at the Enriched Air Workshop included this passage in their concluding summary: "Hosted by the Scuba Diving Resources Group, the Workshop brought together training agencies, manufacturers, retailers, instructors, technical and scientific experts, the academic diving community, and experienced enriched air users from commercial, government, and scientific organizations. The Workshop concluded that Enriched Air NITROX has been established as an alternative breathing medium to compressed air and is considered suitable for recreational diving with proper equipment, gas mixtures, training and certification. Current EANx certification agencies for training users, instructors and dispensers of the gases are adequate and in place."

In conclusion, the popularity of EANx/NITROX diving is rapidly spreading. Many divers will find the benefits of such mixtures to be worth the time and expense of further training. Do not attempt to mix your own NITROX or dive it without seeking out training from a properly credentialed instructor or facility.

Currently, ANDI and IAND offer the only specific NITROX/EANx certification programs but NASDS and NAUI have recognized their training as an approved specialty course and provide insurance coverage. At least two other national certification agencies are considering the same position at press time.

Noted diving professional Bill High, ex-President of NAUI and veteran of over four decades of scientific diving, has this response to the critics who have raised various arguments, "I hear a lot lately about recreational and technical divers being somehow greatly different. It looks as though all good, serious divers are being re-classified as technical divers. Certainly recreational divers, regardless of how technical they have become, *can* and *do* safely dive NITROX. They require no more complex training than was given for basic air scuba." High has a private bet with an associate that by the year 2000 all divers will be using NITROX. At its current rate of growth, his vision of the future may well be attained ahead of schedule.

Richard Nordstrom

CHAPTER 20

Closed Circuit Underwater Breathing Apparatus *(CCUBA)*

In the beginning there was air. Not oxygen. Have you ever noticed how divers are consistently assailed by the question of, "How much oxygen do you have in that tank?". We know it's air, right? Today, you could be wrong!

As the practice of "High-Tech" diving evolves, we see the creation of many new types of both simple and sophisticated devices designed to offer the diver a more fulfilled and safer dive. The U.S. Navy Tables were once above reproach. Today, they are replaced by a large number of new tables and more than 22 Dive Computers. This very large information source can provide a diver's decompression status in a multitude of variations. Who would have expected such a change ten years ago?

As the Siren's song beckons divers to greater challenges, inventors and manufacturers strive to keep up with the evolving process of greater demands from diving consumers. As progress evolves it's not only the "High-Tech" diver who benefits, but all divers as the technology trickles down. From the first 10 commercially viable dive computers sold in 1983, today, the dive industry sells tens of thousands of units annually.

As a diver, there are only three items absolutely necessary to sustain your life when submerged. Gas to breath, the tank to hold the gas and a regulator to deliver it. Note that breathing gas is the common item and the other components are designed to support its delivery. As you probably already know, divers generally use a binary (two component) breathing gas called air.

The quest for breathing systems to allow man the right to explore more than 70% of the earth's boundaries has resulted in many interesting inventions.

The earliest illustration of a person diving was found on an Assyrian Bas Relief from 885 BC.It shows the diver breathing from an air filled leather bag strapped to their chest. The first user probably breathed from and into the bag. This technique probably qualifies it as the first rebreather, though I am sure this practice stopped after a few minutes for all of the users. If the carbon dioxide build up didn't get you I am sure the smell of fresh goat skin would.

Submariner's obtain breathing gases for submarines by breaking down the ocean's water molecule and extracting oxygen. A method called electrolysis that requires large amounts of electrical power and heavy machinery. Not easily carried on the back of your average diver.

Over the past twenty years experiments have been performed with semi-permeable membranes, artificial gills and other methods to extract oxygen from sea water. Due to cost, size, and complexity none of them have found real commercial use. The other problem lies in their ability to only provide oxygen, and as we already know, it's not considered a safe breathing gas beyond 21 FSW. So you need a diluent or inert gas to add volume to your breathing mixture and a method to eliminate carbon dioxide. By definition diluent is one of the gases other than pure oxygen that provides volume to the breathing mixture. It can be pure nitrogen, but it is usually an oxygen / inert gas mixture that can sustain a diver's life independent of adding more oxygen to the mixture. Compressed air is frequently the diluent gas for shallow diving in a rebreather. The issue is complex and these experimental methods of creating the ultimate water breather (Gillman) are not yet feasible.

Siebe invented his first surface supplied diver dress in 1837, but as you may already know the first recognized or perhaps commercially viable underwater breathing device was created in 1943. We give that credit to Gagnan and Cousteau during World War II in occupied France. It would not be distributed in the United States until 1950. The free swimming unit they developed is almost identical to what we today call Self Contained Underwater Breathing Apparatus or SCUBA.

Almost all of the available consumer based diving equipment today can be listed under the classification of open-circuit scuba. This type of Portable Life Support System or PLSS consists of a compressed air cylinder and demand regulator from which the diver breathes. Exhaled gases are ported to the outside water hence the open-circuit designation (Figure 1).

Most improvements in open-circuit scuba equipment over the last forty years have centered around breathing performance and the volume of available air. High flow regulators can provide the most exerted diver with all the air they can breathe at depths to 250 fsw. Newer high pressure steel tanks provide 120 cubic feet of air instead of the present industry norm of 80 cubic feet. Until the mid-1970's the normal sized scuba tank was only 71.2 cubic feet of air. With the advent of these larger and higher pressure tanks, new captured o-ring valves were introduced to provide a more reliable seat on the valve to regulator connection. Associated instrumentation has also kept up with the latest integrated pressure / decompression computers to help the diver plan a more productive and controlled dive.

With these improvements, the range of open-circuit scuba has, for all practical purposes, been maximized. Beyond 5000 psig (the pressure now commonly used with composite Scuba cylinders) the amount of gas which can be stored for a given increase in pressure becomes smaller because of molecular interaction which follows the real gas laws.

Furthermore, at pressures much greater than 6000 psig, three stage regulators, which are not readily available nor price effective for underwater work, become essential to prevent premature failure of the first stage piston seat.

None of these technological details change the basic characteristics of open-circuit Scuba. The reason for this lies in the fact that only a fraction of the Respiratory Minute Volume (RMV; the volume of gas inhaled and exhaled during normal breathing) is actually used to sustain human metabolic function. There is a tremendous waste of usable oxygen with each exhaled breath. As a result of the laws of physics, the volume of oxygen lost in this manner for a Scuba diver increases with depth.

Figure 1

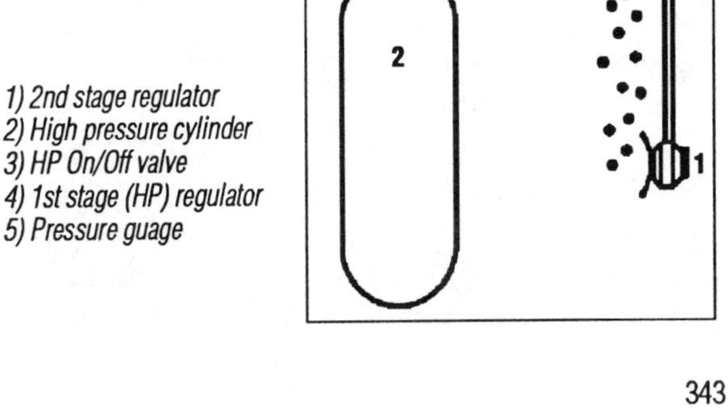

OPEN-CIRCUT SCUBA

1) 2nd stage regulator
2) High pressure cylinder
3) HP On/Off valve
4) 1st stage (HP) regulator
5) Pressure guage

Dr. Bill Stone and his team of explorers using various types of Cis-Lunar rebreathers to prepare for the most extensive cave penetration ever make. A high level of system reliability and ease of use is necessary for this application. Photo by Clarita Berger.

As we look at the efficiency of open-circuit Scuba, it's clear that increased costs and complexity began to provide a diminishing return to the user.

The answer to this diminishing return lies in the use of another type of PLSS known as Closed-Circuit Underwater Breathing Apparatus (CCUBA) or more commonly called a "Rebreather". In essence this apparatus is a closed-circuit scuba system as outlined in Figure 2. In a closed system nearly 100% use is made of the oxygen content of the breathing gas. This is done by recycling the divers exhaled breath through a scrubbing mechanism — often an alkaline hydroxide or superoxide filtration device — which removes the carbon dioxide. Breathing gas is added to the system only when the system volume drops below a certain minimum value. Volume decrease in the system is due to metabolizing oxygen; absorption of carbon dioxide; and the loss of gas resulting from mask purging and gas expansion in the breathing bag from ascending.

The difference in performance over an open-circuit is substantial: a standard 80 cubic foot sport diving cylinder used in open-circuit mode at a depth of 300 fsw will provide approximately 30 breaths before the tank runs dry; the same cylinder, if filled with pure oxygen and used to drive a closed-circuit system, could sustain a diver at 300 fsw for more than two days. This example emphasizes a key point: that closed-circuit scuba has an underwater range which is independent of depth. The range for closed-circuit Scuba is controlled predominantly by the individual diver's rate of metabolism (oxygen consumption).

Early designs date back to the late 1800's where caustic potash was used as a carbon dioxide scrubber material. In the early 1900's Draeger designed the first pure oxygen closed-circuit system for fire departments. These systems were required since the existing compressor technology was very limited in high pressure storage and volume.

The same systems were adapted for miners due to their light weight. Modern closed-circuit development started around 1912, but the first effective underwater rebreather design of any success was developed around 1941 just prior to World War II. Draeger Works in Lubeck, Germany created a very small and compact pure oxygen rebreather that was originally designed as an escape device from U-Boats.

The Draeger "Oxygen-Recycling" underwater apparatus was extensively tested by Hans Hass in 1942. He explored the Mediterranean and

As in all diving activities, preparation and training play an important role in the correct use of new equipment. Photo by Richard Nordstrom

probed the unit's limitations as a free swimming device throughout the war. Little was known about the physiology of pure oxygen under pressure and accidents did happen. A similar unit was used by the Italian Navy to sink British ships during the war.

Today there are two types of closed-circuit systems being used in government and industry: A pure oxygen version which is limited to a depth of 25 fsw (Some are now advocating 21 fsw), and a mixed gas version normally used for underwater work at great depths. Let's start with the pure oxygen system for simplicity sake (Figure 2).

An oxygen rebreather consists of an open-circuit oxygen delivery system driving a process loop, in which the user breathes from a flexible counterlung (a flexible breathing bag) attached to the carbon dioxide scrubber. The exhaust breath is cycled back into the scrubber. As oxygen is converted into carbon dioxide via metabolic activity and the carbon dioxide is removed by the scrubber system, the volume of gas in the counterlung begins to decrease. When the breathing bag collapses due to oxygen deple-

Two scientists prepare for the final part of his dive by checking the interactive computer on CIS-Lunar's MK-2S rebreather for data and verification of projected dive plan changes. Photo by Nick Caloyianis

Light and compact this rebreather provides the air equivalent in open-circuit of ten 80 cubic foot tanks. Photo by Richard Nordstrom

tion, a second stage pneumatic switch is triggered and oxygen is added to the system.

The Draeger LAR V (a chest mounted system in use since 1981) and the Carleton CCR 25 (a back mounted unit developed in the early 1970's) are the two most widely used pure oxygen rebreathers for military applications today. Each one provides about three hours of submerged time in warm water at minimum exertion. Other units are available, but in terms of operation they are all very similar and all retail for about $6,000 each.

From a control standpoint, oxygen rebreathers are quite simple: they require no active control of the gases. This is not the case with free-swimming mixed gas rebreathers (Figure 3). The first mixed gas units were developed in the 1960's to solve the problems of nitrogen narcosis at depth and to eliminate the oxygen toxicity situation which limited the safe diving depth of pure oxygen rebreathers. Rebreather systems played an important role in early programs like *Sealab* and *Tektite*, where men worked and lived at depth for long periods of time.

The earlier U.S. Navy free swimming closed-circuit systems were in fact not completely close looped, but intentionally allowed escape of gas from the system. These systems were labeled as semi-closed circuit systems such as the U.S. Navy MK 6.

With the advent of Biomarine's MK 15 the Navy had a true free-swimming closed-circuit apparatus. The commercial version of the MK 15 is called the CCR 155 and is now manufactured by Carleton Technologies. The U.S. Navy's version was limited to 150 fsw using a diluent of air and the CCR 155 is capable of depths in excess of 300 fsw using Heliox as a diluent. In water at 70° Fahrenheit, this system will sustain a diver up to six hours. The commercial version of the system is about $30,000.

Australian military combat divers used the Draeger FGT I/D in Desert Storm military operations during the Persian Gulf War in 1991. Unlike other systems this one must have its operating depth set and the dive plan followed accordingly. This unit provides a diver 70 minutes of bottom time at 165 feet.

In the early mixed gas rebreathers the complexity of design increased dramatically as electronics were added to allow automated functions. Two early rebreathers were distributed by Beckman Electronics and General Electric. One of the earlier rebreathers designated the "electrolung" was later given the nickname "Silver Death" as a result of its uncompromising operational characteristics. Many users felt the nickname was well de-

This diver is spending time at a ten foot decompression stop breathing pure oxygen from his rebreather. This Cis-Lunar rebreather allows an on the fly oxygen set point, thus pure oxygen is available to the diver at depths above 21 FSW. The integrated decompression computer accounts for thechange in gas mixture to offer an optimized or, if preferred, more conservative decompression schedule. Photo by Richard Nordstrom

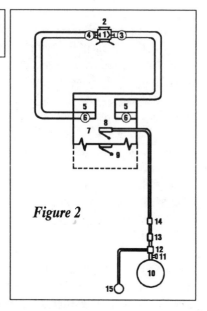

GENERIC PURE-OXYGEN REBREATHER

1) Breathing manifold
2) Breathing manifold shutoff
3) Upstream checkvalve
4) Downstream checkvalve
5) Carbon dioxide scrubber
6) Moisture trap
7) Counterlung (breathing bag)
8) Oxygen addition valve
9) Overpressure checkvalve
10) HP oxygen supply
11) Oxygen on/off valve
12) First stage regulator (O_2)
13) Oxygen filter trap
14) Oxygen metering orifice
15) Oxygen pressure gage

Figure 2

served. Large amounts of preparation were necessary for a few hours of diving and the cost was prohibitive. All of the mixed gas closed-circuit systems on the market today have limited electronic controls and still frequently rely on the diver to be the main control for adequate gas delivery. The complexity of mixed gas and oxygen partial pressures make an ideal problem to be solved by today's more sophisticated yet reliable low power CMOS (Complementary Metallic Oxide Semiconductor) electronic designs.

A sensor controlled mixed gas closed-circuit system consists of two independent gas supplies, and a process loop (the internal workings of the system, including the gases) which is regulated by electrochemical sensors to monitor the partial pressure of oxygen. The two gas supplies are func-

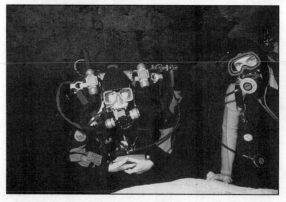

Dr. Bill Stone prepares one of Cis-Lunar's rebreathers for a six hour excursion to further evaluate his most recent modification to its Head-Up-Display (HUD). Photo by Richard Nordstom

tionally different. The first type is known as the diluent gas. This contains either compressed air or a special mixed gas such as Enriched Air (NITROX), Heliox (Helium-Oxygen), Neox (Neon-Oxygen), or Trimix (Helium-Nitrogen-Oxygen), which can be breathed in an open-circuit mode at the designed operating depth of the system. This gas supply is used to maintain system volume as the diver goes to depth, preventing the counterlung from compressing which would reduce the divers breathing quality.

A new type of closed-circuit system called the MK-2 series has been recently introduced by Cis-Lunar Development Laboratories. This new design provides numerous improvements over existing technology. One feature is its ability to allow a quick switch from closed to open-circuit allowing the optional use of diluent gas as a bailout source in the event of total system failure. This approach is part of a new trend to provide rebreather divers with a true redundancy design.

A typical diluent supply consists of a high pressure open-circuit system but with a manual bypass which can be used in the event of a malfunction in the pneumatic (second stage) switch. This pneumatic switch automatically adds diluent as the counterlung is compressed during descent from the surface.

Complimenting this is a second gas source of pure oxygen, similarly designed to the diluent side, which provides the make-up gas as oxygen is converted to carbon dioxide through metabolism.

GENERIC MIXED-GAS REBREATHER

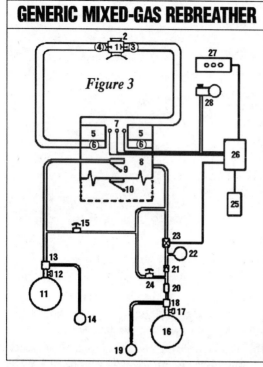

Figure 3

Note that part numbers 1-6 are identical to those of figure 2; parts 8-10 = 7-9 Figure 2.

7) Oxygen sensors
11) HP diluent supply
12) HP on/off valve
13) Diluent first stage
14) Diluent pressure gage
15) Diluent bypass gage
16) HP oxygen supply
17) HP valve (on/off)
18) Oxygen first stage
19) Oxygen pressure
20) Oxygen filter
21) Metering orifice
22) LP accumulator (O_2)
23) Oxygen solenoid
24) Oxygen bypass valve
25) DC power supply
26) Logic circuitry
27) Primary display
28) Analog display

It is important that the system not allow diluent gas to be used for oxygen make-up since this will lead to hypoxia. The principle design difference between the oxygen and diluent supply is that oxygen addition is achieved by means of an electronically controlled valve (newer systems only).

The valve is opened whenever the oxygen sensors residing in the process loop indicate a partial pressure of oxygen below some pre-established set-point. This set-point is typically defined to be 0.7 atmospheres for U.S. Navy rebreathers, although at least one commercial diving company has used a set-point of 1.3 atmospheres on an experimental basis to decrease decompression time.

The Cis-Lunar MK-2 series rebreather allows the user to interactively modify the set point during the course of a dive. This interaction allows an optimization of decompression by maintaining oxygen levels that reduce or eliminate nitrogen content of the breathing mixture. In other words, the unit becomes a pure oxygen rebreather above 21 fsw and a mixed gas rebreather below this depth. In essence, when using an Enriched Air (NITROX) or air diluent, the system can be set to maintain a maximum amount of oxygen (a partial pressure of oxygen that will avoid oxygen toxicity problems) to maximize the reduction in nitrogen on-gassing. The result is a more conservative de-compression schedule and extended bottom time.

As a point of reference, the U.S. Navy presently recommends a maximum oxygen partial pressure for sustained diving of 1.4 atmospheres; by contrast hypoxic blackout symptoms will begin to appear at an oxygen partial pressure of 0.12 atmospheres. These two limiting points are critical in the proper use of rebreather equipment.

The process loop for the mixed gas system is essentially identical to that of the simple oxygen rebreather, consisting of a carbon dioxide scrubber and counterlung; a flexible output hose connected to a mouthpiece;

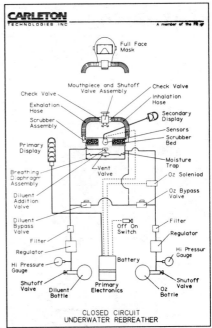

Self Explanatory. Photo by Draeger

and a flexible return hose. The breathing gas is made to flow in a single direction by the means of a series of check valves usually located in the mouthpiece or hoses.

The scrubber section of the rebreather is both functionally critical and usually the limiting factor for dive duration (remember that closed-circuit rebreather's gas supply is normally independent of depth). Carbon dioxide absorbing material can be soda lime, baralyme, or lithium hydroxide.

There are numerous other types of these materials under varying trademarks such as Sodasorb). These materials can vary substantially in particulate size, moisture content, temperature sensitivity and carbon dioxide absorption aggressiveness.

As the exhausted gas passes over the scrubber material, an exothermic (heat producing) reaction takes place and the carbon dioxide in the exhausted gas is chemically bound to the scrubber granules surface. The scrubber material will also remove some of the excess water vapor from the gas. Too much water vapor in the exhaust gas causes the particulates to be coated with moisture, thus creating a barrier that stops the binding reaction. The quantity of carbon dioxide absorbed will depend on the type of absorbent used, the inlet gas temperature and humidity, the external

Working with old explosive ordnance is a dangerous job. You don't want bubbles, sound or magnetic properties setting them off. The U.S. Navy's MK 16 ffrom Carleton was designed for EOD work. Photo by Carleton Technologies, Inc.

water temperature, the canister design and gas flow rates across the scrubber particulates.

When used in a cold water environment most scrubber materials quickly loose their ability to remove carbon dioxide. Lithium hydroxide is the most efficient scrubbing material in cold water, but tends to be too reactive for most rebreather systems. The specific problem lies with the design of most rebreathers. When water enters the mouthpiece and downstream to the scrubber material a reaction occurs which is very exothermic (hot) and forms a caustic gaseous material. This material is passed through the system and on to the diver.

Figure 4

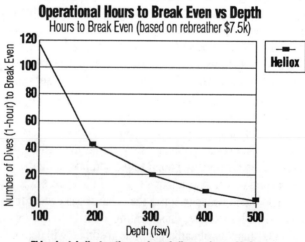

Operational Hours to Break Even vs Depth
Hours to Break Even (based on rebreather $7.5k)

This chart indicates the number of dives using a Cis-Lunar rebreather on Heliox mixture in order to have the unit pay for itself.

The Draeger LAR V is one of then most popular pure oxygen rebreathers today. Photo by Draeger

The potential for inhaling a caustic cocktail is real and not a pleasant experience for the diver. The inhalation of a warm caustic concoction from the scrubber will do serious damage to the lungs and mouth tissues. These caustic burns make it difficult for the diver to continue breathing from the unit which can be disastrous for the diver deep into a decompression dive. This result is also possible with the other less reactive types of scrubber materials and is directly related to the scrubber's design.

One solution to this problem has been developed by Cis-Lunar in their MK-2 series rebreathers. A proprietary process prevents the mixing of water and scrubber material in the scrubber stack. In fact, this rebreather allows the purging of water without hindering the scrubber material's ability to absorb carbon dioxide. As a result of this the more effective lithium hydroxide absorbent can be used without the possibility of a serious caustic reaction.

When you look at the carbon dioxide absorption capability of various types of scrubber materials you begin to see the advantage of using lithium hydroxide. As Dr. Bill Stone of Cis-Lunar has shown with the MK-2 series rebreather, lithium hydroxide removes 2 - 2.3 times more carbon dioxide than the other materials. The down side is that it costs about $25 per pound versus $3 per pound for HP Sodasorb) or about eight times more.

Another factor that can reduce scrubber performance is channeling. Channeling is the separation of scrubber particulates where gas begins to

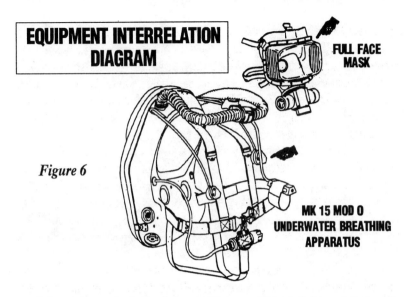

EQUIPMENT INTERRELATION DIAGRAM

FULL FACE MASK

Figure 6

MK 15 MOD 0 UNDERWATER BREATHING APPARATUS

work its way past the bulk of the scrubber material via "channels", thus the potential surface area for carbon dioxide absorption is reduced.

As you already know, carbon dioxide bypassing the scrubber is a serious problem for the diver. This situation usually occurs when the scrubber particulates are not correctly compacted, they are improperly sized or the scrubber itself has a mechanical problem. Most rebreathers require the user to compact their own scrubbers with loose bulk scrubber materials.

Both Carmellon Research and Cis-Lunar rebreathers will provide a pre-filled disposable carbon dioxide scrubber cartridge in the near future for easier and more consistent scrubber packing.

All rebreathers have unique characteristics, but for simplicity lets take a look at the features found in a typical rebreather. From a functional perspective they all operate on the same principles, with varying degrees of reliability and ease of use. Safety features usually include manual controls, multiple oxygen sensors, warning LEDs (Light Emitting Diodes) on simple control panels, and a few have diluent bailout systems. Not a lot of complexity or high technology.

One of the most modern free swimming mixed gas rebreathers in use today by the U.S. Navy is the MK 15, by Carleton Technologies. A special version of the MK 15 is called the MK 16, it is used in EOD (Explosive Ordnance Diver) missions where noise emission and magnetic characteristics are carefully controlled for use in underwater explosive mine detection. Accepted by the U.S. Navy in 1968 the MK 15 / MK 16 represents the present state of the art in most commercially available rebreathers.

Like most rebreathers, the driving force behind the MK 15's creation was mission driven. The military wanted an underwater PLSS that produced minimum bubbles; provided extended submerged duration and operating depth; used mixed gas to reduce decompression and narcosis; and, in general, provided the diver with stealth like characteristics. Ease of use was one feature not high on the priority list. The system requires a diver's constant attention and is manually operated.

As you read this, the U.S. Navy is busy creating their first new rebreather in 24 years called the XE-19. This system incorporates new electronics technology and offers the user more automated features. The MK 15 provides up to six hours of bottom time to depths in excess of 300 fsw. The XE-19 appears to have a depth capability of 1,500 fsw and a longer bottom time than the MK 15. It's top secret for now, but more information should become available in the next two years.

In evaluating the present systems on the market, it becomes clear that they are heavy, difficult to use, mechanically complicated, require complex pre-dive protocol preparation, have high maintenance costs, provide little if any redundancy, and are very expensive. Prices range up to $45,000 each and scuttlebutt has it the XE-19 will cost the taxpayers more than $85,000 each.

Commercial divers have also used rebreathers, but more as back-up systems when diving very deep. Some of the new one atmosphere suits also use a rebreather system. The commercial industry prefers their divers to be tethered and the practice of saturation diving has also reduced their need for rebreathers.

ASSEMBLY DISPLAYS AND CONTROLS

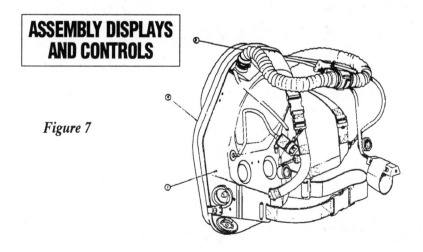

Figure 7

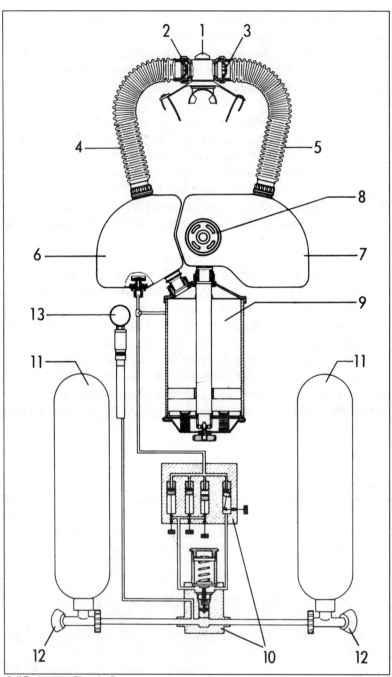

Self Explanatory. Photo by Draeger

If rebreathers are so expensive and difficult to use, then why do we find such an attraction to them? Scientific diving, underwater archaeology, exploration, and many other uses can be found for these devices. The technology was never fully developed since the existing systems were adequate for that use (primarily military use) and scuba seemed to serve the needs of the other markets.

Two firms have recently entered into the rebreather market from different perspectives. Carmellon Research has taken the U.S. Navy's MK 15, renamed it the Gas Pack and removed many of the military based functions for easier use. They added a decompression computer, adjustable helium / oxygen ratio controls, digital oxygen sensing package, on board lighting system, and a manual override capability. The system still uses the back mounted counterlung and all of the basic features of the standard MK 15.

Cis-Lunar Development Laboratories, Inc. has taken a different approach by designing its own concept from the ground up and using state of the art electronic control systems. The MK-2 series is user friendly (totally automated), light weight, with a high reliability factor and redundancy built in at all levels, minimal maintenance requirements, and best of all a reasonable purchase price. This is the one we have been waiting for. It was created with the user in mind and with a mission objective of providing the efficiency of rebreather diving to many.

The MK-2 series rebreather offers an integrated decompression computer that allows user interaction to control the gas supply for maximization of decompression schedules or the ability to build-in a conservative decompression schedule. It allows the use of all binary (two gas systems) breathing gas mixtures from air to Heliox. It also provides redundant analog, digital, and Head-Up-Display (HUD) control/instrumentation sub-systems. HUD's are devices that place data in front of the diver's eyes to eliminate the need for the diver to pick up and read a digital console. The sport version will weigh in at less than 45 pounds (versus the Genesis 120 cubic foot steel tank at over 56 pounds with regulator and buoyancy compensator) and offer the diver up to a 12 hour dive duration to 218 fsw. The professional version is a little heavier with a depth capability of 500 fsw and up to 12 hours of dive duration. Each model has multiple sensing electronics and can tell the diver whether gas has other contaminants such as carbon monoxide and even if the diver is breathing.

This is the only system that has carbon dioxide sensing capability. Four systems were recently used to train deep caving specialists. According to Cis-Lunar founder Dr. Bill Stone, "we waved good-bye to the guys on the twin 120's and just kept going". The cost to wave good-bye with a mixed

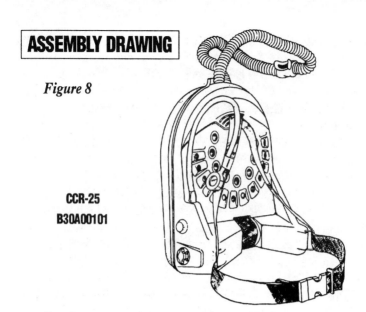

Figure 8

CCR-25
B30A00101

gas rebreather from Cis-Lunar will be less than $10,000 when the firm starts production later next year.

The specialized MK-2R Explorer model is actually two separate rebreather systems linked to provide a maximum amount of redundancy for cave explorers. This model will provide a depth capability of 900 fsw and allow the diver to stay submerged up to 27 hours.

As you can see, there are numerous aspects about the present state of commercially available rebreathers that would make even the most dedicated and qualified diver think twice about using one. These devices require in-depth instruction and extensive practice. U.S. Navy military divers are trained to become proficient in these types of systems and spend a great deal of time in honing there skills and operational capabilities.

Does this mean that the complexity and expense override their feasibility for use in other areas. The answer is a resounding no! Cis-Lunar and Carmellon Research are just the tip of the iceberg as private industry gears up to provide the scientific and technical sport divers with an old tool that has a new capability and mission objective.

Imagine going on a week long liveaboard dive trip to Fiji and taking a closed-circuit scuba rebreather with integrated tanks, buoyancy control device, open-circuit regulator, full instrumentation package, decompression computer, HUD display, and numerous other redundant systems weighing less than 45 pounds. With the same package and a few 3 pound disposable

/ recyclable scrubber modules you won't have to look at a compressor on your entire vacation. Because the system is neutrally buoyant and no buoyancy changes occur from large tanks you can even reduce the weights on your belt.

We can't stop here because you now have to look at the gas efficiency of your diving. The cost of air at 200 fsw is about $3.00 per hour on a rebreather versus a $15.00 per hour on open-circuit scuba. If you use Trimix or Heliox the cost increases to about $86 per hour on open-circuit scuba and only $3.50 per hour on a rebreather. If using open-circuit scuba, don't forget to add the cost of purchasing all of those cylinders for tremendous gas consumption at deeper depths and staging hours of decompression stops.

Remember carrying those heavy cylinders down to the beach on your first open water check out? Imagine having 100 times more capability in a device that weighs less than a filled 80 cubic foot cylinder with attached BCD! A rebreather can be 1000 times more efficient than open-circuit scuba.

What's the payback if you invest in a rebreather? If you decide to consistently use a heliox diluent breathing mixture, it only takes about 40 hours of bottom time on dives to about 200 fsw to make up the cost difference of

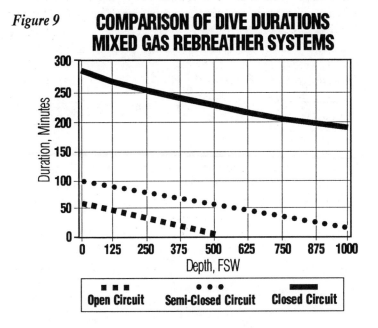

Figure 9 **COMPARISON OF DIVE DURATIONS MIXED GAS REBREATHER SYSTEMS**

open-circuit scuba (Figure 4). Notice the figures at 400 fsw. For the scientific diver who makes research excursions to the twilight zone (350 - 450 fsw) the payback is very attractive.

With the silence of a rebreather, the underwater photographer can now eliminate those troublesome exhaust bubbles. You enter the underwater environment in a less intrusive manner that allows behavioral observations not possible in the past. With a rebreather you become part of the ocean environment instead of a temporary intruder. Even the delicious invertebrate *Homarus americanus* (Maine Lobster) is less likely to flee as you approach.

Price competitiveness; ease of use; integrated functionality; redundant systems; high operational reliability; extended depth range; and a substantial increase in dive duration will bring the concept of rebreathers to the forefront in diving as we approach the 21st century.

CHAPTER 21

The Future is Now: Deep Submersibles As Operational Tools

There is really nothing new about deep diving submersible vehicles in our industry. Ed Link dreamed up models back in the 1960's that seemed like they were excerpted from the pages of a Jules Vern novel. Originally, these subs were employed in pioneering oceanographic and scientific projects and were responsible for opening doors to the oceans' depths that had previously been considered unexplorable. As submersible technology became more affordable and diversified, the expanding commercial diving market quickly adopted such applications for survey and inspection work. In many instances, this proved far more cost effective than subjecting a diver to such an exposure.

Quite a few of these specialized subs were constructed to meet the global commercial diving demands of the seventies but later were left idle as that industry slacked off. Today it's possible to purchase a submersible for a fraction of its original construction cost and many remain completely operational with only minor upgrades required. None the less, the opportunities for persons outside the scientific/commercial community to ever get to actually dive in these vehicles were roughly equivalent to the annual options for snow skiing in Miami. Rather limited.

Thanks to the entrepreneurial vision of Research Submersibles Ltd. (RSL), a division of Atlantis Submarines International Inc., a chance to take part in one of life's truly unique diving adventures now is available and affordable. Located in Grand Cayman, RSL began operation in the early eighties and features two refurbished Perry subs with operational

Launching the PC-1203 from aboard ship. Photo by Bret Gilliam

depth ratings of approximately 1200 feet. Each can carry two passenger/observers and a pilot. Cost is only $265 for the one hour excursion and will showcase the dramatic west drop-off wall to a depth of 800 feet.

The highlight of the dive is an up-close inspection of the wreck of the 170 ft. ship *Kirk Pride* which sunk in a 1976 tropical storm. Locals had often theorized as to the wreck's location but it took RSL chief pilot Stewart Mailer almost a year of searching before he stumbled onto the wreck precariously clinging to the wall at just over 780 feet. The *Kirk Pride* had rolled over the drop-off after breaking her anchor chain only to be checked by two enormous limestone boulders known as "haystacks". The wreck sits virtually upright and is remarkably well preserved due to the cold water and low oxygen levels.

The sub operators really couldn't have dreamed up a better attraction as a climax to what already is an epic high-tech adventure. They schedule four dives a day to the site and, while I was visiting in February 1992, nearly every slot was booked. Lesson: reserve in advance!

My dives would be in PC 1203 piloted by Troy Engen, a former blimp pilot from the Midwest. On this particular morning Dennis Hurd, President of Atlantis Submarines, would be joining us for his first dive since acquiring RSL's operation. Dennis is an affable Canadian who oversees Atlantis' far flung operations in such venues as Cayman, Hawaii and the Virgin Islands. Their primary business is tourist sub excursions in special craft capable of carrying 46 passengers to depths of 100 feet. The deep diving submersible business is new to Atlantis but it's a logical extension and the RSL operation was a proven product with an excellent staff already in place.

I am the first to enter PC 1203 and am struck by the fantastic visual field provided by the expansive acrylic dome mounted in the sub's bow. The observers seem to literally be accommodated *within* the dome's panoramic 160 degree window to the sea. The interior is also more

Bret Gilliam enters submersible through main hatch in conning tower. During loading operations the sub is almost completely awash and transfers are made by inflatable boat. Photo by Lynn Hendrickson

spacious than I had imagined; Dennis and I are able to sit comfortably side by side with Troy perched above and behind us on the pilot's chair. This is a marked contrast from the cramped conditions and limited view ports in submersibles that I piloted during Navy and research projects back in the early seventies. Troy goes over a review of the life support and emergency procedures, conducts a communications check with alternate pilot Patrick Lahey on the surface to monitor our status, and then we begin our descent.

Water temperature at the surface is around 82° F. and the sub is initially warm and humid. Two small fans circulate the interior air for comfort. This is, of course, a one atmosphere vehicle so no pressure changes will be sensed by the occupants. There is no need to equalize your ears or to plan decompression stops, a good thing since our planned depth will exceed 800 feet. Try working that out on your dive tables!

Troy drops us quickly over the steep wall and activates the powerful flood lights mounted on the bow framing. A kaleidoscope of colors envelopes us only a few feet away as we pass through the richly forested gorgonian and sponge populations between 200 and 500 feet. Cayman is blessed with superb underwater visibility anyway but it is even grander as we approach the 650 foot level. The loom of the wreck is visible almost 250 feet deeper as Troy shuts down the lights. Ambient light at even 800 feet is still sufficient to see quite clearly and the spectre of the dramatic wall is even more awe inspiring without the external floods. Inside the sub, we are blessed with a cool natural air-conditioning reflecting the water temperature now pegged at 65°.

Our pilot skillfully maneuvers the PC 1203 under the stern of the *Kirk Pride* to reveal her name and hailing port still legible after 16 years of entombment. Troy throws a switch and engulfs the wreck in a wash of high intensity light. The affect is almost surreal. Parts of the ship look as though the crew might only have just walked away from their stations. Other sections reveal the damage caused in her wild tumble to the abyss. We pass slowly over the pilothouse and observe the engine room telegraph still fully intact as though the *Kirk Pride* still awaits commands to answer bells. Peering into the cargo hold we can see a brand new 1976 Volkswagon, Dennis and I speculate on if it would start.

A local Caymanian businessman had contracted for the car's delivery only to see it disappear with the ship. The RSL staff treated him to a tour of the ship, and his aging but extremely low-mileage VW, on a recent dive. The fiberglass body shows no signs of wear and only needs a garish sales sticker-price to complete the bizarre scene: "vintage VW, one owner, sold as-is where-is, low down payment". Real low, 800 feet.

We've been submerged now for over 40 minutes and Troy begins ascending. He keeps up a snappy patter of descriptive lecture on deep water crinoids, rare commensals and a gigantic sea fan almost eight feet in diameter at 720 feet. All too soon, we arrive back at the surface just over an

PC-1203 descending over the steep Cayman drop-off wall. Photo by Bret Gilliam

hour after departure. It's like returning to earth from a space voyage, you're happy to be back in one piece but can't wait to go again!

Dennis Denton, RSL's operations manager, spends some time with me in their waterfront office conveniently adjacent to what may arguably be the most expensive Burger King in the western world. Lunch for two broke the $30.00 barrier; Dennis wisely brownbags his chow from home. He is a qualified sub pilot as well and frequently trades off with Troy and Patrick so each member of the team can remain current. Dennis is a wealth of information on the technical details of the subs and happy to share his considerable experience. Like all of RSL's staff, he is instantly likeable and completely professional.

The next day we plan a photo shoot to capture the PC 1203 in action. I will make the dive with local dive instructor Erin Nelson as a camera assistant. Patrick once again provides the topside assistance from RSL's inflatable while Troy and Lynn Hendrickson operate the sub. Our plan

The wreck of the freighter KIRK PRIDE at a depth of nearly 800 feet. Viewed from the bow dome of the submersible, the high intensity flood lights clearly illuminate the ship's stern. Photo by Bret Gilliam

calls for Erin and me to mount the sub after it submerges and ride it to 240 feet where a colorful wall formation provides a suitable photo background. Folks, there is nothing quite like this way to travel to a deep diving site.

Erin finds a convenient perch on the starboard side while I position myself by the port windows on the pilot's conning tower. I can look Troy right in the eye as he sits inside at his command station, communicate with hand signals, and yes, pass the occasional rude gesture. Troy is not much of a deep diver himself and is concerned with our safety at this depth but relaxes after realizing that Erin and I are completely comfortable and enjoying the ride. Indeed, with no swimming effort and my camera equipment stowed on the sub, it's an effortless diving experience. Sort of the ultimate diver propulsion vehicle.

At our arranged depth, Troy maneuvers next to the wall and holds his position. I untangle myself and cameras from the sub's midships and swim away feeling much like an astronaut on a space walk. The sub looks like a giant cyclops and I can actually feel the heat of the flood lights as I swim

Diver Erin Nelson gives the OK sign to Gilliam as he rides the sub's deck to 240 fsw. Both divers were able to maintain eye contact with pilot during descent and communicate via hand signals and taps. Photo by Bret Gilliam

in front of the dome. Lynn and Troy wave and look for all the world like some picnic couple that just happened to park at the ocean floor for chicken and potato salad. After about a 15 minute bottom time and two rolls of film, I re-board the sub's back and we are off to rendezvous with our decompression line and back-up tanks at 40 feet. While we begin the required staged stops, Troy circles around us before hovering at the ten foot level.

Our longest hang is at ten feet and for years this has been where I usually pass the time reading a book or simply "zoning out". This time it's different. Lynn is in the dome only inches away and Erin and I carry on an animated sign language conversation in response to her written messages held up for us to read. The time passes quickly and we emerge confident that the photos will be exciting.

Patrick and I got into a discussion of submersibles and how their technology can be applied to the emerging high tech diving community. Vehicles such as PC 1203 would be an invaluable tool for free-swimming divers to utilize in support for wreck diving or deep wall exploration. Up to six divers in a team could easily be accommodated on the sub as riders to the dive site. Extra gear, back-up cylinders, lights, decompression gases, cameras, tools etc. could be packed on deck and effortlessly transported. The divers would be relieved of the exertion of handling such an equipment package and could breathe from large storage cylinders mounted underneath the sub during transit. This would preserve their back carried gas supply for actual exploration. Continuous communications would be possible not only with the surface but with the divers, and the pilot and observer could function as on-site dive supervisors to record and coordi-

Hovering at 240 feet, the photographer catches Lynn Hendrickson seated in the observation dome. Photo by Bret Gilliam

nate the dive schedule. Changes in the dive plan could easily be improvised and the sub would provide guaranteed delivery to the exact decompression level regardless of current or other natural conditions. The
possibilities are endless. And that's just for open circuit gear. Imagine this
on the Andrea Doria or the Monitor.

My mind skipped ahead to the implications of using these subs or
actual lock-out vehicles to deliver me and a dive team on mixed gas
rebreathers for a dive on the *Kirk Pride* as free swimming divers. I know
Tom Mount, Rob Palmer and Sheck Exley (world record mixed gas diver)
would be first in line for the ultimate wreck dive. Who knows, maybe we
will see if that VW will start!

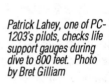

*Patrick Lahey, one of PC-
1203's pilots, checks life
support gauges during
dive to 800 feet. Photo
by Bret Gilliam*

The RSL people are first class. If your diving vacation plans bring you
to Cayman, take my word for it, do not miss this opportunity to make a
submersible dive with them. You will remember it the rest of your life. For
those of you who have any cautions about feeling confined or overall
safety, put your worries aside. RSL has conducted thousands of dives
without mishap and they are held to an extremely high standard of
certification and maintenance. Each sub is equipped with back-ups to
every system and the pilots are some of the best I've seen in the industry.
About five mintes after submerging you'll never give another thought to
worry because you'll be totally consumed with the experience of the dive
itself. They will even video tape the entire adventure for you with a camera
mounted in the dome.

I asked Patrick if he had ever had problems with claustrophobia for
passengers. "I think only twice in the history of the company have we had
people feel uncomfortable and it always happened right at the surface
before we even closed the hatch", he replied. "We simply helped them
back out and that was it. All the rest of the passengers are fascinated. We
have a hard time getting them to leave when the dive is over!"

He continued, "You know, the only bad experience I've ever had in a submersible was on a North Sea job when I was still in the commercial business. I was assigned a company technical representative and took him on a 1000 foot dive on a cold winter day off Scotland. When we reached the bottom, I decided to liven up his ride by squirting him in the back of the neck with a water pistol. It might as well have been a .357 Magnum. He jumped to his feet in unholy terror, crashed his head into the overhead and passed out cold. I thought he would kill me when we got back to the surface and he revived. We don't play those games anymore."

If you get the chance, make the dive with these guys but you might want to frisk Patrick before closing the hatch!

Contact information:

> *Research Submersibles Limited*
> *Box 1719, Georgetown*
> *Grand Cayman, British West Indies*
> *Telephone: 809-949-8296; FAX: 809-949-7421*
> *Dennis Denton: Operations Manager*

APPENDIX A

The Art of Breathing

the philosophy is "take what you accept and use it", and with an open mind see the practical results of correct breathing. The reader can use the techniques without modifying their basic philosophies. All who incorporate the breathing exercises and practices described will become more efficient and relaxed both in water and in their everyday lives. Breathing is the key to relaxation and mental control. Any discussion of such practices runs the obvious risk of the author being tagged with a "metaphysical, touchy/feely" label. Westerners typically are not accustomed to many custom philosophical disciplines, and so I urge the reader to continue with an open mind and perhaps some of the following theory may prove of worth to you. Remember: what works, is what works for you. Feel free to improvise.

In eastern philosophy, breathing is the means of bringing the energy of the universe into one's being. The substance of the universe is known as akasha, or infinity, all encompassing universal material. In this concept, all thought, all knowledge, is contained in the akasha. Prana sustains the akasha, it is the total energy of the universe or cosmic energy. A person who controls prana has learned to control the energy of the universe. The practice of prana enables one to control their own mind and body. Just simple breathing exercise and the development of correct breathing patterns enables one to cope with stress and to become more relaxed in everyday living or diving. When meditation is practiced in conjunction with breathing exercise, total control of the mind and body evolve.

Eastern philosophies have long addressed the importance of breathing. Through both practical demonstration and their belief system, it has been shown that one's internal environment is measurably improved and controlled by simple application of breathing. In the western sciences, it is now recognized that control of breathing is vital in therapy associated with numerous physiological and psychological disorders. Indeed, we realize the effect of emotions on breathing: fear, passion, being startled, and stress act as stimuli on respiration. When left under the auspices of the A.N.S., fright or flight breathing patterns occur. If one simply uses conscious control of respiration this stimuli is overridden. A side benefit occurs with continued control of respiration that we, through breathing, now control the emotional reactions of our mind. In other words, we control our emotional reactions instead of being a victim of them. We become one continuous bio feedback network establishing equilibrium within our selves. The reason for this control is we are now beginning to master the flow of energy in our physical bodies by directing the mind through breathing. Obviously for diving in technical frontiers this is an important ability to comphrehend.

A student of life who takes the time to study and control his/her breath learns to direct energy (prana) in its many forms and qualities. One should strive to become aware of every breath to achieve totally mastery. The person who controls the breath controls the mind. One who controls the mind has learned to control the breath. From this practice the person attains a higher feeling of well-being or spiritually. We often accomplish the impossible and survive against insurmountable odds.

Belief comes from the control of the mind. We are what we believe, be it good or bad. Our entire lives are a success story based on our belief. The success may not be what one desires. It is possible that one lives in constant frustration and does not view that situation as success. However from the mind's (subconscious) point, the person achieves exactly what they believe is to be. Thus to change our success story, we must change the self image of our belief system. The first and foremost step is that of breathing and directing the flow of energy. Soon the doors to one's mind are opened and we may reprogram ourselves. The second step which is to be combined with breathing is meditation. Meditation is essential to reprogram our minds and to get into touch with ourselves.

Divers who are exploring new and exciting frontiers, venturing in the twilight zone of innerspace must learn to control breathing and thus the mind. In all our explorations we face possible stressful or threatening situations, without control of the breath and thus the mind it is easy to fall victim to perceived life threatening situations. But with just a little practice a whole new universe is opened safely to the adventurer. It is all so simple, JUST BREATHE, not as before, but really breathing for most is, in itself, a new discovery.

In an Eastern model of the human body, a body within a body is envisioned. This same application is also presented in western religions where one is concerned with the soul. In the east the "subtle body" also has its own anatomy and physiology. In both approaches, the energy of the soul or subtle body, or metaphysical (beyond physics, the eternal energy), exist after death of the physical body. Death of the physical body results when prana (energy) is no longer derived to the physical body through respiration. It is documented upon death that a measurable (electromagnetical-kirlin photography) energy departs the physical body within 24 hours of death. It is due to this delayed departure that some religions do not prepare the physical body for disposal until 24 or more hours following death.

Indeed, in the animal world this departure is sensed by other members of the pack. A few years ago, one of my dogs had to be put to sleep. We elected to do this at our home where he would be at rest and the animal almost sensed the day and time. His name was Moose and he had been suffering from cancer. As our veterinarian Jim Harrington had explained, Moose would let us know by his own behavior when to make the decision.

The day arrived and on this day Moose pulled up energy to share a last and rewarding day with the family. In the evening the vet arrived. Moose crawled up next to me and laid his head in my lap, as to say "I'm ready" and he did not move again. Shortly after the injection our young dog, Ninja, let out a chilling howling call and almost attacked the vet and myself. We believe Ninja sensed the release of Moose's energy field (subtle body-soul etc.).

The physiology and anatomy of the subtle body (energy field-soul) in eastern philosophy is composed of a minimum of 72,000 nadis, or the channels through which prana (energy) flows. Fourteen of these are more important than the others, with six of these being yet more valuable in the channeling of energy. The most prevailing of these are the three which most directly affect energy flow and are within easy access of our direct control. One of these flows through the right nostril (pingala- surya). The second one is directed via the left nostril (ida- chandra), and the third is channeled with the flow of both nostrils. In mediation, control of these allows freedom from outside distractions and non-directed thoughts from the conscious mind. All three major nadris originate at the base of the spine and travel upwards. The junctions where these nadris crisscross is known as "chakras". In addition, other nadris also cross at these junctions developing them as major energy fields. There are seven principle chakras. All of these chakras are highly sensitive to breathing and are "charged" when directing the breath and flow of energy while in a meditative state.

Most people do not use the total of the stored energy (prana) available to them. Thus a vast energy potential is stored as a "seed" state. This stored energy, that with study and practice can be tapped into, is called kundalini. If a person is successful in developing the cultivation of the kundalini, they experience great peace and have the potential to fully control life forces. The release of total kundalini energy is the source of uniting with cosmic consciousness. Along the path of study and the development of breath control, one benefits by developing tremendous healing powers. An even greater discovery is that through correct breathing, we now control the right brain and thus entry to the ability to direct the mind. With this occurrence, we become highly resistant to disease. Disease is an imbalance in prana caused by improper breathing, stress and negative states of mind.

Prana is subdivided into the ten functions it performs. Within these ten divisions there are five major and five minor forms of prana. These pranas are identified by the functions of the body/physiology they affect. For an in depth discussion readers are referred to *"The Science of Breathing"*. The most external manifestation of prana is the breath and prana governs breathing. By control of the breath a person can gain access and control to all the other subtle forms of prana.

To better grasp the cause and effect of prana (energy fields) a review of the nervous system is in order. The nervous system dictates the actions of all other systems in the physical body. The nervous system is segmented into the central nervous system and its continuation, the peripheral nervous system consisting of twelve pairs of cranial nerves in the brain, and thirty one pairs of spinal cord nerves. These nerves spread throughout the body forming a complex network of nerve fibers, efferent, or motor nerve fibers. These carry messages outward from the C.N.S. to the nerve endings. Afferent or sensory nerve fibers transmit intelligence back to the C.N.S. from the extremities. Examples of this action include the simple movement of an arm to the reaction to a stubbed toe.

The control of inhalation and exhalation by either eliminating pauses in breathing or retention of a pause directly effects our nervous system and the organs of the body. By regulating breath the heart and vagus nerves are controlled. The autonomic nervous system normally regulates the so-called involuntary functions of a person. These include secretion, control of lungs, control of the heart and control of our internal environment (emotions, temperature regulation etc). Herein lies a contradiction in that WE may if WE chose control respiration. The control of respiration is the first step to controlling all functions of the body, thus control of the A.N.S.

Examination of the A.N.S. reveals a division into the sympathetic and parasympathetic systems. These systems oppose each other to insure body/nerve functioning and reaction to stimuli. For instance the parasympathetic system tends to slow the heart. On the other hand, the sympathetic system speeds it up. The combined reactions regulate a "normal" heart activity. The sympathetic system consists of two vertical rows of ganglia or nerve cell clusters on either side of the spinal column. These branch out to glands and viscera in the thorax and abdomen, forming integrated plexuses with nerve endings of the parasympathetic system. The vagus nerve is the tenth cranial nerve and is the focal point of the system. The vagus is connected with the hind brain and travels downward along the spinal cord through the neck, chest, and abdomen sending out branches to form various plexuses within the sympathetic system. It ends in a plexus that, in return, is connected to the solar plexus. Furthermore, through filaments, it is connected with the lower plexuses. It is noteworthy to observe these plexuses are at the junctions of the nadris called chakras. It is the function of the nerves and plexus to belong to the physical body. The chakras are parts of the subtle body. Currents of energy flowing through the chakras are counterparts to nerve impulses. In reality, these energy paths can be directed to control the human nerve impulses.

There are two ways to gain control of our involuntary (A.N.S.) nervous system. The first and most easy to obtain is the control of respiration. This control is accomplished by performing breathing exercises and then incorporating correct breathing habits into everyday living. Control of breathing regulates heart function bringing the right vagus nerve under control. This action allows access to the A.N.S. and its conscious direction.

A second means to control the A.N.S. is by development of the will. This is best done by the practice of meditation. By meditation we can sharply focus mental energy. Of course, the best means of self control incorporates the use of breathing and meditation. Respiration is the most important function of the body. Breathing is the source of all life sustaining energy. Breathing dictates emotional stability, health and happiness. A stressed person will tend to breathe shallow and rapidly. By controlling the breath and concentrating on slow deep breathing stress and tension are released. This is a mandatory way to breathe when facing life threatening or physically threatening events underwater. To gain good respiratory habits, exercise is a most. Just as to tone the body we do physical exercise, we must tone the entire human mechanism by doing breathing exercise. There are many forms of breathing exercise: Taichi, Yoga, Chi, etc. All of these have common roots in the application of the breath. As a martial artist most of my life, correct breathing has been a lifetime pursuit. Through correct breathing practice, I have been saved from death or serious injury on more than one occasion.

An example of breath control as related to resistance of force is: I have my students learn (by doing slow relaxed breathing) the ability to make their arms unbendable by a much stronger person. Pool cue sticks are placed in the neck of students and the attacker attempts to push the stick through the students neck. Meanwhile, the student literally pushes the offender across the room. Ladies in the Chinese circus bend two steel bars with their chest. People walk on fire without being burned. The list of feats that are simply breath and focus controlled could extend for many pages. The fact is, breath and breathing is our means of controlling our reactions. To maximize these effects focus the mind with meditation.

BREATHING EXERCISE

First one must learn to do rhythmic diaphragmatic breathing. Most folks use chest muscles to breathe and usually have a shallow breath. In this type breathing, the lower lobes of the lungs do not receive sufficient air to promote gas exchange. When diaphragmatic breathing is incorporated there is increased suction giving better venous return of the blood. This, in itself, reduces the work of the heart and enhances circulatory efficiency. The habit of diaphragmatic breathing must be developed. To start, lie down on your back with one palm placed on the center of the chest and the other on the lower edge of the rib gage where the abdomen begins. Inhale and feel the lower edge of the rib cage expand and the abdomen rise. Upon exhalation the opposite will occur. During this process there should be little upper chest movement.

Next evolve to harmonious rhythmic diaphragmatic breathing. Observe both the rate and depth of the breath. A rate of 16 to 20 times minute is "normal" but with practice and slowing the inhalation down this rate drops significantly. Respiratory rates of six to ten per minute are not uncommon.. Upon inhalation, plasma from the capillaries ooze into the alveolar space and nutrients from the blood ooze into the air sacs. There is ample supply of enzymes in the alveoli to act on the nutrients. Thus lengthening the inspiration increases the time for metabolic action within the lungs. More oxygen is brought into the circulatory system and thus transported to cells. The venus return is increased. An increased blood supply is brought to the capillaries of the alveoli. In this exercise, all breathing is through the nose. Practice lying down, sitting down, standing up and even while walking, or exercising. Practice should also be done while swimming with a snorkle or on scuba with breathing through the mouth.

The next exercise is what I call "breathing pattern one". In this exercise, the practicer stands with legs at shoulder width. The knees are slightly bent and the spinal cord straight. With hands in front of you, be as relaxed as possible. Slowly exhale from the mouth for six to eight seconds without forcing. Now inhale through the nose for six to eight seconds filling the lungs as fully as possible without forcing them. Once again exhale. Repeat this procedure for a minimum of five repetitions. With each breath concentrate on relaxation, feel yourself become heavier and heavier.

Once comfortable with the two exercises above, assume the stance in breathing pattern one. On this exercise, "breathing pattern two", as you inhale through the nose slowly bring the arms up to above the head in about a six to eight second interval. This allows additional expansion of the lungs and aids in release of bodily tension. It results in increased oxygen in the tissues, often accompanied with tingling in the extremities. Once the breath is full and the arms above the head, exhale slowly lowering the arms for six to eight seconds. Duplicate this breathing technique while walking, then while exercising. When walking, perhaps a good rhythm is to inhale for four to five steps then exhale for four to five steps. Repeat swimming in snorkel or scuba except breathing through the mouth with inhale four to eight kicks exhale four to eight kicks.

The next exercise is identical to breathing pattern two except that we pause at each end of the respiratory cycle for two to three seconds. This is to be performed after becoming proficient in the first three breathing exercise presented so far. Repeat walking with the retention of breath for one to three steps. When swimming, use retention for one to three kicks. This is the best air consumption breathing rhythm. In scuba, the lungs are not expanded to maximum capacity as in the static exercises. When diving it is simply deep slow inhalation... pause... slow full exhalation... pause... and repeat. The pause can last one to three kicks. The exact sequences will vary from individual to individual and change with practice. It should always be comfortable.

For the next exercise a sandbag is needed. This bag is to weigh between ten and fifteen pounds. Place the bag between the chest and abdomen. With teeth clenched practice diaphragmatic breathing, as explained earlier, with this added resistance.

To incorporate exercise into habit, these skills must be practiced while involved in daily activity. Train yourself to use these techniques in each moment you can think of them. When exercising in a gym or whatever: utilize these techniques. I use these breathing applications while doing martial arts, while working out on the stair master at capacity, when swimming and in resistance training as well as when stretching. One of the most beneficial times to use the exercise is while stretching the musculature of the anatomy. Used in this fashion, correct breathing habits become a natural extension of one's habits.

Another prime use of breathing is while meditating. In fact, meditation is the best means to learn how to direct the breath. When meditating, strive to be free from distraction. Begin by slow relaxed breathing with eyes closed. Advanced meditations often are done with eyes open. Concentrate on relaxation, you may wish to direct the breath or relaxation to the various parts of the anatomy. Once totally relaxed, one can do a freeform meditation or direct an active visualization towards an objective. Meditations normally last ten to twenty minutes. For newcomers to meditation, guided tapes afford an outstanding introduction. These tapes are available at most metaphysical book stores. One of the most outstanding sets of tapes that I personally follow and have benefited from are those produced by Jonathan Parker of the Gateways Institute. An excellent breathing meditation to begin with is *"Breathing is the Key"* by Lucinda Green and a chakra balance tape of great benefit is *"Chakra Balance"* by Dick Sutphen. Works by Shakti Gawain are outstanding for understanding the role of visualization in one's life. Her book *"Creative Visualization"* is a must for an easy understanding of the benefits of visualization and an apprenticeship in metaphysics.

Finally, there is an additional exercise to extend air duration on a dive: bradycardia breathing. This technique is performed by emerging the face underwater while breathing through the mouth and exhaling through the nose. No mask is worn as it is designed that the face be exposed to the water. Again slow inhalation and slow exhalation. For best benefits, about three to five minutes of this pattern should be performed.

The information presented in this chapter is broad-based balanced in western science and metaphysical doctrines. A few exercises have been included to enable one to develop good breathing habits. Digest all that is essential to your personal needs to understand correct breathing then practice and grow from the benefits of breathing as nature intended us to do. In addition to better air duration when diving, you will be amazed at the overall results of proper breathing.

REFERENCES

Science of Breathing ;Swami Rama, Rudolph Ballentine M.D., and Alan Hymes M.D. Himalayan institute.

Wheels of Life; Anodea Judith Llewellyn publications

Quantum Physics

GLOSSARY

A

ANOXIA

Total lack of oxygen

ATA

Atmospheres absolute or total pressure absolute pressure measure of pressure exerted on an object or gas from all sources including water pressure (depth) and atmospheric pressure (weight of air)

ACUTE CNS OXYGEN TOXICITY

Effects of breathing oxygen at partial pressures in excess of 1.6 ATA, also known as the Paul Bert effect. An extremely dangerous manifestation which can include convulsions and collapse

ADAPTATION THEORY

Theory supported by subjective reporting that cumulative experience in deep diving environments will lesson or retard onset and severity of inert gas narcosis. This may also include the effects of DCS and O_2 toxicity

ALVEOLI

Plural of aveolus. It is the alveoli that rupture when a lung overexpansion injury occurs

ALVEOLUS

Small air cells in the lungs

ALVEOLAR EXCHANGE

The exchange of carbon dioxide for oxygen as a process of respiration

AMBIENT PRESSURE

The surrounding pressure

ANDI

American NITROX Divers Inc.

ANALYSIS

Term applied to the precise determination of percentages of gases in a breathing mixture. Most diving operations will analyze for oxygen only. In more complex Trimixes, it can be desirable to analyze for the inert gases as well

APNEA

Cessation of breathing for short intervals of time

AGE OR ARTERIAL GAS EMBOLISM

A lung overexpansion injury that involves air bubbles escaping from the lungs into the pulmonary capillary bed. The bubbles can then travel to the heart and eventually follow the circulatory route to the brain. In severe cases, AGE can be fatal. Treatment is immediate O_2 breathing and transport to a recompression chamber. Also known as air embolism. Symptoms may be similar to Type II DCS

ATMOSPHERE

Measure of weight equal to 33 fsw or the weight of air surrounding the earth, approximately 14.7 psi

B

BACKMOUNTS

Breathing cylinders worn on the diver's back

BC OR BCD

Buoyancy compensating device

BIBS

Built In Breathing Systems, deamnd masks to deliver pure O_2 or other therapy gases to patients in recompression chambers

BOTTOM MIX

A breathing mixture uses at the deepest portion or "working depth" of a dive

BRADYCARDIA

Slowness of the heartbeat

C

CARBON DIOXIDE BUILD-UP (HYPERCAPNIA)

An undue amount of CO_2 in the blood caused by improper breathing habits, inadequate venting or chambers or diving helmets, and incomplete scrubbing of breathing gases in closed circuit re-breathers

CCBA

Closed circuit breathing apparatus

CEILING

A minimum depth to which a diver may ascend within the limits of his computer or decompression table

GLOSSARY

CNS
Central nervous system

COMPOSITE TANK
Dive cylinder composed of reinforced fiber covering a metal core

CYANOSIN
A bluish discoloration of the skin that results from a oxygen deficiency in the blood

D

DCAP
(Decompression Computation and Analysis Program) Dr. R.W."Bill" Hamilton's proprietary computer program to generate decom schedules for various mixes, including air, including accelerated decompression

DCIEM
Defence and Civil Institute of Environmental Medicine, Canadian table producers

DCS
Decompression sickness, "the bends"

DECOMPRESSION LINE
A line used as a point of reference or loose attachment for divers who are decompressing

DECOMPRESSION MANAGEMENT TOOLS
Tables, wheels, dive computers and various decom softwear used to calculate decompression exposures

DECOM REEL
A diver-carried reel with typically 300 or more feet of line and a small liftbag that can be tied off to a wreck or weighted and hung from the liftbag in the event that the primary "up line" is missed

DEHYDRATION
A loss of bodily fluids, can contribute to DCS

DILUENT
An inert gas, usually nitrogen or helium, that provides volume in a breathing mix to ensure the partial pressure of oxygen remains within safe limits of exposure

DIVE PROFILE
The depth/time measurements of a particular dive

DIVING REFLEX
A reaction to a mammal's physiology following immersion in water. Typified by a slowing or respiration and pulse

DIN
(Deutsche Industrie Norme, or German industry standard), valve and regulator fittings featuring the "captured o-ring" design whereby the regulator is screwed into the cylinder valve. Adaptable to higher pressure ratings, typically in excess of 3000 psi. Generally considered to be more reliable than yoke type systems

DOPPLER DEVICE
Used to detect sub-clinical or so-called "silent bubbles" as indicators of DCS stress in divers

DPV
Diver propulsion vehicle or scooter

DUMP VALVE
A term for the exhaust fittings on dry suits, lift bags and BC's. Not currently related to any bodily excretory functions and their removal from suits

E

EAD
Equivalent air depth, means of equating gas mixtures to conventional air Tables

EANx
Enriched air NITROX, a mixture containing more than 21% oxygen

END
Equivalent narcosis depth, means of equating the relative narcotic influence of inert gases to conventional air Tables

F

FFW
Feet of fresh water depth

FSW
Feet of sea water depth

FULL-FACE MASK
A diving system with the regulator built into a diving mask that completely covers the face, nose and mouth. Provides extra safety margin with high PO_2 exposures and is easily adaptable to communications units

GLOSSARY

H

HABITAT

An underwater dwelling for divers in saturation. Recent operations have employed derivatives of this with the so-called "decom habitat", a shallow water dry station for more comfortable decompression

HALDANE, JOHN

Early theorist in decompression models. His work provided the base for most diving tables

HANG TIME

Decompression time

HELIOX

Breathing mixture of helium and oxygen

HOME-BREW

Term applied to mixing gas at home or at the dive site, generally by the partial pressure method

HYDRALIOX

Breathing gas consisting of a mixture of hydrogen, helium and oxygen, practical use proved to 1700 fsw

HYDROX

Breathing mixture of hydrogen and oxygen

HYPERLITE

Portable recompression chamber manufactured by SOS Ltd

HYPOXIA

Lack of or low oxygen partial pressure in a breathing mixture

I

IAND

International Association of NITROX Divers

INERT GAS

Those gases present in the breathing mixture which are not metabolized

INERT GAS NARCOSIS

The intoxicating effects of inert gases such as nitrogen when the diver is exposed to elevated partial pressures at depth

J

JON LINE

A three to six foot line with a handloop that can be clipped around a decom line. Named after its inventor, Jon Hulbert. The line serves as a dampening device for the up/down motion of the sea in rough swells. Also used for DPV tows

L

LIFT BAG

A bag-like device that is inflated underwater to lift objects from the bottom. Also used as decompression surface float

M

MEYER-OVERTON HYPOTHESIS

Theory of the relationship of the nacotic effect of a gas to its solubility in lipid tissue

MGR

Mixed gas rebreather

MINI-OX

Portable, hand-held oxygen analyzer manufactured by Catalyst Research

MIXED GAS

Any mixture for diving that alters from standard atmospheric air

MOD

Maximum operating depth of a gas mixture controlled by the partial pressure limit of oxygen exposure

MULTI-LEVEL DIVE

A type of dive that will not conform to a maximum depth and time profile. Ideally, such dives are conducted with the deepest sections first and then the diver ascends progressively to various shallower depths.

MULTI-PLACE, MULTI-LOCK CHAMBER

A treatment chamber designed to accommodate two or more patients and consisting of two or more pressure chambers to allow efficient transfer of staff or materials without losing pressure

GLOSSARY

N

NEOX

A breathing mixture of neon and oxygen

NIGGLE

A transient, minor symptom of DCS

NITROX

Literally, nitrogen and oxygen breathing mixture. When the oxygen percentage in the mix is above 21%, this NITROX is also known as SafeAir, Enriched Air etc.

NOAA NITROX I

NITROX consisting of 32% O_2 and 64% N_2, the most prevalent NITROX in scientific and sport diving. Depth limit of approximately 130 fsw

NOAA NITROX II

NITROX consisting of 36% O_2 and 68% N_2, depth limit approximately 110 fsw

NORMOXIC

a breathing mixture that yields a percentage or partial pressure of oxygen at normal (21%) levels

O

OCTOPUS

Aside from the obvious, in equipment nomenclature, an extra breathing second stage for sharing in the event of out-of-gas scenarios with a diving buddy

OTU

Oxygen tolerance unit, derived from Hamilton's Repex calculation method

OVERHEAD ENVIRONMENT

A diving environment that does not allow direct escape to the surface such as caves and wreck penetrations. Many divers consider stage decompression to be a form of "overhead diving" due to the obligation of a decom ceiling

OXTOX

Oxygen toxicity

OXYGEN TOXICITY

Short or long term physiological effects of elevated partial pressures of oxygen

P

PARTIAL PRESSURE

the portion of the total gas pressure exerted by a single gas in a breathing mixture, expressed as Pg for an unknown gas or PO_2 in the case of oxygen

PONY BOTTLE

A small scuba cylinder commonly used as an emergency breathing system, also know as a "bailout bottle"

PRE-MIX

A specified gas mixture that has been dispensed by a commercial gas supplier in bulk

PROPRIETARY TABLES

Private, exclusive custom-generated tables for diving

PSI

Pounds per square inch

Q

QUADS

A set or rig consisting or twin double cylinders

QUATEK PRO-FILE

British programmable NITROX diving computer

R

RECOMPRESSION

The accepted treatment for decompression sickness and AGE. Treatment is instituted by "returning" to higher pressure in a metal chamber capable of simulating the hyperbaric environment

REDUNDANCY

The concept of carrying fully functional back-up systems to replace primaries in the event of failure

REPETITIVE DIVE

Any dive following a previous dive within a particular time frame. This will vary according to the decompression model used e.g. a repetitive according to the U.S. Navy model is any dive within a 12 hour period

GLOSSARY

S

SET

A diver's equipment configuration or rig

SIDEMOUNTS

Breathing cylinders worn on the sides of the diver

SPG

Submersible pressure gauge

STAGE BOTTLE

Extra diving cylinder carried in addition to main gas supply. Usually carried on front or side mount clips. These cylinders are designed to provide additional bottom mix gas supply or to provide alternate mixtures for decompression efficiency

SURFACE DECOMPRESSION OR SUR-D

Decompression performed in a surface decompression chamber removing the diver from the water environment

SQUARE PROFILE DIVE

A type of dive that involves staying at one particular depth for the entire bottom time and then ascending directly

T

TACHYCARDIA

Excessive rapidity of the heartbeat

TANK BANDS

The metal bands that secure a breathing cylinder to the diver's backpack or harness

TEST OF PRESSURE

20 minute breathing period on pure oxygen at 60 fsw in a recompression chamber to observe patient for relief or improvement of DCS or AGE symptoms

THIRDS RULE

Gas management policy of using one third of gas supply for initial dive penetration, one third ot exit, and holding one third as a contingency reserve

TRAVEL MIX

An intermediate breathing mixture used for maintaining proper PO_2 exposures or to promote more efficient decompression. Generally associated with "traveling" to the dive site or working depth and back to the surface

TRIMIX

A breathing mixture of three gases usually oxygen, nitrogen and helium

U

UPTD

Unit of pulmonary toxicity dose, measurement of "whole body" O_2 toxicity similar to the OTU method

V

VERTIGO

A loss of the sense of balance accompanied by dizziness or confusion, spatial disorientation

W

WINGS

BC worn as back-mounted unit

Y

Y-VALVE

A single cylinder valve that allows two separate regulators to be mounted to one cylinder

Z

ZEPP

Slang term for Aqua-zepp, a German DPV or scooter

BIBLIOGRAPHY

BOOKS

Advanced Wreck Diving Guide, Gentile,Gary (1988), Cornell Maritime Press

Andrea Doria: Dive to an Era, Gentile, Gary (1987), Gary Gentile Productions

The Application of Enriched Air Mixtures, Betts, Ed (1992) ANDI

Cave Diving: The Cave Diving Group Manual, Bedford, Bruce (editor), Mendip Publishing, England

Caving, A Blueprint For Survival, Exley, Sheck, NSS-CDS

Deep Diving: An Advanced Guide to Physiology, Procedures and Systems, Gilliam, Bret and von Maier, Robert, (1992) Watersport Publishing, Inc.

Deep Into Blue Holes, Palmer, Rob, Unwin Hyman, England

Diving Accident Management Field Guide: Oxygen Administration and Recompression Therapy, Gilliam, Bret, Ocean Tech Publications

Dive Computers: A Consumer's Guide to History, Theory and Performance. Loyst, Ken, (1991) Watersport Publishing, Inc.

Diving Medicine, Second Edition, Bove & Davis (1990) Grove & Stratton

Diving and Subaquatic Medicine, Edmunds, Lowery Pennegather (1983) Best Publishing Co.

Evaluating Enriched Air (Nitrox) Diving Technology, Hamilton, R.W. (editor) SDRG

Field Guide for the Diving Medic, Daugherty, Gordon (1985), Best Publishing Co.

Living and Working in the Sea, Miller, James W. and Koblick, Ian G., Van Nostrand Reinhold Co.

The Physician's Guide to Diving Medicine, Shilling, Carlston & Mathias (1984) Plenum Press

The Physiology and Medicine of Diving, Third Edition, Bennett & Elliot (1982) Best Publishing Co.

NITROX Manual, Rutkowski, Dick (1991) Hyperbarics International

Recompression Chamber Life Support Manual, Rutkowski, Dick (1990) Hyperbarics International

Ultimate Wreck Diving Guide, Gentile, Gary (1992), Gary Gentile Productions

U.S. Navy Diving Manual, Vol. II Mixed Gas, NAVSEA (1992) Best Publishing Co.

PERIODICALS

AquaCorps, c/o KeyWest Divers 1MM 4.5 US 1 Stock Island, Key West FL 33040

Discover Diving, Watersport Publishing, Inc. Box 83727, San Diego, CA 92138

Scuba Times, 14110 Perdido Key Drive, Suite 16, Pensacola, FL 32507

Underwater USA, Press-Enterprise Inc., 3185 Lackawanna Ave., Bloomsburg, PA 17815

RESOURCE GUIDE

TRAINING FACILITIES

Bellingham Dive-N-Travel
{Larry Elsevier}
2720 West Maplewood Ave.
Bellingham, WA 98225
(206) 734-1770 (800) 338-6341

The Gas Station
{Bart Malone, Lou Sarlo}
831 Charles St.
Gloucester City, NJ 08030
(609) 456-4316

Hyperbarics International, Inc.
{Dick Rutkowski}
490 Caribbean Drive
Key Largo, Florida 33037
(305) 451-2551

ISC Management Corporation
{Ed Betts}
74 Woodcleft Ave
Freeport, Ny 11520
(516) 546-2026

Key West Divers:
High-Tech Training Facilities
{Bill Deans}
MM 4.5 US 1
Stock Island, FL 33040
(305) 294-7177 (800) 873-4837

National Diving Center
{Ray Jarvis}
4932 Wisconsin Ave., NW
Washington D.C. 20016
(202) 363-2631

Ocean Odyssey Dive Centre
{Capt. Wings}
2345 S. Rodeo Gulch Road
Santa Cruz, CA 95062
(408) 475-3483

Ocean Tech
{Bret Gilliam}
HC 33, #7 Stone Tree Rd.
Arrowsic Island
Bath, ME 04530-9401
(207) 442-0998

Scuba Adventures
{Jim Baden}
253 E. Redland Blvd.
San Bernardino, CA 92408
(714) 825-2502

Sheck Exley
Cathedral Canyon
Rt. 8, Box 374
Live Oak, FL 32060
(904) 362-7589

Steamboat Dive Inn
{Dustin Clesi}
Box 1000
Branford, FL 32008
(904)-935-3483

Submariner Research
{John Crea}
Box 1906
Bainbridge, GA 31717
(912) 246-9349

Tom Mount
1545 NE 104th St.
Miami Shores, FL 33138
(305) 754-1027

SPECIALIZED EQUIPMENT

AquaZepp
Steiner Strasse 20 A
8000 Munchen 70
Germany
011-49-89-723-1188
-diver propulsion vehicles

RESOURCE GUIDE

Carmellen Research, Ltd.
Box 8311
Port St. Lucie, FL 34985
(407) 337-2631
-mixed gas rebreathers

Carter Lift Bags
29500 Green River Gorge Rd.
Enumclaw, WA 98022
(206) 886-2302
-lift bags

Cis-Lunar
1 Ridgeway Drive
Chaddsford, PA 19317
(215) 388-2303
-mixed gas rebreathers

Dive Comm, Inc.
11720 Sunrise Valley Drive
Reston, VA 22091
(703) 620-9283
-underwater communications

Dive Rite Manufacturing
{Mark Leonard}
Rt. 14, Box 136
Lake City, FL 32055
(904) 752-1087
-Specialized manufacturer of doubles, BCD's, linereels, lights and accessories, nitrox computer.

DUI Inc.
1148 Delevan Drive
San Diego, CA 92102-2499
(800) 325-8439
-dry suits

English Enginereeing, Inc.
{Lamar English}
Route 3, Box 54
Greenville, FL 32331
(904) 948-3311
-Custom U/W lights rated to extreme depths (850+ fsw), line reels and custom DPV's.

ISC Management Corporation
{Ed Betts}
74 Woodcleft Ave.
Freeport, NY 11520
(516) 546-2026
-Full engineering consulting for any high-pressure applications, air compressors, oil-free systems, etc.

Key West Divers
{Bill Deans}
MM 4.5 US 1
Stock Island
Key West, FL 33040
(305) 294-7177 (800) 873-4837
-Specialized deep diving equipment, DPV's, lights and thermal suits.

Ocean Tech
{Bret Gilliam}
HC 33, #7 Stone Tree Rd.
Arrowsic Island
Bath, ME 04530-9401
(207) 442-0998
-Consulting for specialized deep diving systems and compressor/filling systems. Oxygen equipment and recompression chambers. Vessel design, construction, operation and management. Books and reference materials.

Ocean Technology Systems
2610 Croddy Way, Unit H
Santa Ana, CA 92704
(714) 754-7848
-underwater communications

Underwater Applications Corporation
{Randy Bohrer}
427-3 Amherst St., Suite 345
Nashua, NH 03063
508-433-6586
-Specialized deep diving equipment, oxygen-clean breathing systems, booster pumps, oxygen analyzers and custom tables.

RESOURCE GUIDE

Reimers Enginereing
6314-A Gravel Ave.
Alexandria, VA 22310
(703) 922-0606
-compressors, mixed gas systems and distribution panels

Sherwood South
4332 Sullivans Lake Drive
Greensborough, NC 27410
(919) 854-8337
-cylinders and valves

Sherwood
3 Chrysler
Irvine, CA 92718
(714) 581-1300

SCUBAPRO
3105 E. Harcourt
Rancho Dominguez, CA 90221
(800) 382-2211
high pressure/high volume cylinders, valves, high performance regulators

Viking Diving Inc.
9043 Dutton Dr.
Twinsburg, OH 44087
(216) 963-0301
-dry suits

Underwater Application Corporation
{Randy Bohrer}
427-3 Amherst St., Suite 345
Nashua, NH 03063
(508) 433-6586

Watersport Publishing, Inc.
P.O. Box 83727
San Diego, CA 92138
(619) 697-0703
specializing in technical diving publications

CUSTOM (PROPRIETARY) TABLES

Hamilton Research, Ltd.
{Bill Hamilton}
80 Grove St.
Tarrytown, NY 10591
(914) 631-9194

Submariner Research, Ltd.
{John Crea}
Box 1906
Bainbridge, GA 31717
(912) 246-9349

INDEX

INDEX

INDEX

INDEX

INDEX

INDEX

INDEX

OTHER TITLES BY WATERSPORT BOOKS